JOINT
NATURE
CONSERVATION
COMMITTEE

DEPARTMENT of ARTS, CULTURE and the GAELTACHT

Atlas of the dragonflies of Britain and Ireland

ITE research publication no. 9

R Merritt, N W Moore and B C Eversham

Centre for Ecology and Hydrology

London: The Stationery Office

Natural Environment Research Council

Published in Great Britain by The Stationery Office

The Institute of Terrestrial Ecology (ITE) is a component research organisation within the Natural Environment Research Council. The Institute is part of the Centre for Ecology and Hydrology, and was established in 1973 by the merger of the research stations of the Nature Conservancy with the Institute of Tree Biology. It has been at the forefront of ecological research ever since. The six research stations of the Institute provide a ready access to sites and to environmental and ecological problems in any part of Britain. In addition to the broad environmental knowledge and experience expected of the modern ecologist, each station has a range of special expertise and facilities. Thus, the Institute is able to provide unparalleled opportunities for long-term, multidisciplinary studies of complex environmental and ecological problems.

ITE undertakes specialist ecological research on subjects ranging from micro-organisms to trees and mammals, from coastal habitats to uplands, from derelict land to air pollution. Understanding the ecology of different species of natural and man-made communities plays an increasingly important role in areas such as monitoring ecological aspects of agriculture, improving productivity in forestry, controlling pests, managing and conserving wildlife, assessing the causes and effects of pollution, and rehabilitating disturbed sites.

The Institute's research is financed by the UK Government through the science budget, and by private and public sector customers who commission or sponsor specific research programmes. ITE's expertise is also widely used by international organisations in overseas collaborative projects.

The results of ITE research are available to those responsible for the protection, management and wise use of our natural resources, being published in a wide range of scientific journals, and in an ITE series of publications. The Annual Report contains more general information.

The Biological Records Centre is operated by ITE, as part of the Environmental Information Centre, and receives financial support from the Joint Nature Conservation Committee. It seeks to help naturalists and research biologists to co-ordinate their efforts in studying the occurrence of plants and animals in Britain and Ireland, and to make the results of these studies available to others.

B C Eversham
Environmental Information Centre
Biological Records Centre
Institute of Terrestrial Ecology
Monks Wood , Abbots Ripton
HUNTINGDON, Cambs PE17 2LS
Tel: 01487 773381   Fax: 01487 773467

CONTENTS

FOREWORD

Having been on the fringe of the work leading up to the preparation of this *Atlas* has enabled me to see the fruits of formidable amounts of work being harvested, processed and refined into a satisfying result. Like a good wine, it has the subtleties of its component parts, which the discerning user will be able to detect, but it also provides a complete and rewarding whole.

The *Atlas* is a prime example of the collaboration between volunteers and those employed to compile data for research and conservation. National dragonfly recording began within the Insects Distribution Maps Scheme in 1968. This Scheme was set up by the Biological Records Centre (BRC) and was administered by the late John Heath, assisted by Mike Skelton. Progress was slow because of the absence of a readily available identification guide. However, in 1977 Basil Harley, then of Curwen Press, masterminded the publication of a well-illustrated guide by Cyril Hammond. This publication made a recording scheme truly viable and has remained in print ever since, in an edition revised by Bob Merritt and published by Harley Books in 1983.

When David Chelmick took responsibility for organising the Scheme in 1977, recording was already beginning to increase, but his energy and his enthusiasm were soon to influence a growing number of recorders. By 1979, the second edition of the *Provisional atlas*, edited by David, showed considerable improvement on the earlier edition (1978) which had been edited by John Heath, but based on the work of Mike Skelton.

In 1981 Bob Merritt succeeded David Chelmick as scheme organiser. Over the next nine years Bob devoted enormous energy and personal commitment to the Scheme and has continued to foster a level of interest in this group of insects which would have been unimaginable 20 years ago. Above all, Bob has ensured that the standards of recording are the very highest. The excellence of the quality of the data held at BRC and summarised in this *Atlas* is almost entirely due to Bob's thorough knowledge of the dragonfly fauna through his extensive fieldwork in Britain and Ireland, and to his meticulous checking of records before their submission to BRC.

Norman Moore's involvement with the preparation of this *Atlas* is particularly welcome. Norman was joint author of the much sought-after early New Naturalist volume *Dragonflies*, and his influence on the study and conservation of the group has become apparent over the years, both at home and overseas.

My colleague, Brian Eversham, has devoted considerable time and energy to work on the data for dragonflies and has been able to make some initial analyses for this *Atlas*, together with preparing some of the text.

It is my personal pleasure that the *Atlas of dragonflies* has now been published after so much work by all concerned, including, of course, the cohorts of volunteer recorders. I have strong memories of working with all the personalities mentioned above, but particularly with the three authors, so that to pick up this *Atlas* will bring me a host of personal recollections.

Quite apart from my own pleasure in this volume, I am confident that it will prove to be as significant a stage in the study of dragonflies in Britain and Ireland as were the publications of *Dragonflies* in 1960 and *The dragonflies of Great Britain and Ireland* in 1977. It places the fauna of these islands on record in such a way that it is now possible to relate the distribution of our species to their occurrence in several other western European countries where similar studies have been undertaken. The data summarised in the *Atlas* are held at BRC and will be put to a wide variety of uses, especially in research and nature conservation.

I now look forward to seeing further results from the recording effort of the last 20 years and to new recording to provide fresh insights into the ecology and distribution of these impressive and captivating insects.

Paul T Harding
Biological Records Centre
ITE Monks Wood
February 1995

PREFACE

The purpose of this book is to summarise the information gathered from the Recording Scheme set up a quarter of a century ago at the Biological Records Centre (BRC) to record the distribution of British and Irish dragonflies. In addition to discussing the present and changing status of species, their distribution in relation to their habitat requirements, and to reviewing some of the more important historical records, it provides an opportunity to indicate some of the other uses to which the information is being put.

Few of the people who submitted their records to BRC in the late 1960s and early 1970s could have envisaged the comprehensiveness both of the maps published in this *Atlas* and of the information contained in the text. The data held at BRC now provide a baseline with which future studies can reasonably be compared.

In the early years of the Scheme, recorders were presented virtually with a blank page, for most of what was known about dragonfly distribution was buried either in the scientific literature or in out-of-print books that were difficult to obtain. For the participants, it was a pioneering time in which all fieldwork was instantly rewarding, significantly improving our knowledge. Slowly, a picture began to emerge: first, of the main areas of recorder activity, but, gradually, of the distribution of dragonflies themselves. Along the way, important (re)discoveries were made of the rarer breeding species, for example that of *Lestes dryas* in England and *Somatochlora metallica* in Scotland, but perhaps the most notable discovery was that of *Coenagrion lunulatum* in Ireland: a damselfly that had never been recorded before from either Ireland or Britain.

That so much has been achieved is due to the enthusiasm and dedication of a great many people, and this *Atlas* is a testimony to their endeavour.

It is heartening to see the increasing interest in dragonflies being reflected in the growing membership, activity and influence of the British Dragonfly Society. It is reflected also in the recent publication of a large number of detailed county surveys. Most are of high quality owing to the effort put in to ensure that the data are fully checked, and thus reliable, or suitably qualified in the case of those historical records which cannot be verified. It is hoped that this *Atlas* will give further impetus to the study of dragonflies.

I would like to express my thanks, and that of my co-authors, Brian Eversham and Norman Moore, to those people who have been involved in the

publication of this book – to Paul Harding, head of BRC, for his help and support; to David Chelmick, my predecessor as national scheme organiser, for laying the foundations upon which the Scheme was built; to Colm Ronayne, who took over responsibility for Irish records in 1983; to Steve Coker, Tony Fox, Betty Smith, Lee Thickett and Noelle and (the late) Tony Welstead, who were appointed regional recorders in 1987, for their contributions up to and since that date, and for helping me to transfer a large quantity of museum and field survey data to BRC record cards; to Philippa Adams for her help with this task also; and to Steve Cham, David Clarke, Alan Hold and Brian Nelson, additional current regional recorders, for dealing with post-1988 data, much of which have been used in this *Atlas*. Thanks are due to the many county and local organisers who, throughout the duration of the Odonata Recording Scheme, have done so much to achieve thorough coverage in many parts of the country. They are too numerous to mention here, but the names of many appear in the references and the species accounts: without their efforts, the maps would have been immeasurably poorer. Thanks are also due to Steve Brooks, Tony Irwin, Steven Jones, Bob Kemp, Howard Mendel and Graham Vick for their speedy response to requests for information concerning certain details in the text of the *Atlas*. Special thanks are due to Robert Thompson, of Banbridge, Co Down, who provided all the photographs of adult dragonflies and larvae; and, finally, our thanks go to all the individual recorders who submitted records to BRC – their names are listed in the **Acknowledgments**.

Bob Merritt
Chesterfield
January 1995

ACKNOWLEDGMENTS

The following list includes the recorders whose data are included in this *Atlas*. Most have supplied records directly to the Odonata Recording Scheme; some figure in the literature; and others are responsible for specimens in the major museum collections. The latter provide a valuable historical perspective. Thanks are due to the keepers and curators of the museums cited in the text.

Abbott, A.; Abbott, R.; Abrahart, D.; Abrehart, T.; Acheson, V.; Adams, A.J.; Adams, J.H.; Adams, Miss P.A.; Adams, T.H.L.; Addington, R.; Adey, J.P.; Adkin, N.R.; Agnew, A.; Albertini, M.; Alderson, Miss E.M.; Aldren, T.; Aldridge, M.; Alexander, J.; Alexander, K.N.A.; Allan, C.; Allen, B.; Allen, B.M.; Allen, C.A.; Allen, J.E.R.; Allen, Miss K.; Allen, Mrs C.; Allen, P.M.; Allen-Williams, L.J.; Allenby, K.G.; Allison, L.; Allison, M.; Allnut, A.C.; Allport, A.; Allport, A.M.; Amphlett, A.; Amsden, A.F.; Anderson, C.; Anderson, R.; Andress, R.; Andrew, L.; Andrew, R.H.; Andrewes, Sir C.H.; Andrews, E.W.; Andrews, J.; Annett, H.E.; Antram, C.B.; Appleton, T.; Archdale, M.; Archer, M.; Archer, P.; Archer-Lock, A.; Ardron, P.A.; Arkel, J.; Arkle, J.; Armitage, J.; Armitage, J.S.; Armstrong, I.; Armstrong, J.D.; Arnold, G.A.; Arnold, H.R.; Arnold, M.A.; Arnold, N.; Arnott, J.G.L.; Arnott, P.A.; Arthurton, W.; Ascott, Mrs J.; Ashby, B.; Ashby, C.B.; Ashby, E.B.; Ashdown, W.J.; Ashington, S.W.; Ashton, J.M.; Ashwell, D.A.; Ashworth, D.; Ashworth, M.; Askew, D.; Askew, R.R.; Aston, W.H.; Atherton, P.; Atkin, K.; Atkins, J.; Atkins, R.; Atkinson, J.; Atkinson, L.; Atlee, H.G.; Attside, D.; Attwood, P.J.; Atty, D.; Aubrook, E.W.; Audcent, H.; Ausden, M.; Austin, E.M.; Averill, M.T.; Averis, A.B.G.; Avery, L.; Ayre, K.; Babbs, S.; Bacon, J.C.; Badenoch, C.; Badenoch, C.O.; Badmin, J.S.; Baguley, R.; Bailey, B.; Bailey, E.B.; Bailey, G.S.; Bailey, M.; Baily, W.E.; Bainbridge, A.; Bainbridge, I.; Bainbridge, J.; Baker, A.; Baker, B.; Baker, B.R.; Baker, F.E.S.; Baker, H.; Baker, M.R.; Baker, P.; Baker, R.; Baker, R.E.; Baker, T.; Baker, W.B.; Bakewell, D.N.; Balchin, C.S.; Baldock, D.; Baldock, N.M.; Baldrick, Mr.; Baldwin, Miss S.I.; Balfour-Browne, F.; Ball, H.N.; Ball, M.E.; Ball, Miss M.; Ball, S.G.; Ballantyne, G.H.; Ballantyne, I.; Ballantyne, J.; Banks, B.; Banks, Mrs.J.; Bannister, P.A.; Banwell, A.; Barclay, R.J.; Barefoot, J.; Barham, Mrs K.; Barker, A.M.; Barker, G.; Barker, L.; Barker, M.V.; Barlow, S.; Barnard, C.C.; Barnes, H.; Barnes, L.; Barnes, S.; Barnett, R.J.; Barnham, V.; Barrand, B.; Barratt, P.; Barrett, C.G.; Barrington, Mrs; Barton, T.; Barwick, M.; Barwick, S.; Batchelor, D.M.; Bates, B.L.; Bates, J.K.; Bates, P.; Bateson, C.; Bateson, G.; Bateson, J.; Bath, W.H.; Bathe, E.C.; Bathe, G.M.; Batt, C.M.; Batty, B.D.; Batty, D.; Batty, H.; Batty, L.; Batty, Mrs P.M.; Batty, P.; Batty, S.; Baxter, E.V.; Baxter, R.; Bayley, A.; Bayley, J.A.; Bayne, D.; Bayne, D.M.; Baynes, E.S.A.; Beales, C.; Beaufoy, S.; Beaumont, A.; Beaumont, J.L.; Beaumont, Mrs S.; Bebbington, J.; Beckitt, W.; Beer, T.; Beere, W.; Beirne, B.P.; Belden, P.; Belden, P.A.; Bell, G.A.C.; Bell, P.; Bell, S.; Bell, S.L.; Bell-Marley, H.W.; Belle, J.; Belringer, R.M.; Bennett, G.; Benstead, J.P.; Benstead, M.; Benstead, P.J.; Bentley, Miss N.; Benton, E.; Berry, I.; Bertenshaw, S.; Bertram-Lloyd, Mrs; Betton, Mrs E.; Betts, C.R.; Betts, S.; Bevan, D.; Beveridge, Mrs J.; Beynon, T.G.; Bhatia, Zul; Biggs, D.T.; Biggs, J.; Biggs, L.S.; Bignal, Dr; Bignell, G.C.; Biltcliffe, C.; Biltcliffe, M.; Bilton, D.T.; Bindon, L.; Binge, J.C.; Bingham, J.; Birchall, Miss J.; Birchall, Mr; Bird, G.M.; Bird, H.; Bird, M.; Bird, P.F.; Birkenhead School; Birmingham Museum Collection; Birtwistle, S; Bishop, E.B.; Bishop, W.; Black, I.; Black, J.; Black, J.M.; Blackburn, J.; Blackett, D.; Blackledge, A.; Blackman, A.W.; Blackman, R.A.A.; Blackwood, G.G.; Blackwood, J.J.; Blackwood, Mrs K.M.; Blades, D.; Bladon, C.M.; Blair, C.G.; Blair, K.G.; Blake, W.E.; Blakeley, D.S.; Blamire, S.; Bland, K.; Bland, Mrs V.A.; Blanning, P.E.; Blatchley, I.; Blathwayt, L.; Bleay, R.; Blenkarn, S.E.; Blindell, R.; Blinkarn, S.A.; Blood, E.J.; Bloomfield, E.N.; Bloomfield, P.J.; Blunt, A.G.; Bolton, D.; Bolton, D.E.; Bolton, Mrs A.E.; Bolton, Mrs L.; Bond, G.; Bond, K.G.M.; Bondi, S.R.; Bone, K.; Booker, Mrs; Bookham, A.; Boon, C.; Boosey, E.; Boote, M.D.; Bossom, P.; Bostock, E.D.; Bostock, N.; Boston, R.N.; Bowden-Smith, Mrs; Bowers, J.K.; Bowey, K.; Bowhill, J.W.; Bowles, S.; Bowman, N.; Bowtell, G.; Boxall, P.G.; Boyd, D.A.; Boyd, I.; Boyd, J.M.; Boyd, T.; Boyd, W.; Boyd, W.C.;

Boyer, J.A.J.; Boyle, A.; Boyne, R.; Bracegirdle, M.; Bracken, C.W.; Bradford, M.; Bradford, R.; Bradley, J.D.; Bradley, R.C.; Bradley, S.; Bradney, R.J.; Bradshaw, H.; Bradshaw, R.; Braithwaite, M.E.; Braithwaite, Miss P.J.; Bramhall, A.; Brassley, Mrs P.; Bratton, J.; Bratton, J.H.; Bray, R.P.; Brayshaw, S.; Breeds, J.M.; Brennan, D.; Breton, Mrs A.; Brett, R.; Brewer, E.G.; Brewster, D.; Brewster, Mrs M.A.; Brian, M.C.; Bricknell, I.; Bridges, Mrs D.; Brierley, S.B.; Brierley, S.J.; Briggs, C.A.; Briggs, H.M.; Briggs, R.S.; Brind, R.; Brind, R.A.; Brindle, J.H.; Brinklow, R.K.; Brinn, D.; Britnell, A.J.N.; Britten, E.B.; Britten, H.; Broad, R.; Broadbank, A.R.; Brocklebank, A.; Brocklesby, J.S.; Brodie, E.S.; Brodie, I.; Brook, G.; Brook, G.G.; Brook, J.; Brook, M.; Brook, S.; Brooks, A.D.; Brooks, J.E.; Brooks, P.; Brooks, S.; Brooks, S.J.; Broomfield, Mrs M.; Broughton, E.E.; Broughton, W.B.; Brown, A.J.; Brown, C.R.; Brown, D.G.; Brown, E.; Brown, E.S.; Brown, H.H.; Brown, J.; Brown, J.M.; Brown, L.; Brown, N.; Brown, P.W.; Brown, R.C.; Brownett, A.; Brownlie, J.; Bruce, C.; Brummitt, J.M.; Brunstrom, S.; Bryanston Natural History Society; Brydson, J.A.; Buchanan White, F.; Buchanan, J.; Buck, F.D.; Bucke, C.; Buckham, A.; Buckingham, D.; Buckle, P.J.; Bucknall, A.; Buckstone, A.A.; Buckthorpe, Mrs S.; Budworth, D.; Bull, A.L.; Bull, Mrs; Bullock, E.F.; Bullock, I.D.; Bullock, R.W.; Bunce, W.M.; Bundy, A.; Bundy, G.; Burfield, J.; Burges, D.J.; Burkill, H.J.; Burlison, J.; Burn, A.M.; Burn, D.S.; Burr, M.; Burrow, R.; Burrows, H.L.; Burt, D.; Burt, R.; Burton, J.A.; Burton, J.F.; Burton, P.J.; Burtt, E.; Bush, A.K.S.; Butcher, P.; Butcher, R.; Butler, C.G.; Butler, E.A.; Butler, M.; Butler, S.G.; Butterfield, D.; Butterfield, I.; Buxton, R.; Bybee, A.K.; Cabot, D.; Cain, R.; Caithness Loch Survey; Cale, S.R.; Callaghan, D.C.; Callan, I.W.; Callaway, T.; Cameron, E.; Campbell, C.; Campbell, E.W.G.; Campbell, J.K.; Campbell, J.M.; Campion, F.W.; Campion, H.; Candlish, P.A.; Cann, D.; Caradon Natural History Field Club; Carley, M.; Carman, B.M.; Carmichael, N.S.; Carpenter, G.H.; Carpenter, P.; Carr, F.M.B.; Carr, R.; Carrington, L.I.; Carstairs, D.N.; Carter, A.E.J.; Carter, D.J.; Carter, J.W.; Carter, M.; Cartwright, Mrs; Carty, P.; Carvell, K.; Casebourne, W.C.; Casement, P.; Caston, A.E.; Catley, G.P.; Catt, M.; Cawdery, Ms S.; Cawley, P.J.; Cawthorne, D.; Chalkley, A.; Chalmers-Hunt, J.M.; Cham, S.A.; Chamberlin, A.; Champion, G.C.; Champion, M.; Chandler, D.; Chapman, B.L.; Chapman, B.M.; Chapman, E.; Chapman, E.A.; Chapman, F.I.; Chapman, F.J.; Chapman, P.; Chapman, R.A.; Charbonnier, H.J.; Charles, J.S.S.; Charles, P.J.; Charlton, L.H.; Charlton, T.; Charlton, T.D.; Charter, Ms E.; Chaston, H.J.; Chater, A.O.; Chave, Mrs J.E.; Chelmick, D.G.; Chenery, J.M.; Chesham and District Natural History Society; Chetwyn, D.; Cheverton, J.M.; Child, Miss M.; Childs, J.; Childs, P.; Chinery, M.; Chitty, L.D.; Christie, C.; Christie, E.R.; Christie, I.; Christie, I.C.; Christie, L.; Church, A.R.; Churchill, C.; Clare, A.J.; Clark, B.D.; Clark, D.J.; Clark, E.C.; Clark, J.; Clark, P.; Clarke, C.; Clarke, D.J.; Clarke, J.; Clarke, P.M.; Clarkson, P.; Classey, E.W.; Claydon, D.G.; Clayfield, P.; Clayton, H.S.; Clayton, J.; Cleland, A.; Cleland, G.C.; Clements, A.; Clements, D.; Clements, D.K.; Clements, H.A.B.; Clemons, L.; Clifford, A.; Clifford, J.; Clifford, J.A.; Clifford, T.; Clift, W.J.; Clinging, R.; Clist, M.J.; Clive, P.R.; Cloudsley-Thompson, J.L.; Coates, G.; Cobb, P.; Cockburn, T.; Cockle, M.J.D.; Cocks, W.P.; Codd, G.M.; Coetzee, E.F.C.; Coker, A.; Coker, Mrs J.W.; Coker, S.J.; Coldwell, J.D.; Cole, A.; Cole, C.B.; Colegate, V.M.; Coleman, D.; Coles, Miss H.E.; Collar, Ms J.; Colley, L.T.; Collier, I.; Collier, R.V.; Collin, C.J.; Collin, P.N.; Collinson, M.P.; Colmer, A.; Colthrup, C.W.; Colthurst, W.B.; Comont, J.; Connold, E.; Connolly, B.; Cook, A.R.; Cook, B.; Cook, I.; Cook, J.; Cook, M.H.; Cook, N.; Cooke, K.; Coombes, D.; Coombs, F.J.; Cooper, D.; Cooper, D.R.; Cooper, E.; Cooper, J.W.; Cooter, J.; Copson, Mrs P.J.; Corbet, P.S.; Corbet, S.A.;

Corbett, H.H.; Corbett, I.; Corke, D.; Corkhill, P.; Cotton, D.C.F.; Cotton, D.C.R.; Coulthard, R.B.; Coupar, A.; Coventry Museum; Covey, S.J.; Cowan, C.F.; Coward, T.A.; Cowdy, S.; Cowin, W.S.; Cowley, E.V.; Cowley, J.; Cowley, Miss B.; Cox, J.R.; Cozens, N.; Cranefield, P.; Cranston, P.; Crawford, E.; Crawshaw, D.; Crawshaw, Mrs R.; Cremona, J.; Crewe, M.D.; Crick, K.; Crick, P.V.; Cripps, N.; Crofts, D.; Crofts, D.A.; Croker, J.; Crompton, D.W.T.; Cropper, R.S.; Crosby, T.S.; Cross, E.J.; Cross, I.C.; Cross, S.; Crossley, C.; Crossley, R.; Croucher, B.; Crowe, A.; Crowther, N.; Cruttwell, G.H.W.; Cullen, D.; Cullen, J.M.; Cullen, W.R.; Cundale, G.C.; Cundale, J.G.; Curtis, J.; Cutting, K.; D'Oyly, M.; Daborn, R.; Dale, C.W.; Dale, J.C.; Dale, K.; Dale, M.; Dale, W.S.; Dallman, A.A.; Dalton, R.A.; Daltry, H.W.; Daniels, E.T.; Dannreuther, T.; Dapling, J.; Darley, P.L.; Darlington and Teesdale Naturalists Field Club; Darwin; Davey, S.R.; Davidson, J.R.; Davidson, R.; Davidson, T. McLean; Davidson, W.F.; Davies, D.; Davies, D.A.L.; Davies, J.; Davies, M.; Davies, S.; Davis, A.; Davis, A.R.; Davis, G.A.N.; Davis, M.J.; Davis, N.; Davis, P.; Davis, P.E.; Davis, P.S.; Davis, T.A.W.; Davis, W.G.; Daws, J.; Dawson, C.; Dawson, D.G.; Dawson, I.K.; Dawson, J.; Dawson, Mrs N.; Dawson, N.; Day, C.D.; Day, F.H.; Day, J.J.; Day, K.; Day, Ms R.; Day, P.; Dean, A.R.; Dean, M.; Delhanty, J.E.; Dell, D.H.; Dell, J.M.; Dempsey, Mrs M.; Dempster, J.P.; Dempster, P.; Denis, E.; Denman, D.; Dennis, G.C.; Dennis, M.C.; Dent, G.E.; Denton, M.; Derby, E.J.; Dettmar, S.; Deuchar, G.L.; Devonald, S.; Dey, D.; Diaper, L.; Dick, Mrs P.M.; Dickinson, J.; Dicks, D.E.J.; Dickson, B.; Dickson, B.R.; Digby, J.; Dimmock, D.; Dimmock, D.P.; Dingle, T.J.; Dingley, R.N.; Distant, W.L.; Diver, C.; Dixon, A.; Dixon, T.E.; Doarks, C.; Dobson, J.; Dobson, R.; Dobson, R.M.; Dodd, I.; Dodds, R.M.; Dohrn, M.M.; Doidge, H.; Doller, C.W.; Dolling, W.R.; Doncaster, R.; Donisthorpe, H.St.J.K.; Donnithorne, N.J.; Donovan, J.W.; Donovan, P.; Doogue, D.; Doran, R.; Dorman, Mrs; Dorset Countryside Park Force; Dorset Natural History and Archaeological Society; Dorset Naturalists' Trust; Doubleday, H.; Dougall, T.; Douglas, A.; Dove, N.R.; Dove, T.; Dowling, D.; Dowling, N.; Downer, V.J.; Downes, J.A.; Doyle, J.E.; Drake, C.M.; Draper, Mrs F.; Driscoll, R.J.; Driver, A.J.; Driver, C.; Drury, W.D.; Du Feu, G.R.; Ducker, S.; Duddington, J.; Duffin, B.S.; Duffy, H.; Duigan, C.; Dunbar, J.; Duncan, A.B.; Duncan, D.W.; Duncan, P.B.; Duncan, Sir A.B.; Duncan, W.; Dunlop, G.A.; Dunn, Mrs D.; Dunn, P.; Dunn, R.H.; Dunn, T.C.; Dunston, A.; Durkin, J.; Durose, K.; Durrant, K.C.; Dutson, G.M.; Dwyer, P.; Dyson, W. Edwards; Dyson, W.E.; Eales, H.T.; Eales, T.; Earley, J.; East, A.; Eastmead, J.; Eatogh, C.; Eaton, J.C.; Eccles, P.; Eckstein, M.; Edelsten, H.M.; Eden, R.; Edgar, A.; Edmonds, M.R.; Edwards, J.; Edwards, J.S.; Edwards, K.; Edwards, Mrs J.; Edwards, R.M.; Edwards, S.; Eley, Mrs.J.R.; Elias, D.O.; Elkins, N.; Elliott, A.; Elliott, G.A.; Elliott, R.; Ellis, A.E.; Ellis, D.; Ellis, D.E.; Ellis, E.A.; Ellis, P.; Ellis, P.M.; Ellison, G.; Ellison, N.F.; Elphick, D.; Ely, W.A.; Emley, D.; Emmett, E.E.; Emmett, V.S.; Enfield, M.; English, G.; English, P.; Ensor, T.N.; Espin, G.; Evans, A.M.; Evans, C.E.; Evans, D.R.; Evans, E.; Evans, G.; Evans, I.M.; Evans, M.; Evans, Ms F.; Evans, P.A.; Evans, R.; Evans, S.B.; Evans, T.; Evans, W.E.; Evans, W.F.; Eve, H.C.; Everingham, Ms F.; Eversham, B.C.; Exley, J.J.; Exton, Mrs; Eyre, E.; Eyre, M.D.; Eyre, S.; Fair, J.; Fairclough, K.; Falk, S.J.; Faris, R.C.; Farley, P.; Farmer, J.; Farrar, D.A.; Farrell, L.; Farren, G.P.; Farren, J.; Farrow, F.J.L.; Fawcett, J.E.; Fawkes, W.L.; Featherstone, B.; Fehrsen, J.; Felton, C.; Fenton, J.; Fenton, R.; Ferguson, J.; Ficklin, A.; Fiddler, W.; Field, C.M.; Fieldhouse, D.S.; Fielding, J.; Fielding, T.J.; Filby, R.A.; Finch, G.; Fincher, F.; Fitch, E.A.; Fitter, R.S.R.; Fiwek-Smith, C.; Flecknoe, J.; Fleming, J.M.; Fletcher, J.E.; Flinders, I.; Flint, J.B.; Flint, J.D.; Flint, J.H.; Flint, Mrs H.E.; Flory, J.E.; Flumm, D.S.; Fonseca, E.A.d'Assis; Foot, J.B.; Foott, K.G.; Forbes, W.; Ford, L.H.; Ford, R.L.E.; Ford, W.K.; Fordham, W.J.; Formstone, B.; Formstone, P.; Forster, A.P.; Forster, Canon; Forsyth, J.; Fosbury, Mrs I.O.; Foster, A.P.; Foster, G.; Foster, G.N.; Foster, J.; Foster, J.A.; Foster, Mrs.R.; Foster, R.G.; Foster, S.; Fowler, D.; Fowler, S.V.; Fowles, A.P.; Fox, A.D.; Fox, B.W.; Fox, Mrs A.E.M.; Fox, R.; Fox, R.C.E.; Foxwell, D.J.; Frame, J.H.; Francis, I.S.; Fraser, A.; Fraser, F.C.; Fraser, P.A.; Frazer, J.F.D.; Freeman, Ms T.; Freeman, R.H.; Fremlin, H.S.; French, J.; Freshwater Biological Association; Friday, D.N.; Friday, L.E.; Friday, R.D.; Frith, M.; Frost, R.A.; Fry, Mrs, J.; Fry, R.M.; Furley, J.M.; Furneaux, P.J.S.; Gabb, R.; Gabb,

R.G.; Gabbitas, Miss L.; Gaddum, J.H.; Gaffney, Mrs J.E.; Gallagher, H.; Galliford, A.; Gamble, I.B.; Gamble, P.H.; Gambles, R.M.; Gane, C.W.V.; Gardener, P.; Gardener, S.; Gardner, A.E.; Gardner, E.; Gardner, P.; Garland, S.P.; Garner, P.G.; Garner, R.; Garnet, P.; Garrad, Ms L.S.; Garratt, G.; Garside, A.; Gater, A.F.; Gauld, S.; Gaunt, R.G.; Gay, Mrs.C.; Geddes, C.; Geddes, Miss R.; Gee, K.; Geeson, J.D.; Gent, C.J.; Gent, D.R.; George, W.; Gibbons, M.; Gibbons, N.; Gibbons, R.; Gibbs, D.J.; Gibbs, R.; Gibson, C.; Gibson, I.; Giddings, P.; Gifford, D.; Gilbert, Ms D.; Gilbert, O.L.; Giles, S.; Gill, A.; Gill, D.; Gill, Ms E.; Gillam, B.; Gillam, M.; Gillam, Mrs B.; Gilles, W.S.; Gillespie, Mrs E.; Gittings, T.; Gladwin, T.W.; Glaves, D.; Gledhill, T.; Gliddon, D.; Gloaguen, A.; Gloaguen, M-P.; Glover, J.; Glover, Miss S.; Gobbett, R.; Goddard, D.; Goddard, D.G.; Goddard, J.H.; Godfrey, A.; Godfrey, D.U.; Godfrey, R.; Godfrey, R.D.; Goff, R.W.; Going, Rev; Goldsmith, J.G.; Gomersall, C.H.; Gomes, R.; Gondriss, P.; Gonter, M.; Good, J.A.; Goodall, Mrs A.L.; Goodall, R.N.; Goodwin, Miss P.; Goodyear, C.; Goodyear, K.G.; Goom, N.; Gooseman, M.P.; Gordon, P.R.; Gorman, C.; Gorton, E.; Goss, H.; Gotham, P.; Gourlay, D.; Gowenlock, J.; Goyvaerts, P.; Gradwell, A.W.; Graham, A.W.; Graham, E.A.; Graham, M.; Graham, Ms R.; Grainge, C.; Grant, D.; Grant, D.R.; Grant, G.C.; Grant, H.C.; Graves, P.P.; Graves, T.; Gravett, P.; Gray, A.; Gray, J.R.; Gray, T.; Grayson, A.; Grayson, F.W.; Green, A.St.J.; Green, D.; Green, E.; Green, G.; Green, G.P.; Green, J.; Green, K.J.; Green, L.J.; Green, M.; Green, R.; Green, R.E.; Green, S.V.; Green, V.A.; Greenhalf, P.; Greenhill, J.S.; Greensill, Mr; Greenwood, J.; Greer, J.H.; Greville, Dr; Grewcock, D.T.; Grey, P.; Grey, R.N.; Grierson, R.; Griffin, B.; Griffith, D.; Griffiths, D.; Griffiths, M.E.; Griffiths, P.; Griffiths, W.; Grigg, A.D.; Grimshaw, P.H.; Grinstead, K.; Grove, S.J.; Groves, Mr; Grummitt, G.; Grundy, L.; Guest, J.; Guest, J.P.; Gunn, I.; Gush, G.H.; Hadley, M.; Haes, E.C.M.; Haggar, J.; Haigh, T.; Haines, F.H.; Haines, Miss; Halbert, J.N.; Halbert, L.; Hale, J.W.; Hall, C.G.; Hall, C.R.; Hall, G.; Hall, L.; Hall, L.E.; Hall, M.; Hall, Miss M.C.; Hall, R.A.; Hallett, M.; Halliday, J.; Halliday, M.G.; Halligan, C.T.; Halls, J.M.; Halls, L.; Hämäläinen, M.; Hamilton Meikle, J.B.; Hamilton, A.; Hamilton, W.; Hamlet, T.; Hamlett, A.; Hamm, A.H.; Hammersley, D.P.; Hammond, C.O.; Hammond, E.C.; Hammond, H.E.; Hancock, C.; Hancock, E.F.; Hancock, E.G.; Hancock, P.G.; Hanford, D.M.; Hannah, J.; Harcombe, D.J.; Harding, B.D.; Harding, P.T.; Hare, D.; Harle, B.; Harley, A.; Harley, B.H.; Harlington, J.; Harman, T.; Harper, K.G.; Harpley, D.; Harries, H.; Harris, A.; Harris, D.; Harris, J.I.; Harris, L.; Harris, R.; Harrison, F.; Harrison, J.; Harrold, R.; Harrop, A.; Hart, Miss W.; Hartley, B.C.; Hartley, D.; Hartley, J.C.; Harvey, I.; Harvey, I.F.; Harvey, P.; Harvey, R.; Harwood, B.; Harwood, P.; Harwood, W.; Harwood, W.H.; Haskins, L.; Hastings, R.; Havers, S.J.; Hawell, J.; Hawker, D.M.; Hawkins, K.; Hawkins, Miss K.M.; Hawkins, R.D.; Hawkswell, A.; Hawley, R.; Hawley, R.G.; Haycock, R.J.; Haydock, K.; Hayhow, S.J.; Hayman, P.V.; Haynes, J.; Haynes, P.G.; Hayward, H.H.S.; Haywood, P.; Hazelwood, A.; Hazlehurst, G.; Headley, A.D.; Heardman, C.; Hearn, J.; Heath, J.; Heath, J.J.; Heath, K.; Heath, Mrs.K.; Heath, P.J.; Heaton, A.; Heaver, D.J.; Hedley, I.; Heeley, A.; Hemsley, J.H.; Henderson, A.; Henderson, M.; Henderson, Mrs B.; Henderson, T.W.; Hendry, C.H.; Henegan, K.; Henrickson, L.; Henrickson, W.; Henry, Ms M.; Henson, H.E.; Henton, A.; Henty, C.J.; Herbert, C.; Herlihy, Ms D.J.; Herring, C.M.; Herring, J.L.; Heslop-Harrison, G.; Heslop-Harrison, J.W.; Hewer, T.F.; Hewetson, Miss A.; Hewitson, D.; Hewitt, D.J.; Hewitt, P.M.; Hewitt, S.; Hewitt, S.M.; Hewson, F.; Hewson, H.E.; Hey, W.C.; Hick, A.E.; Hickey, P.; Hickin, N.E.; Higgins, M.; Higgins, R.C.; Higgott, J.B.; Higgs, A.B.; Hignett, J.; Hignett, S.; Hill, J.E.; Hill, P.; Hill, R.N.; Hillcox, P.; Hills, S.G.; Hilton, B.S.; Hilyer, C.; Hinchcliffe, G.; Hinchon, G.; Hincks, W.D.; Hind, S.; Hind, S.H.; Hipkin, P.; Hipperson, D.; Hirst, D.J.; Hirst, W.R.; Hobbs, A.; Hobbs, J.; Hobbs, N.; Hockin, D.; Hodge, H.; Hodges, J.; Hodges, R.; Hodgetts, N.G.; Hodgkinson, R.F.; Hodgson, Mr; Hodgson, S.B.; Hodson, A.; Hogg, Ms S.; Hoines, P.H.; Hold, A.; Hold, A.I.; Hold, A.J.; Holden, C.R.; Holland, Mrs S.C.; Holland, W.; Holliday, S.; Holloway, D.; Hollowday, E.; Holmes, A.; Holmes, J.D.; Holmes, J.W.D.; Holton, N.; Honey, Mr; Hooton, G.P.; Hooton, S.; Hopcroft, D.J.; Hopkins, D.J.; Hopkins, G.; Hopkins, P.; Hopkirk, A.; Horne, F.; Horne, S.; Horton, G.A.N.; Horton, P.J.; Hosking, C.F.; Houghton, A.; Houghton, J.T.;

Howard, G.; Howard, L.W.; Howe, M.; Howe, S.R.; Howell, A.C.; Howells, L.; Howes, Mrs M.; Howson, J.; Hubbard, A.C.; Hubbard, J.K.; Hughes, A.; Hughes, D.; Hughes, J.; Hughes, J.D.; Hughes, M.R.; Hughes, Mrs A.; Hughes, N.; Hughes, P.; Hughes, R.A.D.; Hughes, T.P.; Hull, A.; Hull, M.; Hulme, D.C.; Humphrey, J.; Humphreys, M.; Hunt, D.; Hunt, N.V.; Hunter, A.; Hunter, E.; Hutchinson, G.; Hutton, J.; Hyde, D.H.; Hyde, G.E.; Hynd, W.R.B.; Ikin, Miss H.; Iles, A.C.; Iliff, D.A.; Iliff, J.; Imms, A.D.; Imms, A.W.; Innes, M.; Inns, B.; Inskip, Mrs.C.; Irby, Lt.-Col.; Ireland, D.T.; Irvine, A.; Irwin, A.G.; Ismay, J.; Izzard, M.J.; Jackson, A.; Jackson, B.E.; Jackson, Miss A.C.; Jackson, N.; Jackson, P.; Jackson, R.; Jaeger, M.; Jagger, D.; James, H.; James, M.; James, Mrs M.; Jarman, Miss; Jarman, R.B.; Jarvis, Mrs M.; Jebbett, D.E.; Jeffer, D.; Jeffers, D.; Jeffers, D.J.; Jeffs, J.; Jenkins, C.R.; Jenkins, D.; Jenkins, J.R.W.; Jenkins, R.A.; Jenner, H.E.; Jenner, J.H.A.; Jenner, Mrs G.; Jennings, D.A.; Jenyns, L.; Jermyn, T.; Jewell, D.; Joachim, Prof; Jobe, J.B.; Jodicke, D.; Jodicke, K.; Jodicke, R.; Johnson, C.; Johnson, I.; Johnson, K.; Johnson, V.S.; Johnson, W.F.; Johnston, A.J.; Jones, A.Vaughan; Jones, B.J.H.; Jones, B.L.; Jones, D.A.; Jones, D.G.; Jones, D.H.; Jones, G.; Jones, H.; Jones, H.P.; Jones, J.H.N.; Jones, J.L.; Jones, J.R.E.; Jones, M.; Jones, M.R.; Jones, Mrs C.M.; Jones, P.; Jones, R.; Jones, R.A.; Jones, R.E.; Jones, S.P.; Jones, T.A.; Jourdain, F.C.R.; Judd, S.; Justin. S.H.F.W.; Kand, H.; Kane, W.F. de Vismes; Keall, R.M.; Kearney, Miss J.; Keats, E.M.; Keeler, P.; Keeley, N.; Keeling, Ms. N.; Keen, D.; Keenan, S.; Keeping, A.J.; Kefford, R.W.K.; Keighley, J.; Kelham, Mrs A.; Kelly, P.; Kemp, R.G.K.; Kemp, S.W.; Kempster, D.; Kendall, A.; Kendall, I.; Kennedy, D.; Kennedy, S.; Kerry, J.C.; Kesby, J.; Kettell, M.; Kettle, R.H.; Keylock, J.G.; Keys, J.H.; Khan, R.J.; Kiauta, B.; Killington, F.J.; Kimmins, D.E.; King, D.; King, E.; King, G.J.; King, J.J.F.X.; King, N.H.; King, P.; King, S.; Kingham, D.; Kingham, D.L.; Kinnear, P.; Kirby, M.A.; Kirby, P.; Kirk, P.; Kirkwood, D.S.; Kitching, D.; Kittle, T.; Knight, G.; Knight, R.B.; Knight, R.C.; Knights, R.; Knill-Jones, R.; Knill-Jones, S.A.; Knott, R.A.; Knowler, J.; Knowles, J.T.; Koenigswarter, K. de; Kohli, M.; Kramer, J.; Kruys, I.P.; Kydd, D.W.; Kyle, D.; Kyle, P.; Laddin, S.S.; Ladywalk Nature Reserve Report; Laidlaw, F.F.; Laidlaw, W.B.; Laidler, W.R.; Laing, A.I.; Laing, R.M.; Laing, S.; Lake, S.; Lamb, R.; Lamerton, J.F.; Lane, R.; Laney, T.J.; Lang, G.W.; Lang, W.D.; Lang, W.G.; Langdon, R.; Langham, Sir C.; Langhorne, J.; Langton, P.H.; Lansbury, I.; Larsen, H.; Last, W.J.; Latham, H.A.; Latimer, B.; Laugher, R.C.; Laverick, J.; Lavers, N.; Lawman, J.; Lawson, K.; Lawton, J.H.; Le Boutillier, A.J.; Le Gros, A.; Le Masurier, P.C.; Le Quesne, W.J.; Le Sueur, F.; Leach, A.; Leach, S.; Leach, T.; Leach, W.E.; Leadbetter, M.; Leavett, R.; Lee, M.; Lee, Miss R.; Leece, J.; Lees, A.J.; Leicester Literary and Philosophical Society; Leicester Museum; Lelliott, T.; Lemmon, W.E.; Lepard, G.F.; Lester, D.; Letsche, R.; Leven, M.; Levy, E.T.; Lewis, A.; Lewis, C.; Lewis, D.C.; Lewis, G.E.; Lewis, J.; Lewis, M.; Lewis, N.; Leyshon, O.J.; Lightfoot, K.E.; Limb, K.; Limb, Mrs P.A.; Limbert, M.; Linch, J.R.; Lindsay, M.; Line, J.M.; Ling, S.; Linton, E.J.; Lipscomb, R.J.; List, G.P.; Liston, A.; Little, D.; Liverpool Naturalists' Field Club; Livingstone, A.; Lloyd, B.; Lloyd, Ms S.; Lloyd-Evans, L.; Llyn-Jones, A.P.; Loan, A.; Lock, M.H.; Lockwood, B.; Lockwood, R.G.; Lodge, J.; Lofthouse, T.A.; London Natural History Society; Long, A.G.; Long, Mrs M.; Long, Mrs M.L.; Long, R.; Longfield, Miss C.; Longman, L.; Lonsdale, I.; Lonsdale, M.; Lord, D.J.; Lott, D.A.; Louch, C.S.; Lowe, A.; Lowe, A.F.; Lowe, C.J.; Lowenstein, T.; Lowmass, C.D.; Lucas, B.; Lucas, M.J.; Lucas, Mrs J.; Lucas, W.J.; Luff, W.A.; Lumm, D.S.F.; Lunn, J.; Lyell, Mr; Lynes, M.; Lyon, R.; Lyons, C.; Lyszkowski, R.M.; MacDonald, M.; MacGillavry, Miss; MacLean, G.; MacLennan, A.; MacLeod, I.; MacNeill, N.; MacRitchie, D.; MacVicar, S.M.; Macan, T.T.; Macdonald, A.; Macdonald, M.A.; Mace, H.; Macgowan, I.; Mackay, A.J.; Mackay, J.; Mackenzie, Ms E.; Mackenzie, S.; Mackindlay, V.; Mackinnon, M.; Macklin, R.N.; Mackrill, E.; Mackworth-Praed, C.W.; Macmillan, N.W.; Macneill, N.; Maddison, P.; Madge, S.C.; Magee, J.; Mahon, A.; Mahony, R.H.; Mainstone, C.P.; Maitland, P.S.; Mallet, J.; Malpass, A.; Maltby, Miss M.; Malton, N.; Malton, P.; Manley, S.; Mann, A.J.; Mann, R.B.; Mapplebeck, P.; Mardle, D.V.; Marmont, A.M.; Marquand, E.D.; Marren, P.R.; Marrs, B.; Marsh, A.; Marsh, M.C.; Marsh, P.; Marshall, Mrs J.A.; Marshall, Mrs.H.; Marshall, P.; Marshall, T.A.; Marshall, T.F.; Martin, D.;

Martin, J.; Martin, J.P.; Martin, J.R.; Martin, Miss P.; Martin, N.; Martin, N.A.; Martin, S.; Martin, T.; Martineau, A.H.; Marwick, Miss F.C.; Mash, K.; Maskew, R.; Maslen, R.; Mason, C.F.; Mason, J.L.; Mason, J.M.; Massee, A.M.; Massey, K.; Mather, J.R.; Mathias, J.H.; Matthews, J.; Matthews, M.G.; Mattingley, W.; Mawby, F.J.; Mawdsley, T.; Maxey, D.; May, G.E.; May, M.; Maynard, Mrs; Mayo, M.C.A.; McAleavy, D.; McCabe, E.; McCabe, L.; McCarty, C.; McCarty, H.; McCleary, J.; McConnell, Mrs A.; McConway, J.; McCraw, D.A.; McCreaddie, G.; McCutcheon, D.; McEvry, Mr; McEwen, Ms E.; McFarland, V.M.; McGeeney, A.; McGibbon, R.; McGregor, J.M.; McGregor, T.M.; McKerchar, H.; McLachlan, R.; McLean, I.F.G.; McLellan, J.; McLeod, C.R.; McMillan, Miss N.F.; McMullin, A.; McNamee, M.; McNaughton, J.; McOnie, R.J.; McShane, R.; McVey, D.; Mearns, J.; Measday, A.V.; Meharg, M.; Meiklejohn, J.; Mellor, D.G.; Mellor, M.J.; Melrose, W.; Mendel, H.; Mendham, Mrs M.L.; Menendez, C.T.; Meredith, G.H.; Meredith, G.H.J.; Meredith, J.; Merret, P.; Merrifield, R.K.; Merritt, A.; Merritt, R.; Merritt, W.; Metcalf, F.; Metcalfe, J.W.W.; Michael, P.; Michaelis, H.N.; Michelmore, A.P.G.; Miles, J.; Miles, P.M.; Milford, P.J.; Mill, P.J.; Miller, D.; Miller, K.F.; Miller, K.W.; Miller, P.L.; Mills, R.; Milne, B.S.; Milne-Redhead, E.; Milner, G.; Milton Abbey Natural History Society; Milton, F.; Minihane, J.; Minor, J.W.; Minshall, J.; Mist, B.; Mitchell, D.; Mitchell, G.A.; Mitchell, J.; Mitchell, P.; Mitchell, P.J.; Mitchell, S.H.; Moffat, C.B.; Moffatt, A.T.; Molly, M.; Molyneux, J.; Moon, A.A.; Moon, A.V.; Moon, H.P.; Moon, S.; Moorcroft, Miss S.; Moore, A.; Moore, B.P.; Moore, D.W.; Moore, J.J.; Moore, J.L.; Moore, K.F.; Moore, L.; Moore, N.; Moore, N.W.; Moore, P.; Moralee, A.K.; Moran, S.A.; Moreton, B.D.; Morgan, I.K.; Morgan, J.; Morgan, Mrs M.J.; Morgan, Y.; Moriarty, C.; Morley, C.; Morris, G.J.; Morris, J.; Morris, Mrs F.; Morris, R.; Morrison, J.; Morse, R.; Morss, J.R.; Mortimer, E.; Mortimer, N.; Morton, J.A.; Morton, K.J.; Morton, K.V.F.; Moseley, K.A.; Moseley, M.; Mosely, M.E.; Mosley, S.L.; Mowat, M.; Moxam, D.; Muddeman, J.L.; Muggleton, R.; Muller, A.; Mundell, A.; Mundell, A.R.; Mundell, A.R.G.; Mundy, A.V.; Murdoch, D.; Murphy, D.; Murphy, K.; Murphy, M.D.; Murphy, Ms D.; Murray, A.M.; Murray, D.E.; Murray, K.; Murray, R.; Muschamp, J.H.; Muschamp, P.A.H.; Muscott, Miss J.; Music, A.H.; Music, J.; Music, N.; Nall, J.; Nash, R.; Nathan, L.; Nature Conservancy Council; Nau, B.S.; Naylor, G.; Neal, E.G.; Nelson, B.; Nelson, M.; Nelson, R.J.; Nelson, W.N.A.; Nesbitt, L.; Neville, A.C.; Newbold, C.; Newman, E.; Newman, G.; Newsome-Davies, K.; Newton, A.; Newton, A.H.; Newton, G.E.; Newton, J.; Newton, P.; Newton, R.J.; Nichol, Mrs C.; Nicholls, C.; Nicholls, S.P.; Nicholson, G.; Nicholson, J.B.; Nicholson, P.A.; Nicol, I.M.; Nisbet, R.G.; Nobes, C.; Noonan, G.C.; Norgate, F.; Norman, T.; Norris, A.; Norris, F.; Norris, Mrs A.; Norriss, T.; North Kent Wildlife Preservation Society; North, A.; North, M.; North, S.; Northern Naturalists' Union; Northridge, H.; Northridge, Mrs H.; Northridge, R.; Norton, F.; Norton, J.; Norton, W.J.; Nottage, L.E.; Nottage, R.L.; Nugent, E.W.T.; O'Brien, J.; O'Brine, T.; O'Byrne, D.; O'Carroll, A.; O'Conner, Mrs N.; O'Connor, F.; O'Connor, J.P.; O'Connor, M.A.; O'Donnell, C.; O'Donovan, J.E.; O'Farrell, A.F.; O'Flanagan, C.; O'Keeffe, C.; O'Leary, A.; O'Leary, P.; O'Mahony, E.; O'Meara, M.; O'Neill, M.A.; O'Rourke, F.; O'Shea, T.; O'Sullivan, D.J.; O'Toole, C.; Oakley, E.H.N.; Oates, M.; Odin, N.; Ogilvie, M.; Okill, J.D.; Oldale, R.; Oldham, G.; Oliver, Ms C.; Ollerearnshaw, Mrs J.; Onslow, N.; Orpe, K.J.; Osborne, Mr; Osbourne, R.D.; Osley, N.J.; Osman, J.; Ostler, J.; Oswick, D.; Otsu, Miss M.; Otter, J.; Owen, C.M.; Owen, J.A.; Owen, M.; Owen, Mrs J.; Oxenham, J.V.; Pack-Beresford, D.R.; Packer, L.; Page, A.E.; Page, J.J.; Paget, C.J.; Paget, J.; Palfrey, S.; Palmer, C.; Palmer, D.; Palmer, G.; Palmer, K.W.K.; Palmer, L.G.; Palmer, Mrs M.; Palmer, Q.; Palmer, R.; Palmer, S.; Palmer, S.J.; Palmer, T.W.; Panter, A.; Panter, A.J.; Parfitt, Mr; Parker, A.; Parker, A.P.; Parker, B.N.; Parker, D.M.; Parker, H.G.; Parker, Mrs J.E.; Parker, T.N.; Parker, W.; Parkin, G.; Parmenter, L.; Parr, A.J.; Parr, M.J.; Parrack, J.D.; Parry, J.; Parsons, A.; Parsons, A.J.; Parsons, D.; Parsons, E.; Parsons, R.M.; Parsons, T.; Partridge, J.; Passant, M.; Passey, L.; Patel, D.; Paton, J.A.; Paton, V.S.; Patrick, E.W.; Patterson, D.; Paul, C.; Paul, J.; Paul, M.F.; Paulford, E.; Paull, D.; Pavett, P.M.; Payne, D.; Payne, E.M.; Payne, K.; Payne, R.G.; Payne, R.M.; Paynter, D.; Paynter, R.;

Peacey, A.W.; Peachey, Miss C.; Peers, M.; Pelham, Mrs A.; Pelham-Clinton, E.C.; Pender, S.; Pendlebury, B.; Pendlebury, R.E.; Penfold, N.; Penhallurick, R.D.; Penketh, P.W.; Penn-Smith, E.M.; Pennie, I.D.; Pennington, M.G.; Pepin, C.E.; Perkins, J.F.; Perkins, R.C.L.; Perks, R.; Perrens, C.J.; Perry, A.D.; Perry, A.R.; Perry, D.; Perry, E.; Perry, J.; Perry, J.W.; Peterkin, A.; Peters, J.; Peters, J.C.; Petley-Jones, R.A.; Petrie, A.B.; Pettit, R.C.; Philip, E.; Phillips, J.; Phillips, Mrs. P.; Phillips, N.J.; Phillips, R.A.; Philp, B.; Philp, E.G.; Philp, P.; Philp, T.; Philpott, A.I.; Pickard, B.C.; Pickess, B.; Pickess, B.P.; Pickles, M.E.; Pickup, A.R.; Pickup, J.; Pidgeon, R.N.; Pierce, C.C.; Pierce, L.C.; Pilkington, G.; Pilkington, Miss R.; Pinder, L.C.V.; Pinguey, D.K.; Pinkess, L.H.; Pinney, R.J.; Pinniger, E.B.; Piotrowski, A.K.; Piotrowski, M.S.; Piotrowski, S.H.; Pirie, M.; Pitcher, D.; Pitchers, D.R.; Pitchford, V.L.; Pitt, R.; Pittkin, Mrs D.M.; Plant, C.W.; Plant, S.; Pollinger, B.R.; Pont, A.C.; Pontin, A.J.; Porritt, G.T.; Porter, J.; Porter, K.; Potter, B.J.; Potter, J.; Potts, J.; Poulter, D.; Poulton, E.B.; Powell, Mrs M.; Powers, Mr; Powrie, K.; Powrie, K.J.; Praeger, R.L.; Pratley, P.; Pratt, Mrs M.M.; Prendergast, E.D.V.; Prendergast, N.H.D.; Prest, J.; Preston, T.; Preston-Mafham, K.G.; Price, A.; Price, J.; Price, R.; Price, S.O.V.; Pringle, W.; Pritty, D.G.; Proctor, D.A.; Proctor, H.; Prosser, R.; Pryce, R.D.; Pulford, E.; Pullen, G.; Pummell, B.D.; Pummell, B.E.; Purchas, W.H.; Purves, D.N.; Purves, J.S.; Putnam, C.D.; Pye, D.; Pyman, G.; Pyman, H.A.; Pyman, Q.; Quayle, E.; Quigley, R.L.; Quin, P.C.; Quinn, P.; Quirke, M.; Radford, A.P.; Radford, D.J.; Radley, D.; Radley, Mrs D.; Rae, R.; Raine, P.; Rampton, A.; Randall, H.; Randall-Jackson, A.; Randolph, S.; Rands, D.G.; Rands, Mrs E.B.; Rankin, D.W.H.; Rankin, W.T.C.; Ransom, B.; Ransome, K.; Ratcliffe, D.A.; Ratcliffe, M.J.; Rau, J.; Raven, P.J.; Rawcliffe, C.P.; Rayner, J.; Rayner, Ms J.M.; Raynor, R.; Read, J.; Read, R.W.J.; Reading Museum; Rear, D.; Reavey, S.; Rebane, M.; Rebecca, G.W.; Redgate, N.D.; Redgeley, Mr; Redgrave, J.R.; Redman, B.; Redshaw, E.J.; Reed, A.; Reed, S.; Rees, D.; Rees, J.; Reeve, Dr and Mrs P.J.; Regan, C.; Reid, D.; Reid, Mrs E.; Reid, Mrs M.; Reid, S.; Reinhold, A.; Renals, T.J.; Reynolds, J.D.; Reynolds, Ms J.R.; Rheinholdt, A.; Ribbands, B.; Ribbon, G.; Rice, D.J.; Rice, T.; Richards, A.; Richards, A.J.; Richards, A.P.; Richards, A.W.; Richards, J.; Richards, M.; Richards, O.W.; Richardson, A.T.; Richardson, N.W.; Richardson, P.W.; Richardson, T.; Richmond, D.; Richmond, D.I.; Ridgill, S.C.; Rigden, S.P.; Rigney, S.; Riley, J.; Riley, K.; Riley, Mrs J.; Rimmer, J.; Rintoul, L.J.; Rippey, I.; Ris, F.; Ritchie, A.B.; Ritchie, R.J.; Rivett, A.; Roach, Mrs S.; Robbins, J.; Robbins, M.T.; Roberts, A.; Roberts, F.J.; Roberts, G.; Roberts, J.; Roberts, J.E.H.; Roberts, R.; Roberts, S.; Roberts, W.W.; Robertson, B.; Robertson, D.A.; Robertson, L.R.; Robertson, M.; Robertson, Major; Robertson, T.S.; Robins, Ms M.; Robinson, C.A.; Robinson, H.P.K.; Robinson, K.; Robinson, M.C.; Robinson, P.M.; Robinson, R.; Robinson, T.; Robinson, T.J.; Robinson, W.R.; Robson, J.J.; Roche, P.J.; Roderick, E.; Roderick, H.; Rodger, A.M.; Rodway, D.A.; Roff, D.; Rogers, B.; Rogers, M.; Rogers, P.; Rogers, R.H.; Rogerson, J.P.; Ronayne, C.; Rooke, S.; Roper, Miss I.M.; Roper, P.; Rose, I.; Rotheroe, G.; Rothney, E.; Rowden, A.O.; Rowe, J.; Rowe, L.; Rowland, Mrs K.M.; Royal Society for the Protection of Birds; Royles, K.; Rudd, Mrs W.; Ruddick, H.; Rugby School Natural History Society; Russel, R.J.; Russel, T.; Russell, C.; Russell, H.M.; Russell, M.; Russell, P.G.; Rutherford, C.I.; Ryan, E.; Ryan, E.P.; Ryan, M.; Ryrie, J.; Sadler, D.; Sage, B.; Sage, B.L.; Sage, J.A.; Salmon, M.A.; Salmon, P.; Salter, J.H.; Salter, M.; Sampson, D.; Sampson, Ms C.; Samson, D.; Samuel, R.L.; Samways, M.J.; Samworth, M.; Sanders, J.D.; Sanderson, D.; Sanderson, M.R.; Sanderson, Ms M.; Sanford, M.N.; Sankey, J.H.P.; Sansbury, B.; Saul, K.G.; Saunders, D.R.; Saunders, J.W.; Saunt, G.W.; Sauze, H.A.; Savage, A.A.; Savan, B.; Savidge, J.P.; Sawyer, N.L.; Sayer, C.J.W.; Scampion, B.R.; Scaysbrook, K.R.; Scharff, R.F.; Schaub, R.G.; Schofield, P.; Schofield, T.; Scholey, G.; Schuchard, C.; Scott, A.; Scott, A.G.; Scott, D.W.; Scott, M.; Scott, Miss H.; Scott, Mrs M.E.; Scott, W.; Scrimgeour, C.M.; Scruton, D.; Scudder, G.G.E.; Seaby, D.A.; Seaby, W.A.; Searle, J.; Searle, J.B.; Seawright, D.; Seddon, E.A.; Seddon, J.; Sellers, R.M.; Selys-Longchamps, E. de; Sergeant, C.R.; Service, M.W.; Shackleton, J.; Shanahan, M.J.; Shannon, Mrs G.; Sharman, S.G.; Sharp, D.; Sharpe, N.; Sharrock, N.; Shattock, M.; Shaw, B.; Shaw, C.E.; Shaw, E.; Shaw, P.; Shaw, R.; Shaw, S.; Shayer, C.J.; Sheasby, J.; Sheasby, P.; Sheldrake, V.; Shelton, B.; Shelton, H.M.A.; Shennan, N.M.; Shenton, F.W.; Shepard, B.; Sheppard, D.A.; Sheppard, Mrs F.V.S.; Sheppard, R.; Sherringham, C.; Shetland Entomological Group; Shimmings, P.; Shimmings, P.J.; Shipley, D.; Shirt, D.B.; Shortland, G.; Shortridge-Clarke, H.; Showers, J.; Showler, D.A.; Shreeves, W.G.; Siewruk, J.; Sills, N.; Silock, L.; Silsby, Mrs J.; Simper, I.J.; Simpson, A.N.B.; Simpson, B.; Simpson, P.J.; Simpson, V.R.; Sims, C.; Simson, R.A.; Sinnott, A.; Skeen, R.Q.; Skelton, M.J.L.; Skerritt, J.E.; Skidmore, P.; Skinner, J.; Slack, C.; Slade, A.M.; Slade, B.; Slade, B.E.; Slade, D.J.; Slade, S.; Slater, F.; Slater, H.; Slater, J.; Slater, M.; Sleeman, P.; Small, D.; Small, H.; Small, R.; Smallshire, D.; Smart, P.E.; Smellie, W.J.; Smith, B.; Smith, C.; Smith, D.A.; Smith, D.H.; Smith, D.J.; Smith, E.; Smith, E.J.; Smith, E.M.; Smith, F.T.; Smith, H.R.; Smith, I.D.; Smith, J.L.; Smith, K.G.V.; Smith, L.; Smith, L.N.S.; Smith, L.R.; Smith, M.; Smith, Mrs E.M.; Smith, Mrs G.A.; Smith, N.; Smith, P.; Smith, P.A.; Smith, P.H.; Smith, R.A.H.; Smith, R.E.N.; Smith, R.G.; Smith, R.W.; Smith, R.W.J.; Smith, S.; Smith, S.G.; Smith, S.J.; Smith, T.; Smith, W.E.; Smout, R.; Snow, M.; Soames, P.; Soane, I.D.; Sollis, D.; Solman, D.; Solman, Mrs Z.; Somerville, A.; Sorensen, J.; Sotheby, R.M.; South, R.; Southall, R.; Southern, Mrs; Southwood, R.; Sparshall, J.; Speight, M.C.D.; Speirs, R.A.; Spence, F.; Spencer, A.G.; Spencer, J.; Spencer, J.W.; Speyer, E.R.; Spinks, P.; Spirit, M.G.; Spirit, Mrs M.G.; Spittal, R.J.; Spragge, F.; Spray, C.; Spray, S.; Spriggs, I.; Spriggs, Mrs D.; Spring, N.; Squire, H.; Squires, B.R.; Squires, R.; Stace, H.; Stacey, A.; Stacey, D.R.; Stallwood, B.R.; Stammers, M.; Stanbridge, R.; Stanley, B.; Stanley, J.M.; Stanley, L.; Steeden, D.; Steedman, J.; Steedman, J.C.; Steedon, D.; Steedon, J.; Steel, C.; Steel, D.; Steel, Miss C.; Steel, Mrs C.; Steele, K.; Steer, J.; Stelfox, A.W.; Stephens, D.; Stephens, S.; Stephenson, E.M.; Stephenson, Mrs E.M.; Stevenson, J.; Stewart, L.; Stewart, N.; Still, E.C.; Stirling, A.M.; Stocks, H.; Stokes, H.G.; Stokoe, R.; Stone G.P.; Stone, G.P.; Stone, J.; Stone, Mr; Stonor, C.R.; Stooke, D.; Storer, B.; Storer, L.A.; Storey, C.; Stott, M.; Stout, K.B.; Strachan, I.M.; Strachen, R.; Stratford, A.; Street, L.; Stringer, B.; Stringer, R.N.; Stroud, D.A.; Stuart-Wright, W.; Stubbs, A.E.; Sturdy, P.; Suffern, C.; Summers, P.; Summersby, L.; Summersgill, A.; Summerson, F.C.; Sumner, B.; Sumner, D.P.; Sumner, E.D.; Sumner, J.Q.; Sumner, Mrs J.; Surry, R.J.; Sussex, D.J.; Sutton, R.D.; Sutton, S.; Swailes, R.; Swaine, C.M.; Swale. J.; Swales, J.D.; Swanson, S.; Swinnerton, B.F.A.; Swinnerton, C.F.M.; Swire, P.; Sykes, E.A.; Sykes, M.; Sykes, T.; Symes, N.; Tagg, D.; Tailby, T.W.; Tait, T.; Tait, T.N.; Talbot, G.; Tannett, P.G.; Tarbat, J.E.; Tarpey, T.; Tate, N.; Tattersall, W.; Taylor, B.J.; Taylor, D.; Taylor, H.; Taylor, J.C.; Taylor, J.R.; Taylor, M.; Taylor, M.P.; Taylor, Mrs G.; Taylor, Ms A.; Taylor, N.; Taylor, N.W.; Taylor, P.; Taylor, R.; Taylor, R.T.; Taylor, S.; Taylor, W.; Taylor, W.T.; Teagle, W.G.; Teague, D.; Telfer, M.G.; Tew, I.F.; Thannett, P.G.; Theaker, J.; Theobald, F.V.; Thickett, A.J.; Thickett, L.A.; Thomas, C.; Thomas, D.I.; Thomas, D.L.; Thomas, G.H.; Thomas, J.; Thomas, J.A.; Thomas, K.; Thomas, K.I.; Thomas, M.P.; Thomas, P.J.; Thomas, R.M.; Thomas, S.C.; Thomas, T.; Thompson, B.; Thompson, B.G.; Thompson, D.; Thompson, D.J.; Thompson, E.; Thompson, I.S.; Thompson, J.; Thompson, J.M.; Thompson, Mrs.H.; Thompson, P.; Thompson, R.; Thomson, D.A.R.; Thomson, W.; Thorne, G.; Thorne, R.I.; Thornhill, W.B.; Thornley, A.; Thorpe, E.; Thorpe, R.; Thouless, H.J.; Threlfall, J.H.; Thurgate, H.C.; Thurner, M.; Tickner, M.; Tilling, M.R.; Tinning, P.; Tinning, P.C.; Tipple, D.; Todd, M.V.E.; Tofield, S.; Tolhurst, D.J.; Tomlin, P.; Tomlinson, R.; Tooley, J.; Towns, M.; Toyne, A.; Trail, J.W.H.; Trayner, Mrs M.; Treadwell, P.; Treloar, P.T.; Tremewan, W.G.; Trett, M.W.; Trigg, R.; Trim, H.; Trinder, G.; Trodd, P.; Troup, R.D.R.; Trubridge, M.; Trump, R.D.; Truscott, L.A.C.; Tubb, J.; Tubbs, C.J.; Tucker, D.; Tucker, D.C.; Tufts, I.P.; Tulloch, R.; Tulloh, B.; Tully, H.; Tunnard, J.; Tunnard, T.; Turk, Mrs S.M.; Turner, A.H.; Turner, G.; Turner, H.J.; Turner, J.; Turner, J.H.; Turner, J.R.G.; Turner, Miss A.; Turner, R.; Turner, S.; Turrell, R.; Turrell, R.E.; Tweedie, W.; Tweedle, R.; Tweedy, L.; Twissell, I.; Twissell, Mr and Mrs C.F.; Twissell, Mr; Tyler, M.W.; Underdown, S.J.; Unwin, W.C.; Urwin, W.; Usher, M.B.; Vallins, F.T.; Van Der Klei, J.; Vandome, P.; Varney, P.L.; Vaughan, A.; Vaughan, I.M.; Vaughan, Miss O.; Venables, Mrs A.V.; Verdcourt, B.; Vick, G.S.; Vickers, J.G.; Vickers, S.E.F.; Vincent, E.; Vokins, M.; Wade, P.M.; Wagstaffe, R.; Wain, C.B.; Wainwright, C.W.; Wake, A.; Wake, A.J.; Wakeley, R.; Wakely, S.; Waldie, G.; Walker, A.M.; Walker, B.; Walker, B.D.; Walker, B.J.;

Walker, D.S.; Walker, F.A.; Walker, I.; Walker, J.; Walker, J.J.; Walker, Rev Dr; Wallace, A.; Wallace, B.; Wallace, I.D.; Wallace, T.J.; Waller, C.S.; Waller, G.; Walls, R.; Walls, R.C.; Walpole, M.; Walsh, G.B.; Walter, M.F.; Walton, G.A.; Warbrook, J.P.; Warburton, R.; Ward, J.; Ward, P.H.; Ward-Smith, A.J.; Ward-Smith, J.; Warden, Miss K.J.; Warden, P.; Waring, E.; Waring, P.; Warman, Ms E.; Warman, S.; Warne, A.C.; Warner, D.; Warner, R.; Warnock, D.; Warnock, J.S.; Warren, A.; Warren, D.; Warren, M.S.; Warren, R.G.; Warrington, Mrs J.E.; Warrington, R.; Warwick, C.; Warwick, S.; Wash, J.; Wash, R.J.; Watchman, A.; Waterhouse, E.A.; Waterhouse, M.; Waters, E.G.R.; Waters, R.; Waterston, A.R.; Waterton, P.; Watkins, E.P.; Watkins, M.; Watkins, O.G.; Watson, A.J.; Watson, N.C.; Watson, R.; Watson, R.A.; Watson, W.; Watt, D.; Watt, K.R.; Watt, R.; Watts, B.; Watts, C.E.D.; Watts, H.J.; Watts, N.D.; Weal, R.D.; Weatherhead, Ms R.; Weaver, D.J.; Weaver, J.; Weaver, R.; Webb, C.; Webb, D.F.; Webb, K.; Webb, P.; Webb, P.C.; Webber, G.L.; Webster, B.D.; Webster, E.G.; Weedon, K.; Weeks. A.; Weir, A.J.; Welch, G.R.; Welch, J.; Wells, C.E.; Wells, T.; Welstead, A.R.; Welstead, A.R; Welstead, N.I.; Wenham, Mrs S.; Wentworth, B.; West, B.B.; Westerhoff, D.; Weston, T.; Westwood, W.D.; Wetton, B.; Weyl, R.; Whaley, F.W.; Wheeler, D.; Whellan, J.A.; Whitaker, T.M.; Whitaker, W.J.; White, G.J.; White, H.V.; White, J.R.; White, P.; White, S.; Whitehead, R.; Whitehead, R.W.; Whitehead, T.; Whitehead, T.P.; Whitehouse, F.I.; Whitelaw, A.; Whiteley, D.; Whitlock, D.; Whittaker, O.; Whittles, Mrs C.A.; Wickens, D.; Wicklings, Mrs D.; Widden, B.J.; Wigglesworth, B.; Wilcox, C.; Wilcox, M.; Wild, E.H.; Wild, J.; Wild, O.H.; Wildfowl Trust; Wildridge, G.F.; Wiley, M.; Wilkingson, Mr; Wilkinson, L.; Wilkinson, Miss M.J.; Wilkinson, T.; Willamson, G.R.; Willcox, J.M.; Williams Vaughan, J.; Williams, E.; Williams, E.F.; Williams, G.A.; Williams, G.E.; Williams, I.; Williams, J.; Williams, J.H.G.; Williams, J.W.; Williams, L.R.; Williams, M.J.; Williams, Mrs N.A.; Williams, P.; Williams, R.; Williams, R.W.; Williams, T.R.; Williamson, K.; Willis, M.J.; Willows, R.; Wills, H.; Wilmore, A.; Wilson, A.; Wilson, G.; Wilson, I.B.; Wilson, J.; Wilson, K.D.; Wilson, O.; Wilson, P.H.G.; Wilson, P.J.; Wiltshire, J.T.; Winder, F.; Winder, F.J.; Winsland, D.C.; Winspear, R.; Wise, A.J.; Wise, E.; Wise, N.A.J.; Wistow, R.J.; Withers, P.; Withrington, D.; Withycombe, C.L.; Witter, P.N.; Wolstencroft, G.; Wolstenholme, R.S.; Wolwood, I.; Womersley, H.; Wood, N.R.; Wood, O.; Wood-Homer, H.G.; Woodcock, B.; Woodford, W.; Woodhead, D.; Woodhead, F.; Woods, Mrs R.; Woodward, F.R.; Woodward, N.; Woofe, J.; Wooldbridge, D.B.; Woolfe, J.J.; Woolley, D.; Woolnough, J.; Worsley, B.; Wortham, P.; Worwood, S.; Wragg, A.; Wragg, J.; Wratten, S.D.; Wright, C.; Wright, D.; Wright, D.G.; Wright, E.; Wright, G.; Wright, H.; Wright, M.; Wright, Miss D.; Wright, S.; Wright, W.S.; Wykes, N.; Wylie, W.; Wynde, R.M.; Wyndham Miller, S.; Yates, J.N.; Yates, T.J.; Yerbury, J.W.; Yost, L.; Youden, G.H.; Young, C.; Young, H.; Young, M.R.; Young, S.; Youngman, R.E.; Zasada, K.

The maps in this *Atlas* were produced using the DMAP mapping software written by Dr Alan Morton.

INTRODUCTION

The term 'atlas' might be expected to refer to a book of maps. This volume contains maps of all the resident dragonflies, and the more frequent immigrants are discussed, but, in common with several recent *Atlases* of the British and Irish fauna and flora, it contains far more text than maps. This fact reflects a trend in biological recording which is discussed in the chapter on the **History of recording**, and is reviewed by Harding and Sheail (1992).

The distribution maps of dragonflies presented here are among the most complete available for an invertebrate group. Only the butterflies have enjoyed such a popular following, and the attentions of a co-ordinated group of skilled enthusiasts. Thus, if a dragonfly species is not recorded from a region, there is every likelihood that it is genuinely absent, and that the gap is no mere artefact of recorder effort. This aspect is discussed further in the sections describing the data set and the coverage which has been achieved.

The **Species accounts** which accompany the maps provide a commentary on the British and Irish distributions, and refer to the European and global range of each species. The latter part of this **Introduction** places the fauna in its European context. The **Species accounts** also provide new insight into the habitat requirements of a number of important species, and summarise aspects of dragonfly behaviour which are particularly relevant to recording. They also provide an introduction to the literature on dragonfly biology. A **Glossary** is included to explain the technical terms which may be unfamiliar to non-specialists.

The **Species accounts** highlight gaps in what is known of the British and Irish species, which it is hoped will encourage recorders to observe more closely, and to report their observations in the literature. The emphasis over the 20 years of the Odonata Recording Scheme has moved from simply plotting the geographic distribution of species, to studying many aspects of the biology of species. The methods employed in recording have evolved, encouraged by the newsletters of the Recording Scheme and, more recently, in consultation with the British Dragonfly Society. Methodology is discussed in the chapter on **Fieldwork**, and opportunities for further development of techniques are presented in the chapter on **Future recording**.

More detailed recording provides additional opportunities for examining aspects of the life of dragonflies, apart from their geographic occurrence. The analyses of flight period information from the Odonata Recording Scheme present examples of what is possible.

The emphasis on 'research' is not intended to discourage amateur involvement. Almost all the records summarised in this *Atlas* come from 'amateur' recorders: even the small proportion which derive from the work of professional biologists tend to be the result of spare-time fieldwork. As concern for the environment grows and, with it, a much deeper awareness of the fine details of ecological problems, such as pollution and human-induced climate change, the role of the skilled amateur naturalist is more vital than ever.

Apart from deepening our understanding of the biogeography of dragonflies, the Recording Scheme has focused attention on the need for conservation measures for dragonflies. The chapter on **Dragonflies and nature conservation** here provides a history of conservation in Britain, and the context and a rationale for future efforts. Conservation has been a driving force for many recorders in the past. Recent developments in recording methods, especially the approach adopted in the Key Sites Project, should enable the efforts of recorders to be applied even more directly to ensuring the survival of the British and Irish Odonata.

Throughout this *Atlas*, English names of plants follow Stace (1991); scientific names of plants, also following Stace (1991), are given in **Appendix 2**. Unless otherwise qualified, the word 'dragonfly' is used to mean all members of the order Odonata (see **Glossary** for amplification).

CHECKLIST

The following checklist includes all species of Odonata which have been reliably recorded in Britain, Ireland or the Channel Islands. The sequence and scientific nomenclature follow Askew (1988), except for *Cordulegaster boltonii*, *Oxygastra curtisii* and *Sympetrum fonscolombii*, which are amended following Brooks (1988). The currently accepted scientific name appears in **bold italic**, with synonyms in plain italic. The vernacular names given in **bold** for resident and regular vagrant species are those recommended in the Journal of the British Dragonfly Society (Anon 1991); for Channel Islands species and very rare vagrants, names follow McGeeney (1986).

The synonymy is not intended to be comprehensive, but it includes most of the scientific and English names which are likely to be encountered in 20th century literature on British and Irish Odonata, and in all but the oldest museum collections. A more extensive list of early synonyms is given by Robert (1958) and Askew (1988). Scientific and vernacular names used by the following authors are given: Aguilar, Dommanget and Prechac (1986); Corbet (1962); Corbet, Longfield and Moore (1960); Fraser (1949); Gibbons (1986); Hammond (1977, 1983); Kloet and Hincks (1945, 1964); Longfield (1937, 1949a); Lucas (1900, 1930); McGeeney (1986); and Miller (1987).

(Longfield (1937) uses hyphens in 'dragon-fly' and 'damsel-fly'; these variants are not listed as synonyms.)

Vagrants to Britain or Ireland which have never been known to breed are marked *****.

Species which occur regularly in Britain as immigrants, but do not usually breed, are marked **!**.

Species recorded only from the Channel Islands, and not from Britain or Ireland, are marked **+**.

Species which formerly bred in Britain, but are now believed to be extinct here, are marked **x**.

Order ODONATA

Suborder ZYGOPTERA

Family CALOPTERYGIDAE

AGRIIDAE

Calopteryx virgo (Linnaeus 1758)
   Agrion virgo

Beautiful demoiselle
   Beautiful agrion
   Demoiselle agrion

Calopteryx splendens (Harris 1782)
   Agrion splendens

Banded demoiselle
   Banded agrion

Family LESTIDAE

Lestes viridis ***** (Vander Linden 1825)
   Chalcolestes viridis

Green emerald damselfly

Lestes barbarus **+** (Fabricius 1798)

Shy emerald damselfly

Lestes sponsa (Hansemann 1823)

Emerald damselfly
   Green lestes

Lestes dryas Kirby 1890

Scarce emerald damselfly
   Scarce green lestes

Sympecma fusca **+** (Vander Linden 1820)

Brown emerald damselfly

Family PLATYCNEMIDIDAE

Platycnemis pennipes (Pallas 1771)　　　White-legged damselfly

Family COENAGRIONIDAE

COENAGRIIDAE

Pyrrhosoma nymphula (Sulzer 1776)　　　**Large red damselfly**

Erythromma najas (Hansemann 1823)　　　**Red-eyed damselfly**
　Erythromma naias

Coenagrion mercuriale (Charpentier 1840)　　**Southern damselfly**
　Agrion mercuriale　　　　　　　　　　　　　Southern blue damselfly
　　　　　　　　　　　　　　　　　　　　　　　Southern coenagrion

Coenagrion scitulum **x** (Rambur 1842)　　**Dainty damselfly**
　Agrion scitulum　　　　　　　　　　　　　Dainty blue damselfly

Coenagrion hastulatum (Charpentier 1825)　**Northern damselfly**
　Agrion hastulatum　　　　　　　　　　　　Northern blue damselfly
　　　　　　　　　　　　　　　　　　　　　　　Northern coenagrion

Coenagrion lunulatum (Charpentier 1840)　**Irish damselfly**
　　　　　　　　　　　　　　　　　　　　　　　Irish blue damselfly

Coenagrion armatum **x** (Charpentier 1840)　**Norfolk damselfly**
　Agrion armatum　　　　　　　　　　　　　Norfolk blue damselfly
　　　　　　　　　　　　　　　　　　　　　　　Norfolk coenagrion

Coenagrion puella (Linnaeus 1758)　　　**Azure damselfly**
　Agrion puella　　　　　　　　　　　　　Common coenagrion

Coenagrion pulchellum (Vander Linden 1825)　**Variable damselfly**
　Agrion pulchellum　　　　　　　　　　　　Variable blue damselfly
　　　　　　　　　　　　　　　　　　　　　　　Variable coenagrion

Enallagma cyathigerum (Charpentier 1840)　**Common blue damselfly**

Ischnura pumilio (Charpentier 1825)　　**Scarce blue-tailed damselfly**
　　　　　　　　　　　　　　　　　　　　　Scarce ischnura

Ischnura elegans (Vander Linden 1820)　**Blue-tailed damselfly**
　　　　　　　　　　　　　　　　　　　　　Common ischnura

Ceriagrion tenellum (Villers 1789)　　**Small red damselfly**
　Palaeobasis tenella
　Pyrrhosoma tenellum

Suborder ANISOPTERA

Family AESHNIDAE

Aeshna caerulea (Ström 1783)　　　**Azure hawker**
　Aeschna caerulea　　　　　　　　　Blue aeshna
　Aeschna borealis (Zetterstedt 1840)

Aeshna juncea (Linnaeus 1758)　　**Common hawker**
　Aeschna juncea　　　　　　　　　Common aeshna

Aeshna mixta Latreille 1805
    Aeschna mixta

Migrant hawker
    Scarce aeshna

Aeshna affinis ***** Vander Linden 1823

Southern migrant hawker

Aeshna cyanea (Müller 1764)
    Aeschna cyanea

Southern hawker
    Southern aeshna

Aeshna grandis (Linnaeus 1758)
    Aeschna grandis

Brown hawker
    Brown aeshna

Aeshna isosceles (Müller 1767)
    Anaciaeschna isosceles
    Aeschna isosceles

Norfolk hawker
    Norfolk aeshna

Anax imperator Leach 1815

Emperor dragonfly

Hemianax ephippiger ***** (Burmeister 1839)

Vagrant emperor dragonfly
    Saddle-back dragonfly

Brachytron pratense (Müller 1764)

Hairy dragonfly
    Hairy hawker

Family GOMPHIDAE

Gomphus flavipes ***** (Charpentier 1825)

Yellow-legged dragonfly

Gomphus vulgatissimus (Linnaeus 1758)

Club-tailed dragonfly
    Club-tail dragonfly

Family CORDULEGASTRIDAE

CORDULEGASTERIDAE

Cordulegaster boltonii (Donovan 1807)
    Cordulegaster boltoni
    Cordulegaster annulatus (Latreille 1805)

Golden-ringed dragonfly

Family CORDULIIDAE

Cordulia aenea (Linnaeus 1758)
    Cordulia linaenea Fraser 1937

Downy emerald

Somatochlora metallica (Vander Linden 1825)
    Cordulia metallica

Brilliant emerald

Somatochlora arctica (Zetterstedt 1840)
    Cordulia arctica

Northern emerald

Oxygastra curtisii **x** (Dale 1834)
    Oxygastra curtisi

Orange-spotted emerald

Family LIBELLULIDAE

Libellula quadrimaculata Linnaeus 1758

Four-spotted chaser
    Four-spotted libellula

Libellula fulva Müller 1764

Scarce chaser
    Scarce libellula

Libellula depressa Linnaeus 1758 — **Broad-bodied chaser**
  Broad-bodied libellula

Orthetrum cancellatum (Linnaeus 1758) — **Black-tailed skimmer**
  Black-lined orthetrum

Orthetrum coerulescens (Fabricius 1798) — **Keeled skimmer**
  Orthetrum caerulescens — Keeled orthetrum

Crocothemis erythraea * (Brullé 1832) — **Scarlet dragonfly**

Sympetrum striolatum (Charpentier 1840) — **Common darter**
  Common sympetrum

Sympetrum nigrescens Lucas 1912 — **Highland darter**
  Sympetrum striolatum ssp. — Black-legged sympetrum
  nigrifemur Longfield, nec Sélys-Longchamps

[The specific distinctness of this taxon from *S. striolatum* is still unresolved; see text]

Sympetrum vulgatum * (Linnaeus 1758) — **Vagrant darter**
  Vagrant sympetrum

Sympetrum meridionale * (Sélys-Longchamps 1841) — **Southern darter**

Sympetrum fonscolombii ! (Sélys-Longchamps 1840) — **Red-veined darter**
  Sympetrum fonscolombei — Red-veined sympetrum

Sympetrum flaveolum ! (Linnaeus 1758) — **Yellow-winged darter**
  Yellow-winged sympetrum

Sympetrum sanguineum (Müller 1764) — **Ruddy darter**
  Ruddy sympetrum

Sympetrum danae (Sulzer 1776) — **Black darter**
  Sympetrum scoticum (Donovan 1811) — Black sympetrum

Sympetrum pedemontanum * (Allioni 1766) — **Banded darter**

Leucorrhinia dubia (Vander Linden 1825) — **White-faced dragonfly**
  White-faced darter

Pantala flavescens * (Fabricius 1798) — **Globe skimmer**
  Libellula sparshalli Dale

Note added in proof

At the time of going to press, some extraordinary sightings of migrant dragonflies have been reported, including two species which are new to the British list. These are *Crocothemis erythraea*, which was found by S P Jones and G Sutton on 7 August 1995 at Hayle Kimbro Pool on the Lizard Peninsula, Cornwall, and *Sympetrum pedemontanum,* which was found by I D Smith on 16 August 1995 near Tredegar, Gwent. In both instances, a single male was seen and photographed. Also in August, *S. flaveolum* and *S. fonscolombii* were reported from many locations in southern Britain, and there were several sightings of *S. vulgatum* – the first reliable records since 1946.

The **Checklist** has been amended accordingly, but not the relevant sections in the text.

THE BRITISH AND IRISH ODONATA IN A EUROPEAN CONTEXT

Britain and Ireland support about one third of the European dragonfly fauna, a higher proportion than is found in most groups of plants and animals (Eversham & Arnold 1991). None is endemic to these islands. Table 1 compares the British and Irish fauna with that of the neighbouring continent. Several different types of distribution pattern are apparent in the European dragonflies (Askew 1988), and most of these are represented in the British and Irish fauna.

The only true tundra dragonfly in Europe is *Somatochlora sahlbergi* Trybom, which is confined to areas north of the Arctic Circle and is absent from Britain and Ireland.

Boreo-montane species, which are characteristic of the taiga, the northern coniferous forest zone, include *Aeshna caerulea*. Such species are widespread throughout Scandinavia and northern Russia, but their distribution is restricted to mountain areas further south, such as the Massif Central and the Alps. Another group of northern species has a broadly similar distribution, including relict populations in mountain areas in the south of their European range, but is found also at low altitudes in central European latitudes, and so cannot be termed 'boreo-montane'. This group includes *S. arctica*, *A. juncea*, *Leucorrhinia dubia*, *Coenagrion hastulatum* and *C. lunulatum*.

Most of Britain and Ireland lies within the zone which would naturally be occupied by temperate deciduous forest. There are few species of dragonfly which are confined to this zone in Europe: *Brachytron pratense* and *Gomphus vulgatissimus* are characteristic, being absent from most of Scandinavia and rare or absent in southern Europe.

One species-rich European faunal element has a broadly Mediterranean distribution. Many species in this group have a narrow, southern distribution, and so are absent from Britain, but some are also found in lowland areas further north, and do occur, such as *Coenagrion mercuriale*, *Ceriagrion tenellum*, *A. isosceles* and *A. mixta*, or have bred in the past, such as *Coenagrion scitulum*.

A few dragonflies found in Europe are more typical of tropical or desert regions at lower latitudes, but are capable of long-distance wandering. Of these, *Pantala flavescens* and *Hemianax ephippiger* have reached Britain on rare occasions, and the latter may sometimes breed as far north as southern France and central Italy.

A high proportion of the British and Irish fauna has a wide European range. Species such as *Pyrrhosoma nymphula*, *Enallagma cyathigerum*, *A. cyanea*, *Libellula quadrimaculata*, *L. depressa* and *Sympetrum striolatum* occur from the Mediterranean to Scandinavia. Such eurytopic species were probably among the early colonists after the last glaciation, and are today the species best able to make use of recent man-made water bodies.

Many European species are probably absent from Britain and Ireland simply because of their failure to recolonise at the end of the last glaciation. A few might possibly be overlooked, or be able to colonise in future (particularly if the climate becomes slightly warmer). These species are discussed in the section on **Possible additions to the British and Irish dragonfly fauna**.

Table 1. Comparison of Odonata species resident, or formerly resident, in Britain and Ireland, compared with the nearby continent

Country	Zygoptera	Anisoptera	Total Odonata
Ireland	11	11	22
Britain	17	23	40
Channel Islands	10	13	23
France (excl Corsica)	30	51	81
Belgium	25	40	65
The Netherlands	25	39	64
Denmark	15	30	45
Norway	15	26	41
Europe (total)	**37**	**77**	**114**

The above data have been taken from this *Atlas*, and from Askew (1988), Dommanget (1987) and Geijskes and van Tol (1983). It should be noted that the above figures from countries in continental Europe may not be exact, and may include a few non-resident or migrant species. The figures from Britain and Ireland have taken *Sympetrum striolatum* and *S. nigrescens* as one species. (This point is discussed more fully in the relevant species account.)

HISTORY OF RECORDING

The early history of the British and Irish dragonflies is described by Cynthia Longfield (in Corbet *et al.* 1960). Recording in the 19th century was uneven. Nevertheless, only four resident species have been added to the British/Irish list since 1900 (*Coenagrion hastulatum*, *C. armatum* and *C. scitulum* from Britain and, most recently, *C. lunulatum* from Ireland but yet to be found in Britain). The taxonomic status of a possible fifth additional species, *Sympetrum nigrescens*, is more doubtful (see relevant **Species account**). The first workers, before 1850, concentrated their collecting activity, no doubt out of necessity, in the areas closest to home. In the latter half of the 19th century, the advent of the railways enabled more remote parts of Britain and Ireland to be investigated, including the Highlands of Scotland, where the chance of collecting additional species doubtless seemed greatest. The many papers by Robert McLachlan and others bear witness to this. However, there is scant recorded information on the commoner species in the more accessible and populous areas such as southern England.

In the present century, the appearance of Lucas's monographs on the adults (1900) and the larvae (1930) attracted a few enthusiasts to the order, but the books were soon out of print. The *Wayside and woodland* volume (Longfield 1937, 1949a) revived interest, the second edition coinciding with a Royal Entomological Society *Handbook* to the Odonata (Fraser 1949). During the 1950s there were important studies on the biology of dragonflies, such as those of Philip Corbet on the effects of environmental factors on larval development. Norman Moore drew attention to the role of 'territoriality' in controlling the density of adult males beside water. A E Gardner undertook the captive breeding of many species in order to describe their larvae, and published a series of keys (Gardner 1954, 1955). Unfortunately, only a small proportion of the information on the distribution of species which was generated during this early period has been preserved in publications and museum collections, although some additional records have been retrieved from the notebooks of key workers. As is often the case today, locality details were much more

complete for the rare species than for the common ones. For example, in Longfield's review of the dragonflies of the London area (Longfield 1949b), *Pyrrhosoma nymphula* was described simply as 'abundant throughout' the area in the 1940s, but this is no longer the case: it is now mainly confined to acid water sites, such as parts of Epping Forest and the Surrey heaths (Brooks 1989). This change may indicate a considerable decline, but such comparisons are impossible to quantify without more detailed information on the common species.

Zoological recording in the 1950s followed the pattern of previous decades, with published maps

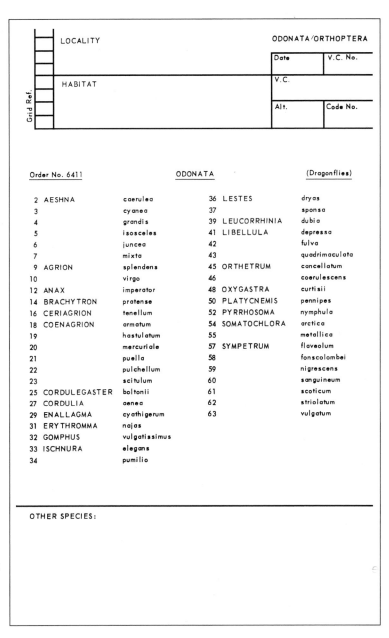

Figure 1. RA4, the first Odonata recording card, February 1968 (actual size 8" x 5")

of distributions of dragonflies using the Watson/ Praeger vice-counties (Corbet *et al.* 1960), which were essentially similar to those produced for other groups of animals for the previous half-century, such as Taylor (1894-1921). However, in 1945, the Ordnance Survey (OS) began publishing the 1:63 360 ('One inch') series of maps showing the national grid (Harley 1975). The potential of this grid for recording purposes was quickly realised, as demonstrated by the initiative of the Botanical Society of the British Isles (BSBI) for co-ordinated surveys by amateurs (Perring 1992). The resulting *Atlas of the British flora* (Perring & Walters 1962), mapping the distribution of species on the 10 km squares of the national grid, was a catalyst for naturalists in other disciplines to begin more systematic recording.

In 1964, the Biological Records Centre (BRC) was set up at Monks Wood Experimental Station, within the then Nature Conservancy (Harding & Sheail 1992), to manage the results of the BSBI survey and to introduce the same methods to other groups of organisms. Shortly after the appointment of John Heath to the staff of BRC in 1967, as the Centre's first invertebrate specialist, a project to record Odonata was launched within the Insect Distribution Maps Scheme, and the first standard recording card for Odonata, the RA4, was produced (Figure 1) in February 1968. Reports of the Insect Distribution Maps Scheme appeared at intervals in the entomological journals (Heath 1971). At this stage, Odonata recording was coupled with a scheme for the Orthoptera, both orders being the province of only a handful of dedicated devotees. The joint scheme was later managed by M J L Skelton, also on the staff of BRC.

In 1973, the Nature Conservancy was split to form two independent organisations, the Nature Conservancy Council (NCC) and the Institute of Terrestrial Ecology (ITE). After some uncertainty, BRC remained at Monks Wood, as part of ITE, within the Natural Environment Research Council (Harding & Sheail 1992), with annual funding support from NCC and its successor agencies. In 1974, the first maps showing the distribution of Odonata in the 10 km squares of the national grid were prepared and circulated to recorders (Skelton 1974). Coverage at this time was very patchy, with one or two counties fairly well recorded, but large areas of central England, most of Wales, and almost all of Scotland and Ireland completely lacking records (Figure 2). However, the maps were a great incentive for recorders to submit their existing records and to target their future fieldwork on some of the gaps.

During the 1970s, the increasing number of invertebrate mapping schemes being co-ordinated by BRC, coupled with the transfer of Skelton to ITE's research station at Furzebrook in Dorset, and especially the success of the Macrolepidoptera

Scheme which was Heath's personal interest, led Heath to seek outside volunteers to organise some of the mapping schemes for their specialist groups. In 1977, he recruited David Chelmick, a true enthusiast who had already been very active mapping the dragonflies of Sussex and surveying Odonata in other parts of Britain for NCC, to run the national Odonata Mapping Scheme.

In 1978, a *Provisional atlas* including maps of all the resident species of dragonfly was published (Heath 1978). Coverage had improved significantly (Figure 3), but many large blanks remained. The solution was found in May 1977, with the circulation of an Odonata Mapping Scheme newsletter, edited by David Chelmick. For the first time, there was a means of guiding the enthusiasm and efforts of recorders. The other landmark of 1977 was a new identification guide (Hammond 1977), which filled the gap left because the publications by Longfield (1949a) and Corbet *et al.* (1960) were out of print. Cyril Hammond's book also provided the first complete set of accurate and detailed colour plates of males and females for every resident British and Irish species.

With enthusiastic leadership, and a very attractive handbook encouraging many more naturalists to look at dragonflies, the Odonata Scheme gathered such momentum that a revised *Provisional atlas* was produced within two years (Chelmick 1979), based on twice as many records as in the 1977 edition. Coverage was now good enough to reveal the main patterns in species distribution in Britain, and recorders had rediscovered breeding sites for most of the rarities of the Scottish Highlands. They also produced the first records for many years for immigrants such as *Sympetrum fonscolombii*. The announcement of such highlights in the annual newsletter provided just the boost that recorders needed. The success of the Scheme can be judged by the first recorders' meeting, held in London on 7 April 1979, which attracted 72 people, from as far afield as Inverness, Penzance and west Wales. Discussion at the meeting ranged from maps and temperature limits to behaviour, habitat requirements and colour variation. This increased breadth of interest led to a name change, from 'Mapping' to 'Recording' Scheme, emphasising the wider objectives, and recognising the need for detailed breeding site information. With such commitment, the future of the Scheme seemed assured.

However, the Scheme was in danger of becoming the victim of its own success. In the fourth newsletter, in Spring 1980, David Chelmick requested help with the increasing administrative burden. Soon afterwards, Bob Merritt, who had helped compile the 1979 *Provisional atlas*, offered to assist, and was given the title 'national recorder',

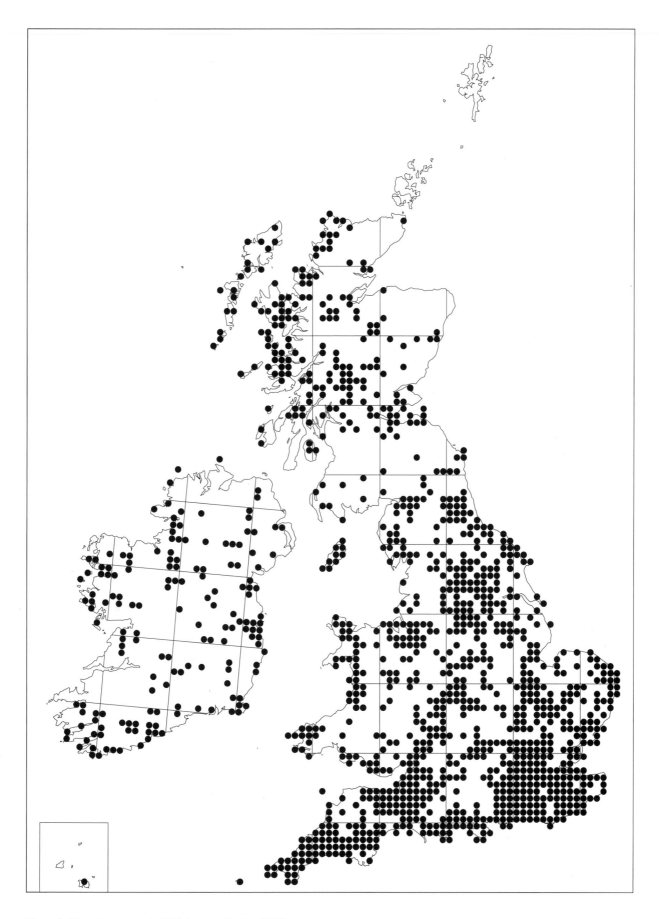

Figure 2. Map of coverage in 1974 (source: Skelton 1974)

Figure 3. Map of coverage in 1977 (source: Heath 1978)

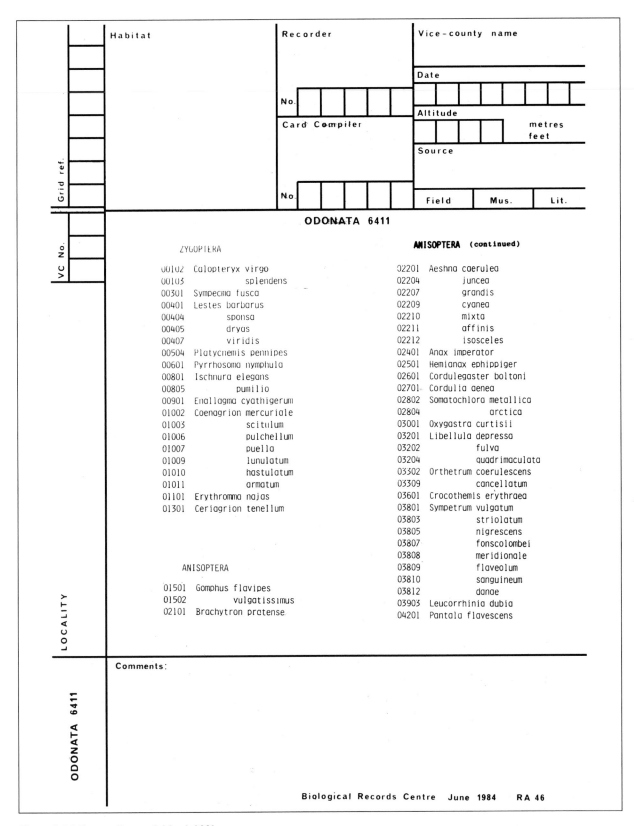

Habitat	Recorder	Vice-county name						

| Grid ref. | | | | | | | | | |
| VC No. | | | |

ODONATA 6411

ZYGOPTERA

00102	Calopteryx virgo
00103	splendens
00301	Sympecma fusca
00401	Lestes barbarus
00404	sponsa
00405	dryas
00407	viridis
00504	Platycnemis pennipes
00601	Pyrrhosoma nymphula
00801	Ischnura elegans
00805	pumilio
00901	Enallagma cyathigerum
01002	Coenagrion mercuriale
01003	scitulum
01006	pulchellum
01007	puella
01009	lunulatum
01010	hastulatum
01011	armatum
01101	Erythromma najas
01301	Ceriagrion tenellum

ANISOPTERA

01501	Gomphus flavipes
01502	vulgatissimus
02101	Brachytron pratense

ANISOPTERA (continued)

02201	Aeshna caerulea
02204	juncea
02207	grandis
02209	cyanea
02210	mixta
02211	affinis
02212	isosceles
02401	Anax imperator
02501	Hemianax ephippiger
02601	Cordulegaster boltoni
02701	Cordulia aenea
02802	Somatochlora metallica
02804	arctica
03001	Oxygastra curtisii
03201	Libellula depressa
03202	fulva
03204	quadrimaculata
03302	Orthetrum coerulescens
03309	cancellatum
03601	Crocothemis erythraea
03801	Sympetrum vulgatum
03803	striolatum
03805	nigrescens
03807	fonscolombei
03808	meridionale
03809	flaveolum
03810	sanguineum
03812	danae
03903	Leucorrhinia dubia
04201	Pantala flavescens

Comments:

ODONATA 6411

Biological Records Centre   June 1984   RA 46

Figure 4. RA46 recording card, March 1981

dealing with all the records, while Chelmick continued to handle general enquiries and organisation. In October 1981, David Chelmick stood down as scheme organiser, and Bob Merritt was thereafter responsible for all aspects of the Scheme. A new recording card, the RA46, was produced by BRC in March 1981 (Figure 4), with additional spaces for habitat descriptions and other notes, reflecting the development of the Scheme beyond simple distribution mapping.

The 1980s saw the pace of recording accelerate considerably. Figure 5 shows the coverage at the end of 1982, and Figure 6 the number of records of one of the commonest species, *Ischnura elegans*, each year, a good measure of recorder activity.

Figure 5. Map of coverage at the end of 1982

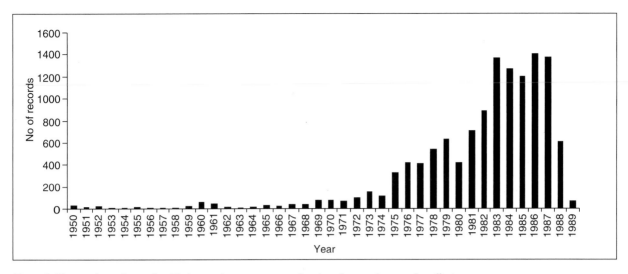

Figure 6. The number of records of *Ischnura elegans* per year, showing changes in recorder effort

By now, there were many local or county recording schemes, and several of the local Biological Records Centres (listed and reviewed by Berry (1988)), which had been established by district or county councils during the 1970s, began to have a serious involvement with Odonata. In most counties, however, dragonfly recording was organised without the involvement of a local records centre, and, as always, the greatest contribution to improved coverage was due to the hard work and dedication of a small band of skilled amateur naturalists. The checking of incoming records by the scheme organiser (explained in the section describing the data set) entailed a very large volume of correspondence with individual contributors, as well as local and county organisers.

In the newsletters in the early 1980s, the suggestion for setting up a society for odonatists in Britain was made, at first tentatively, and then with greater confidence. The result was the foundation of the British Dragonfly Society (BDS) in 1983. The early history of the Society is reviewed by Merritt (1987). Among the benefits of the formation of the BDS have been regular indoor and field meetings, the publication of the *Journal of the British Dragonfly Society* and a newsletter, and the establishment of a number of local groups. Some BDS local groups took on a role in recording immediately, and others were to do so in the coming years. In some areas, this recording is through the regular monitoring of important sites; other groups are studying the distribution and habitats of individual species. The aims of the BDS are wide-ranging, and are not primarily concerned with recording. However, the increased publicity for Odonata and the Recording Scheme, which the activities of BDS have fostered, has undoubtedly introduced new people to the Scheme.

The Odonata Recording Scheme newsletter continued to guide recorders' efforts through the 1980s, providing updated draft maps and summaries of outstanding new records, as well as pointers for fieldwork and advice on identification. The Scheme continued to expand, so that in 1983 a separate organiser was established for Ireland, and in 1987 a network of regional recorders was set up in Britain, to help with the initial vetting of records and the transfer of data to BRC record cards (see **Preface** for personal acknowledgements). This network also introduced the possibility of regular regional reports in the newsletter, and provided a means to strengthen the links with local recording projects and groups.

By the mid-1980s, the overall patterns of species distribution were well known, and new records seldom changed the national picture substantially. In some counties, the focus had already moved to recording and mapping at a smaller scale (1 km or 2 km squares), but the application of Odonata data to nature conservation revealed a shortcoming in many of the records: despite regular requests in the newsletter, most recorders had simply recorded the presence of adult dragonflies, and had not routinely provided evidence of breeding. It has often been shown that adult Odonata frequently occur beside water bodies which may not be suitable for breeding, yet it is the *breeding sites* which conservationists need to protect. To help provide the missing details, a new initiative, the Key Sites Project, was launched in 1988 (Merritt 1988), with a new recordng card, the RA70 (see Figure 12). Records from this Project, up to the end of 1990, are incorporated in the maps in this *Atlas*. The Key Sites Project and other initiatives are described in the chapter on **Future recording**.

FIELDWORK AND DATA MANAGEMENT

METHODS OF RECORDING

Dragonfly recording until relatively recently has largely been a random accumulation of information, dependent on the personal preferences of individual observers. A few prominent workers in the 19th century attempted to collate records for publication, notably Sélys-Longchamps (1846) and McLachlan (1884). In this century, the distribution data in Lucas (1900), Longfield (1937, 1949a) and Corbet *et al.* (1960) testify to the effectiveness of the network of correspondents which had been created. However, only when the data from these periods are presented visually, as on a distribution map, is their patchiness fully revealed.

The key development in recording in the past two decades has been the circulation of draft maps of species distributions within the 10 km squares of the OS grid, in order to target recorder effort on those areas with least information. Much of this fieldwork was initially planned with the aim of producing complete distribution maps, rather than any broader uses. The maps in this volume demonstrate its success in defining species distributions. However, the fieldwork has also proven invaluable in many other ways: the detailed site records which many recorders provided are vital for conservation, both in evaluating individual sites and in documenting the changing status of species. The dates of occurrence may reveal varying patterns of phenology across Britain; and the patterns of co-occurrence of species may tell us more about the ecology of species and the ways in which assemblages of species occupy habitats.

Such additional uses of records which were gathered for less ambitious purposes have focused odonatists' attention on other aspects of data collection. Three areas in particular have attracted interest in recent years:

- the search for larvae and exuviae to provide definite proof of breeding and an estimate of breeding population size;

- transect methods to provide a convenient year-to-year index of abundance of adults;

- comprehensive site monitoring (including proof of breeding, and the assessment of numbers at more than one stage of the life cycle).

Nonetheless, the main method of recording summarised in this *Atlas* has been the observation of adult dragonflies, with the possible exception of a few species, such as *Gomphus vulgatissimus*, for which exuviae provide an equal or greater proportion of the records.

Recording of larvae and exuviae

Work in this field has so far been the interest of only a small minority of dragonfly recorders; indeed, many appear unaware of the opportunities for fieldwork outside the summer months. This lack of awareness results partly from problems with current literature on larval and exuvial identification. The standard keys by Gardner (1954, 1955) were reprinted in Corbet *et al.* (1960) and Hammond (1977, 1983). Most later keys (Miller 1987; Askew 1988) rely heavily on the features used by Gardner. These and other keys are discussed briefly in the **Literature and references** section, and are workable for late instar larvae and exuviae of almost all species.

The need for larval recording is also being addressed by the local groups of the British Dragonfly Society, several of which have organised identification workshops and field meetings devoted to finding larvae.

There are several advantages to working with larvae or exuviae as well as adults. It is an all-weather pursuit: for example, new breeding sites for the rare northern species have often been found in cold or wet conditions, when no adults were flying, by searching for exuviae. Exuviae will remain in position on waterside vegetation for two weeks or so in the absence of rain or strong winds, and can provide a cumulative record of emergences over that time. Also, a few species are easier to record as exuviae than as adults, which spend relatively little time by the water. For instance, dozens or even hundreds of exuviae of *G. vulgatissimus* may be present along stretches of suitable rivers where few or no adults will be observed on a brief visit (Averill 1989). Another advantage of larval recording is that fieldwork is not restricted to the summer months as it is for adult Odonata. Although the larvae of many species are more easy to locate just prior to emergence (especially those with a synchronous emergence - mud-dwelling larvae such as *Libellula depressa* and *Orthetrum cancellatum* congregate in shallow water, whilst weed-dwelling larvae such as *Anax imperator* move nearer to the water surface), larvae of the majority of species can be found by the experienced recorder at all times of year, though larval fieldwork is perhaps least profitable in very cold weather.

The larval ecology of most species is poorly known, but it is apparent that only a small part of a wetland complex may provide suitable larval habitats, even if the adults range widely over the whole site, as is often the case with the larger Anisoptera. Proof of breeding is often crucial in site evaluation and protection, and larvae and exuviae provide the best possible evidence.

Finally, the larvae of Odonata are, in a very different way, as striking as the adults, often subtly coloured and camouflaged, and structurally diverse. In an Order containing rather few British and Irish species, the larvae can provide an extra challenge, requiring a new set of field skills for the observer who has already mastered the adults.

Transect methods

As early as the 1950s, the counting of adult male Odonata along a waterside transect was being used to monitor dragonfly populations (Moore 1953, 1964, 1991c). The method has since become more widely known through its development for butterfly monitoring (Moore 1975; Pollard 1979, 1992). Butterflies are perhaps even better suited to transect counts than Odonata: most butterflies are not strongly territorial, and unlike many Odonata do not move far from their breeding sites. However, if counts of adult male Odonata are repeated regularly (ideally, once a week) in suitable weather conditions (sunny and with little wind) and close to mid-day, they can provide results which are comparable and thus a simple annual index of abundance. This method is very useful in quantifying flight period (see below), and can detect long-term trends in a species, perhaps reflecting site management (Brooks 1993); Moore (1991c) follows the pattern of colonisation and faunal change at ponds at Woodwalton Fen over 27 years using transect methods.

Comprehensive monitoring

Useful though transect counts can be, they are probably best used as part of a wider-ranging programme of monitoring. A review of the techniques for comprehensive monitoring has been provided by Moore and Corbet (1990). They discuss the need for monitoring, and aspects of the behaviour of Odonata which influence the ways in which methods may be applied. They conclude that the choice of survey methods will depend on the habitats involved, especially the accessibility of the water's edge, and the time available for monitoring. They make several recommendations.

• The preferred technique for monitoring Anisoptera is by counting exuviae, which should be collected as frequently as possible, throughout the emergence period.

• Because of the difficulty of finding and identifying their exuviae, Zygoptera are best monitored by counting teneral adults, as frequently as possible, throughout the emergence period.

• Adult counts are comparable only when restricted to adult males by water, and when made within 1–2 hours of mid-day on sunny days with little or no wind.

• Whatever methods of assessment are used, it is preferable if they can be applied at regular intervals, and at the same time each day.

As a minimum, Moore and Corbet recommend that counts of anisopteran exuviae, zygopteran teneral adults, and mature males by water should be made once a week throughout the season. With this required level of commitment, it is important to establish the purpose of monitoring, and to decide what level of detail is required. Can monitoring be focused on one or two species of particular importance? If management is being monitored, can representative sections of habitat be chosen rather than attempting to monitor a whole site? Does the monitoring need to be repeated annually? (A thorough survey every third year may be more useful than incomplete or inconsistent surveys every year.)

DESCRIPTION OF DATA SET

The maps presented in this *Atlas* are based on all records received by the Odonata Recording Scheme up to the end of 1990. Some later records, of particular importance, are mentioned in the species accounts and elsewhere, but do not appear on the maps.

Recording is a continuing process, because species distributions are not static and there remain large gaps in our knowledge of the biology of even the commonest species. The methods of data collection and validation described in this section refer both to the data included in this *Atlas* and to ongoing recording.

Management of data collection

The history of the Scheme and data collection has already been described. For most of the duration of the Recording Scheme, a national scheme organiser has been responsible for collating incoming records and providing feedback to recorders. This feedback has included comments on the significance of the records supplied, and requests for further information in support of particularly outstanding records. Additionally, through the newsletters, recorders have been urged to visit under-worked areas, and encouraged in this by both organised and less formal field excursions.

As well as collating records from recorders, the national organiser's remit included the searching of the scientific literature and museum collections for records that pre-dated the recording scheme, so giving an historical perspective to the database. The establishment of a separate organiser for Ireland in 1983 provided assistance with this task.

A network of regional recorders was set up in 1987. They take responsibility for co-ordinating data collection and vetting records for their region, and, since 1988, the Scheme has been operated entirely by the regional recorders, in direct liaison with BRC.

Vetting of records

All records received by the national scheme organiser or by a regional recorder are assessed on arrival, and any which are unusual (extensions of known range of common species, records of rare species, species in untypical habitats or at unusual times of year) are queried with the originator. Occasionally, they prove to be simple accidents of transcription, and are thus deleted from the card, and never enter the database. In other cases, a recorder may indicate a degree of doubt over an identification: perhaps a dragonfly was seen only fleetingly, or the recorder had not encountered the species before, or was unaware of potential confusion with other species. When this happens, a recorder is encouraged to visit the site again, and obtain clearer evidence that the doubted species is present. Photographs can often help confirm identifications, and the collection of exuviae serves both to prove the identification and to establish that the species is breeding at the site.

Some records can never be satisfactorily resolved. A sighting by an inexperienced recorder, or a brief or distant view of the insect, may not provide sufficient detail for an unequivocal identification. Such records are not entered on to computer, but the details are kept and continually reappraised as new information becomes available. If, for instance, additional, undoubted records of a species are made in the same district, the earlier record may be reviewed.

The need for care applies especially to historical records, some of which may suffer from confusion over the use of names, or weaknesses in other areas. Sometimes it is the method of labelling that causes doubt. For example, there are specimens of *Erythromma najas, Platycnemis pennipes* and *Sympetrum sanguineum* in the J J F X King collection which were apparently taken in Scotland (O'Farrell 1950). However, these specimens are labelled only with numbers, referring to details in King's

notebooks, and may have been misattributed through transcription error. This illustrates the need for each specimen to bear full data, as was King's later practice. Occasionally, museum specimens are discovered which help to confirm or refute a published record, or clarify the site details. For instance, a record of *Leucorrhinia dubia* apparently from 'Dorchester' (in Dorset) in 1837 was eventually traced to a specimen in the Hope Entomological Collections, Oxford, and was found to derive from a mistranscription of the locality label, which reads 'Doncaster' rather than 'Dorchester' (Limbert 1990), so the record came from south Yorkshire and not Dorset.

A small proportion of records will always remain unconfirmed, to be excluded from maps but repeated with due qualification, and at the authors' discretion, in the text of local and national atlases. One important instance in which questionable records found their way into the literature needs to be mentioned in this *Atlas*: that of the dragonflies listed by Henry Doubleday (1871) as having been found in Essex. This extraordinary list cannot be taken at face value (Benton 1988). Although some of the records may be valid, it cannot be known which, and none of them is mapped in this *Atlas*.

When reliable historical records come from an unambiguous site, but cannot be allocated a precise grid reference because the site is too large, or on the border between 10 km squares, they have been assigned to the most appropriate 10 km square for the site, in order that the record can appear on the maps. These records are flagged as such in the BRC database.

All the records that form the basis of this *Atlas*, spanning a period of some 160 years to 1990, have been appraised and vetted by the national scheme organiser. In addition, he has reappraised the records published in earlier *Provisional atlases*. As a result, some records which appear in earlier atlases do not appear in this *Atlas*. This may be due to one of many reasons, not necessarily that the validity of the record was doubted. In some cases, an incorrect grid reference had been overlooked, and the record had simply been misplotted. Often there was not enough supporting information to warrant inclusion.

In addition to taxonomic vetting, the organiser or regional recorder also encourages recorders to supply the fullest possible details with all records, but especially for those involving scarce or rare species, or key dragonfly sites. Precise grid references, accurate locality names, and information on dates of visit and numbers of dragonflies seen all enhance the value of records, and increase the possible uses to which they may be put. Fuller details also facilitate refinding a species at a site in future, which is important if dragonflies are to be conserved.

Table 2. Number of records, and 10 km squares, for each species, also expressed as a percentage of the total 10 km squares with records. These data comprise the combined figures for Britain, Ireland and the Channel Islands

Species	Records	Squares	% total squares
Aeshna affinis	1	1	0.03
Aeshna caerulea	157	57	1.80
Aeshna cyanea	4092	1007	31.88
Aeshna grandis	4942	899	28.46
Aeshna isosceles	147	14	0.44
Aeshna juncea	3762	1194	37.80
Aeshna mixta	2209	597	18.90
Anax imperator	2769	638	20.20
Brachytron pratense	1134	332	10.51
Calopteryx splendens	3553	862	27.29
Calopteryx virgo	2638	645	20.42
Ceriagrion tenellum	989	102	3.23
Coenagrion armatum	11	2	0.06
Coenagrion hastulatum	72	8	0.25
Coenagrion lunulatum	84	33	1.04
Coenagrion mercuriale	376	32	1.01
Coenagrion puella	8085	1453	46.00
Coenagrion pulchellum	1277	439	13.90
Coenagrion scitulum	18	5	0.16
Cordulegaster boltonii	3434	845	26.75
Cordulia aenea	758	136	4.31
Crocothemis erythraea	2	1	0.03
Enallagma cyathigerum	11030	2156	68.25
Erythromma najas	1275	323	10.22
Gomphus flavipes	1	1	0.03
Gomphus vulgatissimus	342	79	2.50
Hemianax ephippiger	10	9	0.28
Ischnura elegans	13153	2121	67.14
Ischnura pumilio	618	165	5.22
Lestes barbarus	4	3	0.09
Lestes dryas	189	64	2.03
Lestes sponsa	4869	1284	40.65
Lestes viridis	10	5	0.16
Leucorrhinia dubia	300	49	1.55
Libellula depressa	3027	777	24.60
Libellula fulva	255	42	1.33
Libellula quadrimaculata	4505	1204	38.11
Orthetrum cancellatum	1650	421	13.33
Orthetrum coerulescens	1659	276	8.74
Oxygastra curtisii	31	2	0.06
Pantala flavescens	2	2	0.06
Platycnemis pennipes	831	203	6.43
Pyrrhosoma nymphula	9663	1976	62.55
Somatochlora arctica	174	48	1.52
Somatochlora metallica	271	43	1.36
Sympecma fusca	1	1	0.03
Sympetrum danae	3246	873	27.64
Sympetrum flaveolum	185	98	3.10
Sympetrum fonscolombii	110	56	1.77
Sympetrum meridionale	2	2	0.06
Sympetrum sanguineum	1710	528	16.71
Sympetrum striolatum/nigrescens	9160	1696	53.69
Sympetrum vulgatum	9	9	0.28

Table 3. Distribution of each species in Britain, England, Scotland, Wales and Ireland, expressed as a percentage of total 10 km squares with records in each country

Species	Britain	England	% of squares in Scotland	Wales	Ireland
Aeshna affinis	0.04	0.07	0.00	0.00	0.00
Aeshna caerulea	2.36	0.00	7.27	0.00	0.00
Aeshna cyanea	41.03	62.91	1.13	43.30	0.14
Aeshna grandis	31.80	53.95	0.13	9.58	18.48
Aeshna isosceles	0.53	0.92	0.00	0.00	0.00
Aeshna juncea	41.20	30.54	55.01	54.41	34.38
Aeshna mixta	24.07	40.62	0.00	6.13	0.00
Anax imperator	25.66	39.49	0.00	27.20	0.00
Brachytron pratense	8.91	12.62	0.88	12.64	17.34
Calopteryx splendens	29.40	45.06	0.00	35.25	23.78
Calopteryx virgo	23.38	26.73	4.51	62.07	13.18
Ceriagrion tenellum	4.15	5.57	0.00	8.81	0.00
Coenagrion armatum	0.08	0.14	0.00	0.00	0.00
Coenagrion hastulatum	0.33	0.00	1.00	0.00	0.00
Coenagrion lunulatum	0.00	0.00	0.00	0.00	4.73
Coenagrion mercuriale	1.30	1.41	0.00	4.60	0.00
Coenagrion puella	52.62	73.55	9.02	72.80	38.11
Coenagrion pulchellum	7.73	10.86	2.13	7.66	37.82
Coenagrion scitulum	0.08	0.14	0.00	0.00	0.00
Cordulegaster boltonii	34.44	22.71	43.86	68.20	0.00
Cordulia aenea	5.33	8.74	0.75	0.38	0.57
Enallagma cyathigerum	77.39	81.73	68.17	80.46	53.15
Erythromma najas	13.30	22.71	0.00	1.92	0.00
Gomphus flavipes	0.04	0.07	0.00	0.00	0.00
Gomphus vulgatissimus	3.21	4.65	0.00	6.51	0.00
Hemianax ephippiger	0.33	0.49	0.13	0.00	0.14
Ischnura elegans	72.83	84.7	50.88	75.48	67.34
Ischnura pumilio	5.33	5.08	0.00	22.61	5.44
Lestes dryas	2.07	3.60	0.00	0.00	2.01
Lestes sponsa	44.81	45.98	38.35	56.70	33.81
Lestes viridis	0.04	0.07	0.00	0.00	0.00
Leucorrhinia dubia	2.03	1.34	3.76	0.38	0.00
Libellula depressa	31.64	46.05	0.00	48.66	0.14
Libellula fulva	1.87	3.24	0.00	0.00	0.14
Libellula quadrimaculata	39.04	38.36	38.35	42.91	39.97
Orthetrum cancellatum	16.43	27.43	0.00	5.75	2.72
Orthetrum coerulescens	8.70	9.24	3.26	21.84	9.31
Oxygastra curtisii	0.12	0.21	0.00	0.00	0.00
Pantala flavescens	0.08	0.14	0.00	0.00	0.00
Platycnemis pennipes	8.38	13.68	0.00	6.13	0.00
Pyrrhosoma nymphula	70.15	67.91	68.67	85.44	61.03
Somatochlora arctica	1.87	0.00	5.76	0.00	0.29
Somatochlora metallica	1.79	2.54	1.00	0.00	0.00
Sympetrum danae	29.61	19.11	45.86	35.25	22.49
Sympetrum flaveolum	3.74	6.21	0.25	0.77	0.00
Sympetrum fonscolombii	2.20	3.39	0.50	0.77	0.14
Sympetrum meridionale	0.04	0.07	0.00	0.00	0.00
Sympetrum sanguineum	17.89	30.25	0.00	4.60	12.89
Sym. striolatum/nigrescens	57.83	73.20	25.31	71.65	55.16
Sympetrum vulgatum	0.33	0.56	0.00	0.00	0.00

Table 4. Vice-county distributions of species in Britain and Ireland (● 1975-90; ○ pre-1975)

ENGLAND AND WALES

SPECIES	W Cornwall (& Scilly)	East Cornwall	South Devon	North Devon	South Somerset	North Somerset	North Wiltshire	South Wiltshire	Dorset	Isle of Wight	South Hampshire	North Hampshire	West Sussex	East Sussex
Calopteryx virgo	●	●	●	●	●	●	●	●	●	●	●	●	●	●
Calopteryx splendens	●	●	●	●	●	●	●	●	●	●	●	●	●	●
Sympecma fusca														
Lestes barbarus														
Lestes sponsa	●	●	●	●	●	●	●	●	●	●	●	●	●	●
Lestes dryas														○
Lestes viridis														
Platycnemis pennipes		●	●	●	●	●	●	●	●		●	●	●	●
Pyrrhosoma nymphula	●	●	●	●	●	●	●	●	●	●	●	●	●	●
Ischnura elegans	●	●	●	●	●	●	●	●	●	●	●	●	●	●
Ischnura pumilio	●			●			●		●		●	○		○
Enallagma cyathigerum	●	●	●	●	●		●		●	●	●	●	●	●
Coenagrion mercuriale	○		●		○				●		●			
Coenagrion scitulum														
Coenagrion pulchellum			●	●							●	●	●	●
Coenagrion puella	●	●	●	●	●	●	●	●	●	●	●	●	●	●
Coenagrion lunulatum														
Coenagrion hastulatum														
Coenagrion armatum														
Erythromma najas			●			●	●	●	●		●	●	●	●
Ceriagrion tenellum	●	●	●	●		○			●	●	●	●	○	●
Gomphus flavipes														
Gomphus vulgatissimus												○	●	●
Brachytron pratense				●	●				●	○	●	●	●	●
Aeshna caerulea														
Aeshna juncea	●	●	●	●	●	●	●			●	●	●	●	
Aeshna grandis					●		●		●		●	●	●	●
Aeshna cyanea	●	●	●	●	●	●	●	●	●	●	●	●	●	●
Aeshna mixta	●		●		●		●		●	●	●	●	●	●
Aeshna affinis														
Aeshna isosceles														
Anax imperator	●	●	●	●	●		●		●	●	●	●	●	●
Hemianax ephippiger		●												
Cordulegaster boltonii	●	●	●	●	●		●		●		●	●	●	●
Cordulia aenea			●		●	○	○		●		●	●	●	●
Somatochlora metallica													●	
Somatochlora arctica														
Oxygastra curtisii			○								○			
Libellula depressa	●	●	●	●	●	●	●	●	●		●	●	●	●
Libellula fulva						●	●	●	●		●	●		
Libellula quadrimaculata	●	●	●	●	●	●	●	●	●	●	●	●	●	●
Orthetrum coerulescens	●	●	●	○	○		●	●	●		●	○		
Orthetrum cancellatum	●	●	●	●	●		●		●	●	●	●	●	●
Crocothemis erythraea														
Sympetrum vulgatum			○											
Sympetrum striolatum/nigrescens	●	●	●	●	●	●	●		●	●	●	●	●	●
Sympetrum fonscolombii	●		●	○	○	○			○		●	●		○
Sympetrum meridionale														
Sympetrum flaveolum	○		○			○			○	○	●		●	
Sympetrum sanguineum	●		●			●	●		●	●	●	●	●	●
Sympetrum danae	○	●	●	●	●	●			●	●	○	●	●	●
Leucorrhinia dubia														○
Pantala flavescens														

SPECIES	East Kent	West Kent	Surrey	South Essex	North Essex	Hertfordshire	Middlesex	Berkshire	Oxfordshire	Buckinghamshire	East Suffolk	West Suffolk	East Norfolk	West Norfolk
Calopteryx virgo	○	●	●	●	●	●	●	●	●	●	●		○	○
Calopteryx splendens	●	●	●	●	●	●	●	●	●	●	●	●	●	●
Sympecma fusca														
Lestes barbarus														
Lestes sponsa	●	●	●	●	●	●	●	●	●	●	●	●	●	●
Lestes dryas	●		●		○	○			○	○		○	●	
Lestes viridis	○													
Platycnemis pennipes	●	●	●	●	●	●	●	●	●	●	○		●	●
Pyrrhosoma nymphula	●	●	●	●	●	●	●	●	●	●	●	●	●	●
Ischnura elegans	●	●	●	●	●	●	●	●	●	●	●	●	●	●
Ischnura pumilio		○									○		●	
Enallagma cyathigerum	●	●	●	●	●	●	●	●	●	●	●	●	●	●
Coenagrion mercuriale														
Coenagrion scitulum			○											
Coenagrion pulchellum	●		●	●	●	●	●	●	●	●	●		●	●
Coenagrion puella	●	●	●	●	●	●	●	●	●	●	●	●	●	●
Coenagrion lunulatum														
Coenagrion hastulatum														
Coenagrion armatum														○
Erythromma najas	●	●	●	●	●	●	●	●	●	●	●	●	●	●
Ceriagrion tenellum		○	●			●		●			○		○	
Gomphus flavipes		○												
Gomphus vulgatissimus	○	●	●											
Brachytron pratense	●	●	●	●	○	○	○	○	○	●			●	●
Aeshna caerulea														
Aeshna juncea		○		●		●		●	●				○	◐
Aeshna grandis	●	●	●	●	●	●	●	●	●	●	●	●	●	●
Aeshna cyanea	●	●	●	●	●	●	●	●	●	●	●	●	●	●
Aeshna mixta	●	●	●	●	●	●	●	●	●	●	●	●	●	●
Aeshna affinis	○													
Aeshna isosceles											●		●	
Anax imperator	●	●	●	●	●	●	●	●	●	●	●	●	●	●
Hemianax ephippiger			○											
Cordulegaster boltonii		●	●	○	●		●							
Cordulia aenea	●		●	○	●	●		○			●		○	
Somatochlora metallica	●		●		●								●	
Somatochlora arctica														
Oxygastra curtisii														
Libellula depressa		●	●	●	●	●	●	●	●	●	●	●	●	●
Libellula fulva	○													
Libellula quadrimaculata	●	●	●	●	●	●	●	●	●	●	●	●	●	●
Orthetrum coerulescens			●			●	○				●	○	○	
Orthetrum cancellatum	●	●	●		●	●	●	●	●		●		●	●
Crocothemis erythraea														
Sympetrum vulgatum				○	○	○				○				
Sympetrum striolatum/nigrescens	●	●	●	●	●	●	●	●	●	●	●		●	●
Sympetrum fonscolombii	○	○	●	●	●		○	○				●		
Sympetrum meridionale														
Sympetrum flaveolum	●	●	●	●	●		○			○	○	○	○	●
Sympetrum sanguineum	●	●	●	●	●	●	●	●	●	●	●	●	●	●
Sympetrum danae	●	○	○			●		●			○		●	●
Leucorrhinia dubia					●									
Pantala flavescens											○			

SPECIES	Cambridgeshire	Bedfordshire	Huntingdonshire	Northamptonshire	East Gloucestershire	West Gloucestershire	Monmouthshire	Herefordshire	Worcestershire	Warwickshire	Staffordshire	Shropshire (Salop)
Calopteryx virgo				●	●	●	●	●	●	●	●	●
Calopteryx splendens	●	●		●	●	●	●	●	●	●	●	●
Sympecma fusca												
Lestes barbarus												
Lestes sponsa	●	●	●	●	●	●	●	●	●	●	●	●
Lestes dryas	○	○	○									
Lestes viridis												
Platycnemis pennipes				●	●	●	●	●	●	●		●
Pyrrhosoma nymphula	●	●	●	●	●	●	●	●	●	●	●	●
Ischnura elegans	●	●	●	●	●	●	●	●	●	●	●	●
Ischnura pumilio	○		●									
Enallagma cyathigerum	●	●	●	●	●	●	●	●	●	●	●	●
Coenagrion mercuriale												
Coenagrion scitulum												
Coenagrion pulchellum	●		○							○		●
Coenagrion puella	●	●	●	●	●	●	●	●	●	●	●	●
Coenagrion lunulatum												
Coenagrion hastulatum												
Coenagrion armatum	○											
Erythromma najas	●	●	●	●	●	●		●	●	●	●	●
Ceriagrion tenellum	○											
Gomphus flavipes												
Gomphus vulgatissimus				○			●					●
Brachytron pratense	●	●	●		○	○	●			○		●
Aeshna caerulea												
Aeshna juncea	◐			●	●	●	●	●	●	●	●	●
Aeshna grandis	●	●	●	●	●	●	○	●	●	●	●	●
Aeshna cyanea	●	●	●	●	●	●	●	●	●	●	●	●
Aeshna mixta	●	●	●				●	●	●	●	●	●
Aeshna affinis												
Aeshna isosceles	○	○										
Anax imperator	●	●	●	●	●	●	●	●	●	●		
Hemianax ephippiger												
Cordulegaster boltonii							●	●	●	○		●
Cordulia aenea	●	●	○				●	●				●
Somatochlora metallica	●											
Somatochlora arctica												
Oxygastra curtisii												
Libellula depressa	●	●	●	●	●	●	●	●	●	●	●	●
Libellula fulva	●	●	●				●	●				
Libellula quadrimaculata	●	●	●	●	●	●	●	●	○	●	●	●
Orthetrum coerulescens		●	○	○			●	●				●
Orthetrum cancellatum	●	●	●	●			●	●			●	●
Crocothemis erythraea												
Sympetrum vulgatum				○								
Sympetrum striolatum/nigrescens	●	●	●	●	●	●	●	●	●	●	●	●
Sympetrum fonscolombii			●				○				●	●
Sympetrum meridionale												
Sympetrum flaveolum	●	○	○	●			●			◐	●	○
Sympetrum sanguineum	●	●	●	●	●	●	●	●	●	●	●	●
Sympetrum danae	○		●	○	○		●	○		◐	●	●
Leucorrhinia dubia									○		●	●
Pantala flavescens	○											●

Table 4 (cont). Vice-county distributions of species in Britain and Ireland (● 1975-90; ○ pre-1975)

ENGLAND AND WALES, ISLE OF MAN, CHANNEL ISLANDS

Column headings (vice-counties, in order):
Glamorgan, Breconshire, Radnorshire, Carmarthenshire, Pembrokeshire, Cardiganshire, Montgomeryshire, Merionethshire, Caernarvonshire, Denbighshire, Flintshire, Anglesey, South Lincolnshire, North Lincolnshire, Leics & Rutland, Nottinghamshire, Derbyshire, Cheshire, South Lancashire, West Lancashire, South-east Yorkshire, North-east Yorkshire, South-west Yorkshire, Mid-west Yorkshire, North-west Yorkshire, Durham, South Northumberland, N Northumberland, Westmorland & N Lancs, Cumberland, Isle of Man, Channel Islands

SPECIES:
- Calopteryx virgo
- Calopteryx splendens
- Sympecma fusca
- Lestes barbarus
- Lestes sponsa
- Lestes dryas
- Lestes viridis
- Platycnemis pennipes
- Pyrrhosoma nymphula
- Ischnura elegans
- Ischnura pumilio
- Enallagma cyathigerum
- Coenagrion mercuriale
- Coenagrion scitulum
- Coenagrion pulchellum
- Coenagrion puella
- Coenagrion lunulatum
- Coenagrion hastulatum
- Coenagrion armatum
- Erythromma najas
- Ceriagrion tenellum
- Gomphus flavipes
- Gomphus vulgatissimus
- Brachytron pratense
- Aeshna caerulea
- Aeshna juncea
- Aeshna grandis
- Aeshna cyanea
- Aeshna mixta
- Aeshna affinis
- Aeshna isosceles
- Anax imperator
- Hemianax ephippiger
- Cordulegaster boltonii
- Cordulia aenea
- Somatochlora metallica
- Somatochlora arctica
- Oxygastra curtisii
- Libellula depressa
- Libellula fulva
- Libellula quadrimaculata
- Orthetrum coerulescens
- Orthetrum cancellatum
- Crocothemis erythraea
- Sympetrum vulgatum
- Sympetrum striolatum/nigrescens
- Sympetrum fonscolombii
- Sympetrum meridionale
- Sympetrum flaveolum
- Sympetrum sanguineum
- Sympetrum danae
- Leucorrhinia dubia
- Pantala flavescens

SCOTLAND

SPECIES	Shetland Islands	Orkney Islands	Outer Hebrides	Caithness	West Sutherland	East Sutherland	East Ross	West Ross	North Ebudes	Mid Ebudes	South Ebudes	Kintyre	Clyde Isles	Dunbartonshire	Argyll Main	West Inverness	East Inverness	Moray (Elgin)	Banffshire	N Aberdeenshire	S Aberdeenshire	Kincardineshire	Angus (Forfar)	East Perthshire	Mid Perthshire	West Perthshire	Stirlingshire	Fifeshire (Kinross)	West Lothian	Midlothian	East Lothian	Berwickshire	Roxburghshire	Selkirkshire	Peeblesshire	Lanarkshire	Renfrewshire	Ayrshire	Wigtownshire	Kirkcudbrightshire	Dumfriesshire
Calopteryx virgo									●	●	●	●			●	●									●	●	●														
Calopteryx splendens			○	●	●	●	●	●	●	●	●	●	●	●	●	●	●	●	●	●	●	●	●	●	●	●	●	●	●	●	●	●	●	●	●	●	●	●	●	●	●
Sympecma fusca																																									
Lestes barbarus																																									
Lestes sponsa	●																																								
Lestes dryas																																									
Lestes viridis																																									
Platycnemis pennipes																																									
Pyrrhosoma nymphula		●	●	●	●	●	●	●	●	●	●	●	●	●	●	●	●	●	●	●	●	●	●	●	●	●	●	●	●	●	●	●	●	●	●	●	●	●	●	●	●
Ischnura elegans		●	●	●	●	●	●	●	●	●	●	●	●	●	●	●	●	●	●	●	●	●	●	●	●	●	●	●	●	●	●	●	●	●	●	●	●	●	●	●	●
Ischnura pumilio																																									
Enallagma cyathigerum		●	●	●	●	●	●	●	●	●	●	●	●	●	●	●	●	●	●	●	●	●	●	●	●	●	●	●	●	●	●		●	●	●	●	●	●			●
Coenagrion mercuriale																																									
Coenagrion scitulum																		○																					●	●	●
Coenagrion pulchellum															●																								●	●	●
Coenagrion puella												●	●	●	●			●					●	●	●		●	●	●	●	●	●	●	●	●	●	●	●	●	●	●
Coenagrion lunulatum																									●																
Coenagrion hastulatum																	●				●																				
Coenagrion armatum																																									
Erythromma najas																																									
Ceriagrion tenellum																																									
Gomphus flavipes																																									
Gomphus vulgatissimus																																								●	
Brachytron pratense												●			●			○																						●	●
Aeshna caerulea					●		○	●	●						●	●	●	●																						●	
Aeshna juncea	○	●	●	●	●	●	●	●	●	●	●	●	●	●	●	●	●	●	●	●	●	●	●	●	●	●	●	●	●	●	●	●	●	●	●	●	●	●	●	●	●
Aeshna grandis							●					●			●		●	●							●																
Aeshna cyanea																																									
Aeshna mixta																																									
Aeshna affinis																																									
Aeshna isosceles																																									
Anax imperator																																									
Hemianax ephippiger																																									
Cordulegaster boltonii		●			●	●	●		●	●	●	●	●	●	●	●	●	●							●	●	●			●	●	●				●		●		●	●
Cordulia aenea	○		○												●		●										●														
Somatochlora metallica								●	○	○					●	●	●	○							●																
Somatochlora arctica															●		●																								
Oxygastra curtisii																																									
Libellula depressa																																									
Libellula fulva																																									
Libellula quadrimaculata	○	●	●	●	●	●	●	●	●	●	●	●	●	●	●	●	●	●	○	●	●	●	●	●	●	●	●		○	●			●			●	●	●	●	●	●
Orthetrum coerulescens									●	●	●	●	●												○															○	
Orthetrum cancellatum																																									
Crocothemis erythraea																																									
Sympetrum vulgatum																																									
Sympetrum striolatum/nigrescens			●	●	●	●	●	●	●	●	●	●	●		●	○	●	●							●			●			●						●	●	●	●	●
Sympetrum fonscolombii				○									○										○					○			○										
Sympetrum meridionale																																									
Sympetrum flaveolum																														○											
Sympetrum sanguineum																																									
Sympetrum danae		●	●	●	●	●	●	●	●	●	●	●	●	●	●	●	●	●	●	●	●	●	●	●	●	●	●	●	●	●	●	○	●	●	●	●	●	●	●	●	●
Leucorrhinia dubia							●	●							●	●	●	●			●	○			○																
Pantala flavescens																																									

Table 4 (cont). Vice-county distributions of species in Britain and Ireland (● 1975-90; ○ pre-1975)

IRELAND

County	Calopteryx virgo	Calopteryx splendens	Sympecma fusca	Lestes barbarus	Lestes sponsa	Lestes dryas	Lestes viridis	Platycnemis pennipes	Pyrrhosoma nymphula	Ischnura elegans	Ischnura pumilio	Enallagma cyathigerum	Coenagrion mercuriale	Coenagrion scitulum	Coenagrion pulchellum	Coenagrion puella	Coenagrion lunulatum	Coenagrion hastulatum	Coenagrion armatum	Erythromma najas	Ceriagrion tenellum	Gomphus flavipes	Gomphus vulgatissimus	Brachytron pratense	Aeshna caerulea	Aeshna juncea	Aeshna grandis	Aeshna cyanea	Aeshna mixta	Aeshna affinis	Aeshna isosceles	Anax imperator	Hemianax ephippiger	Cordulegaster boltonii	Cordulia aenea	Somatochlora metallica	Somatochlora arctica	Oxygastra curtisii	Libellula depressa	Libellula fulva	Libellula quadrimaculata	Orthetrum coerulescens	Orthetrum cancellatum	Crocothemis erythraea	Sympetrum vulgatum	Sympetrum striolatum/nigrescens	Sympetrum fonscolombii	Sympetrum meridionale	Sympetrum flaveolum	Sympetrum sanguineum	Sympetrum danae	Leucorrhinia dubia	Pantala flavescens
Londonderry	●				●				●	●	●	●			●	●	●							●		●	●	●													●					●					●		
Antrim	●				●				●	●	●	●			●	●	●							●		●	●	●													●					●				●	●		
Down	●				●				●	●	●	●			●	●	●							●		●	●	●													●	●				●				●	●		
Armagh	●				●				●	●		●			●		●	●						●		●	●														●	○				●				●	●		
Tyrone	●				●				●	●	●	●			●	●								●		●															●					●				●	●		
West Donegal	●				●				●	●	●	●			●	●								●		●	●														●	●	●			●					●		
East Donegal	●		○		●				●	●		●			●		●							●		○	●														●					●					●		
Fermanagh	●				●				●	●	●	●			●	●	●							●		●	●														●					●					●		
Monaghan	●		○		●				●	●		●			●	●	●									○	○														●					●			○		○		
Louth	●				●				●	●	●	●			●	●	●							●		●	●														●	●				●				●	●		
Cavan	○								●	●		●			●	●								●		●	●														●					○	○				○		
Leitrim	●				●				●	●	●	●			●	●	●							●		●	●														●					●					●		
Sligo	●				●				●	●	●	●			●	●								●		●	●														●	●	●			●					●		
West Mayo	●				●	●			●	●	●	●			●	●								●		●	●														●					●					●		
East Mayo	●		○		●				●	●		●			●	●								●		●	●														●	●				●					●		
Roscommon	●				●				●	●	●	●			●									●		●	●														●	●				●				●	○		
Longford	●		●		●				●	●		●			●	●	●							●		●	●														●					●				●	○		
Westmeath	●		●	●		●			●	●	●	●			●	●	●							●		●	●													●	●	●				●				●	●		
Meath	●				●				●	●	●				●	●								●		●	●														●					●				●	●		
Dublin	●				●				●	●	●	●			●	●	●							●		●						○									●	●	●			●	●				●	○	
Wicklow	●	●		●		●			●	●	●	●			●	●	●							○		●	●														●	●				●				●	●		
Kildare	●			●		●			●	●	●	●			●	●	●							●		●	●														●	●	●			●				●	●		
Offaly	●	●			●				●	●	●	●			●	●								●		●	●														●	●				●				●	●		
NE Galway	●								●	●	●	●			●		●	●						●		●	●														●	●	●			●				●	●		
West Galway	●	●		●		●			●	●	●	●			●	●								●		●	●														●	●	●			●				●			
SE Galway	●	●		●		●			●	●	●	●			●	●								●		●	●	●													●	●	●			●				●	●		
Laois	●	●		○					●	●		●			●	●								●		●	●	●													●	●	●			●				●	●	○	
Carlow	○	●				●	●		○			●			○						○					○	○	○													○					●				○	●		
Wexford	●	●			●				●	●	●	●			●	●								●		●															●					●				●	●		
Kilkenny	●	●		●		●			●	●	●	●			●	●					○			●																	●	●				●				●	●	○	
N Tipperary	●	●			●				●	●		●			●	●								●		●															●	●				●				●	●		
Clare	●	●			●				●	●		●			●	●								●		●	●														●	●	●			●				●	●		
Limerick	●	●			●				●	●		●			●	●								●		●	●														●					●				●		●	
S Tipperary	●	●			●				●	●		●			●	●								●		○	●														●	●				●				●	●		
Waterford	●	●			●				●	●		●			●	●								●		●	●											○			●	●				●				●	●		
East Cork	●	●			●				●	●		●			●	●					○					●															●					●				●	●		
Mid Cork	●	●			●				●	●					●		●									○	●														●					●				●	●		
West Cork	●	●			●				●	●		●			●	●					○			●		●									●						●	●				●				●	●	●	
North Kerry	●	○			●				●	●		●			●	●					●					●	○								●	●					●	●				●				●	●		
South Kerry	●	●		●		○			●	●	●	●			○	●					●			●		●	○								●	●		○			●	●				●				●	●		

Figure 7. Map of coverage up to the end of 1990

Computerisation and validation

Having been fully vetted, so that the identifications are not in doubt, record cards are passed to BRC at Monks Wood. The information on the cards is entered on a desktop microcomputer, and then transferred to a larger machine (currently a MicroVax cluster) for further checking. The data entry is checked by careful proof-reading. The consistency of information is checked by computer to ensure that the grid reference is within the vice-county to which it has been assigned, that the date is possible, and that the species and recorder codes are valid.

The spelling of locality names is standardised to that used by the Ordnance Survey (or, for statutory conservation sites, the managing authority) and, at the same time, the full grid reference is checked, either by computer or manually using OS 1:50 000 maps and gazetteers, and 1:25 000 maps. When all validations are complete, the data are stored within a relational database management system (ORACLE) on a SUN server.

Tables of records and squares per species

Table 2 shows the number of records for each species, and the number of 10 km squares in which each has been found. This information is also expressed as a percentage of the total number of 10 km squares with records. Table 3 shows the percentage of recorded squares in which each species is recorded, for Britain, Ireland, England, Wales and Scotland separately, illustrating how the status of a species varies between the different countries. This aspect is discussed further in the individual species accounts.

Vice-county distributions

Table 4 shows the occurrence of each species in the Watson/Praeger vice-counties in Britain and Ireland. These are shown in Appendix 3, and more detail is given by Dandy (1969) for Britain, and Webb (1980) for Ireland. (NB Current county boundaries may differ from these.)

COVERAGE

Interpretation of strengths and weaknesses

Figures 2 and 3 show that a few southern English counties had received quite thorough coverage as early as the mid-1970s, at least on a 10 km square basis. By 1982, this degree of effort had been achieved over much of England and Wales, parts of Scotland, and a few areas of Ireland (Figure 5).

Figure 7 shows the coverage up to the end of 1990, summarising the data used in the species maps in this *Atlas*. The coverage map shows those 10 km squares from which dragonflies have been recorded, not all the squares which recorders have visited in search of dragonflies. 'Negative records' are exceedingly difficult to establish, and are seldom submitted to recording schemes.

During the mid-1980s, a great deal of effort was spent looking at unrecorded areas. In many 10 km squares, no dragonflies could be found. The gaps in Figure 7, therefore, often coincide with areas where the dragonfly fauna is impoverished. Some gaps represent areas which are largely acid, upland landscape, often barren and windswept, and unsuitable for dragonflies (parts of Scotland, Wales and the northern Pennines of England). In other areas, the paucity of dragonflies is due to the lack of standing water, as in certain chalk downland areas (Salisbury Plain in Wiltshire, the Hampshire Downs, and the Yorkshire Wolds), and intensively agricultural areas (parts of Lincolnshire and the Fens), where pollution is an added problem.

A discussion of patterns of species richness in Odonata compared with other taxonomic groups is given by Prendergast *et al.* (1993) and Lawton, Prendergast and Eversham (1994).

Coverage in Ireland is entirely different from that in Britain. Despite great progress in the 1980s, the coverage map of Ireland still represents, to some extent, areas of recorder effort, and the species maps should be interpreted with caution. However, the broad distribution patterns of many species, eg *Calopteryx virgo*, *Pyrrhosoma nymphula* and *Orthetrum coerulescens*, are beginning to show through. If progress is maintained, recorders in Ireland may be able to produce comprehensive maps of most Irish species in the not-too-distant future.

Future distribution maps

Coverage will never be 100% for any group of plants or animals. Inevitably, therefore, there will be gaps. The maps presented in this *Atlas* are amongst the most comprehensive produced for any invertebrate groups. They provide a clear picture of dragonfly distribution during a fixed period, and are of permanent documentary value. As such, they will never be 'out of date' although, to a varying extent for different species, they will gradually cease to be 'up to date' – an important distinction. Continually adding data to maps, extending their period of coverage, can obscure significant changes in species distributions – expansions or contractions of range, local extinctions, etc.

Having established a reliable baseline, it may be preferable to organise concerted complete resurveys at intervals, rather than amalgamate on-going work with previous surveys. For details of other aspects than geographic distribution, see the chapter on **Future recording.**

SPECIES ACCOUNTS AND MAPS

INTRODUCTION TO THE SPECIES ACCOUNTS

One of the main purposes of the species accounts of resident Odonata is to help interpret the data on the species maps. Apparent patterns of distribution can be better understood if they are studied in relation to the biology of the dragonfly concerned, because distribution depends upon habitat requirements and upon climatic features which affect development. Therefore, if a species has a preference for heathland pools and runnels, we would expect it to have only a very limited distribution in East Anglia. Similarly, if a species is susceptible to the effects of low winter temperatures, its distribution being centred on the Mediterranean region, it would not be expected to occur in northern Scotland.

Each resident species account follows the pattern outlined below. First, there is **a description of the adult dragonfly**, making particular reference to those features which help to distinguish it from similar or closely related species that occur in Britain or Ireland. If the observer is not familiar with the species, the description should be used in conjunction with one of the excellent guides now available for identifying dragonflies.

The next section deals with **habitat**. Dragonflies are strong fliers and so adults may be seen in virtually any biotope, particularly when they are immature and hence in the main dispersal stage. When they are mature they mainly feed away from water, and therefore at this stage will be found in any warm sheltered spot near their breeding place. Thus, a species which breeds in both moorland pools and farm ponds may be found feeding on heather moorland in the shelter of a conifer plantation or in a meadow in the shelter of a hedge. The crucial habitat is the breeding water where larval development occurs, and it is this habitat which is briefly described in the **Species accounts**. Dragonflies are found in a wide range of aquatic bodies. Whilst each species has a favoured breeding habitat or range of habitats, many species can breed under suboptimal conditions, and sometimes attempt to breed under conditions which are very far removed from the optimal. In the latter case, although copulation and oviposition may be observed, breeding is seldom successful in terms of *larval development* and subsequent adult emergence.

In Europe, many species may breed in a narrow range of habitats in one region, yet occupy a broader habitat spectrum elsewhere. For some species at least, such differences also occur between Britain and Ireland, and even within Britain. An attempt has been made, as far as knowledge and space permit, to indicate national and regional differences in habitat occupancy in the relevant species accounts.

The next section deals with **breeding biology**. Unless otherwise stated, it can be assumed that each species has a similar daily routine which is modified by weather. Males fly to water during the late morning on fine days. Their maximal abundance usually occurs at around noon, and they return to their feeding and roosting areas in the afternoon. Females only visit water to mate and lay eggs. Low temperatures, strong winds and rain reduce the number of insects by water or completely prevent them visiting water. Larvae are more difficult to find and identify than adult dragonflies, but at least they can be found whatever the weather.

Special emphasis is put on **territorial behaviour**, because this determines the adult population density of most species at the waterside at the height of the season. Observations at a small pond may show that it is visited by one *Aeshna cyanea* and contains one *Libellula quadrimaculata*, two *Sympetrum striolatum*, five *Lestes sponsa* and ten *Ischnura elegans* at the heights of their respective seasons. The numbers assessed cannot be taken as evidence that the pond is more suitable for one species than for another. They merely reflect differences in the territorial behaviour of the males. A search for larvae may reveal dozens of *A. cyanea* larvae in the pond. In general, larger dragonflies have larger adult territories than small ones, and hence their adult population densities are lower. A useful value is the 'highest steady density', that is the highest number of males per 100 m of water edge which is rarely exceeded for the species concerned (Moore 1964). Highest steady densities are only very approximate (in the **Species accounts**, figures greater than 20 have been rounded to the nearest five), but they give a very useful indication of the maximal density one is likely to find in any species by any water body. Usually the actual density recorded will be below the highest steady density because territorial behaviour causes expulsions of individuals from a pond at densities well below the highest steady density, and because the visit to the pond may often be made before or after the period of greatest abundance.

Territorial behaviour has been widely studied, and it is clear that its nature varies greatly between species. The extent to which it is a matter of simple dominance of one individual over another, or whether it involves different strategies in obtaining a mate, is not certain. The degree of localisation also varies. At one extreme, individuals are merely aggressive wherever they happen to be, and they do not defend a particular place. At the other extreme, a distinct part of the water's edge is defended and an established male may return to it day after day. These points are of great interest, but the effects are very similar: the density of the male population by water is controlled by the behaviour of the insects to a very large extent. If the density observed at a water body approaches the highest steady density for the species, it indicates that the water body is favourable for that species.

Information on other aspects of breeding biology follows. Wherever possible it is based (like that on territorial behaviour) on field observations made in Britain and Ireland, as life histories often vary in different parts of the world. For example, species which require two or more years to complete development in northern Europe may do so in only one year further south. There is also evidence that larval development is slower at higher larval densities in any given area. The subjects briefly covered are **mating behaviour, copulation** time, **oviposition** and the extent to which the males participate in it, **larval development** and habitat, **emergence** and the length of **maturation** of adults. Much is known about these different aspects of breeding biology, but the more that dragonflies are studied the more variable they appear to be. Therefore, none of the information given should be taken as definitive. Much more work is required on almost every aspect of breeding biology. For example, displacement of sperm left in the female at previous matings has been demonstrated in a number of damselflies and dragonflies, but little is known about sperm displacement in British and Irish species. It clearly affects copulation time, which is found not only to vary greatly between species but also within some species. Similarly, there is much variation in oviposition behaviour. There is a growing literature on the relationship between the larva and its habitat and the larvae of other species (Harvey 1985; Harvey & Corbet 1985); nevertheless, it has yet to be shown that one species, either in the larval or adult stage, completely excludes another from a water body. The time spent in larval development appears to vary much more than was originally thought, depending on factors such as water temperature and food supply (Banks & Thompson 1987). The values given in the species accounts may well need to be revised when more observations have been made in different parts of the country. And to what extent does water acidity affect the distribution of species? Foster (1994) found no significant differences in odonate larval number between peat pools in a Galloway bog subject to liming and those in the surrounding untreated area. He suggests that the often-reported association of certain species with acid water is not because they are acidophiles but because of some other factor, or combination of factors.

It should be noted that dragonflies can usefully be divided into two groups, with similar numbers of British and Irish species in each. First, there are the spring species whose larvae pass the winter in diapause in their last larval instar, thus ensuring a synchronous emergence in spring. Second, there are the summer species, which spend the winter in the penultimate or earlier larval instar. Emergence of summer species is not usually synchronised. Many of the summer species, eg *Aeshna cyanea, A. juncea, A. grandis, A. mixta, Sympetrum danae, Lestes sponsa, L. dryas* and sometimes *S. sanguineum*, pass the first winter as diapause eggs. This is an adaptation which enhances the survival of those species which, in Britain or Ireland, may oviposit late in the summer − of all larval stages, newly hatched larvae appear to be least tolerant of low temperatures. *Sympecma fusca*, which has bred in the Channel Islands, is exceptional in that the adult is the diapause stage and overwinters, becoming reproductively active in the spring.

The next section gives approximate **flight periods** and indicates some of the species which may commonly be found with the one under consideration. Flight seasons vary with altitude, latitude, the topography of individual sites, and the weather patterns of particular years, as illustrated in the next chapter; those observed here are very approximate: insects can often be found both before and after the dates given in the text. The flight period tables contain more detailed information.

The penultimate section considers the **status and distribution** of the species, with particular regard to habitat requirements, and indicates threats to such habitats where relevant. It gives a brief appraisal of the data shown on the map. It is recognised that a species considered common in one region may have a different status in another region. So, in discussing important current and historical records, and as far as space allows, an attempt has been made to treat the following four regions separately: England and Wales, Scotland, Ireland, and the Channel Islands. For all but the demonstrably widespread and common species, comments on status and distribution in Ireland are tentative, because recording of dragonflies in southern parts of the island has been insufficient for definitive statements.

Finally, the distribution in Britain and Ireland is put into a **European and world context**. Change of status (decline or increase) has been noted for a number of species which are well documented on the continent.

The species accounts for those Odonata recorded from the Channel Islands but not from the rest of Britain and Ireland are necessarily more brief, but cover the same broad topics; these species are not mapped. The accounts of immigrant and vagrant species mention breeding behaviour only as far as is relevant to the British and Irish occurrence of the species. The next section discusses the likelihood of non-resident species colonising Britain and Ireland, and makes reference to other species, not yet recorded here, which might possibly be overlooked, or which could be expected to occur in future, based on their biology and their European range.

References are not given for statements which are referred to in standard works with good bibliographies. Those references which are included draw attention to some recent studies and to work which may be unfamiliar to British and Irish observers. Further details of the system adopted in giving references appear in the chapter on **Literature and references**.

RESIDENT SPECIES

Calopteryx virgo (Linnaeus)   **Beautiful demoiselle**

Description

The wings of the mature male are almost entirely dark black-brown with blue iridescence, and those of the female are transparent pale brown with a white false-pterostigma near the apices. The body of the male is metallic blue-green, whilst that of the female is metallic greenish bronze. It is much larger (45 mm in length) than other British and Irish damselflies, except for *C. splendens* which is of similar size, although the wings of *C. virgo* are broader than those of the latter species.

Habitat

C. virgo breeds on unpolluted streams and rivers of moderate to fast flow with silt, gravel or stony bottoms, often in heathland or moorland areas though it is not confined to these, also being found on suitable rivers in agricultural areas within its geographical range. It appears to tolerate more shade than *C. splendens*, and often perches on bushes and trees, such as alder, by the water's edge, in addition to bankside herbage in more open areas. The ecology of *C. virgo* and *C. splendens* on rivers on which they coexist is discussed by Prendergast (1988) and Brownett (1994).

Breeding biology

Males are territorial, and open and shut their wings in a threat display. They can occur at high densities. Some males appear to be non-territorial and mate with females as opportunities arise. Unlike most of our other resident dragonfly species, copulation in *C. virgo* is preceded by a courtship display – an aerial dance. Copulation takes from two to five minutes. The female oviposits alone into the submerged tissues of emergent plants, with the male often guarding her from his perch or by hovering nearby. The larvae, which usually take two years to develop, live amongst submerged vegetation, matted tree roots and plant debris.

Flight periods

C. virgo is on the wing from the end of May to late August or early September. On the faster-flowing streams and rivers of western Britain, it is frequently seen with *Cordulegaster boltonii* and *Pyrrhosoma nymphula*. Elsewhere, and further downstream where the current slackens, it may be seen with *Enallagma cyathigerum*, *Ischnura elegans* and *Calopteryx splendens*.

Status and distribution

C. virgo is most abundant in the Weald, south-west England, Wales and the southern part of Ireland. It is found locally in the Lake District and the west of Scotland, including several islands of the Inner Hebrides. Although probably always rare in eastern England and the midlands owing to lack of suitable habitat, it appears to have disappeared from a number of localities, possibly due to agricultural pollution and to the water authority practice of straightening and deepening some rivers and streams, thus altering their profiles, and spraying bankside vegetation with herbicides. It was last recorded in Norfolk on the River Wissey in 1974. *C. virgo* was recently rediscovered as a breeding species in Essex (Benton 1988).

European and world distribution

C. virgo occurs throughout Europe, and east to Asia. It also occurs locally in North Africa. There are several subspecies.

Calopteryx virgo (Linnaeus)

Beautiful demoiselle

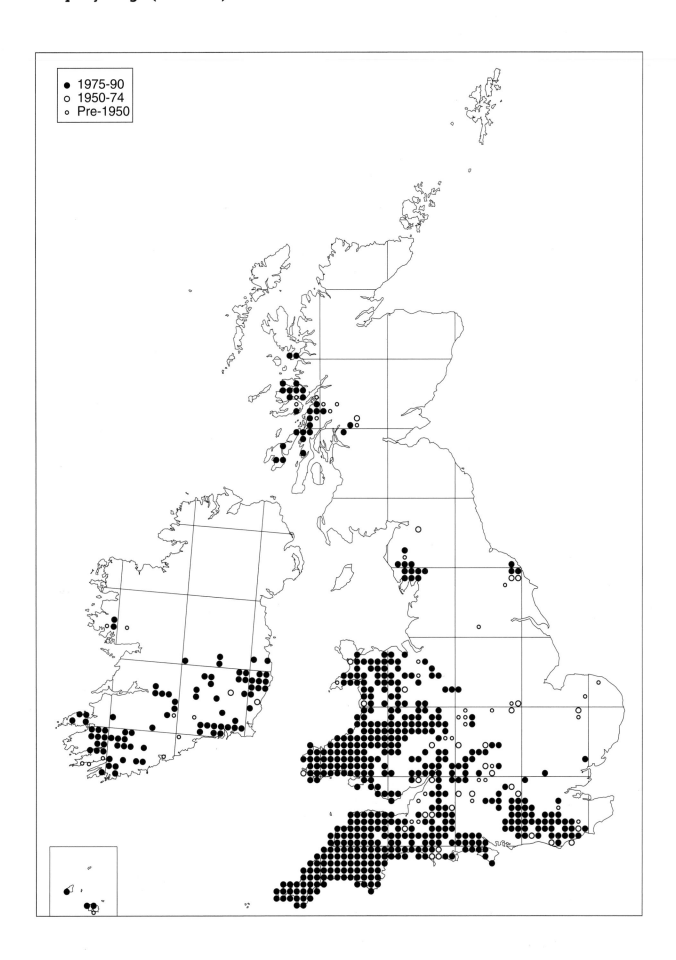

Legend:
- ● 1975-90
- ○ 1950-74
- ○ Pre-1950

Calopteryx splendens (Harris)   **Banded demoiselle**

Description

This damselfly is, with *C. virgo*, the largest that occurs in Britain and Ireland and, like that species, it has brightly coloured wings. In both sexes, the wings are narrower than those of *C. virgo*. In males, there is a broad iridescent dark blue patch on each wing, extending from the node towards the wing tip, and the body is metallic blue-green. The wings of the female are transparent pale green, due to the vein coloration, with a white false-pterostigma on each wing near the apex, and the body is metallic green-bronze. Despite the difference in wing coloration and breadth between females of *C. splendens* and *C. virgo*, inexperienced observers should exert caution in separating the two species unless both are present at the same site and a direct comparison can be made.

Habitat

C. splendens favours slow-flowing rivers, often meandering and with muddy bottoms, in which to breed, and may also be found along the margins of canals and, very rarely, lakes. It frequently perches on tall emergent and bankside vegetation such as reed canary-grass and may occur in large numbers.

Breeding biology

The males are territorial, but population densities can be quite high. Like *C. virgo*, males of *C. splendens* perform an aerial courtship dance in front of the perched female. In the dance, the wings are moved alternately, not together as on other occasions (Ruppell 1985). Copulation takes about one minute. The female oviposits alone into the tissues of floating and emergent plants, eg water-crowfoot and yellow flag, sometimes going completely under water to do so. The male guards her by hovering or perching nearby. The larvae, which live amongst submerged vegetation and plant debris, can thrive in quite muddy water and usually take two years to develop. Emergence usually occurs on the stems of tall bankside plants, but also on short grasses at the top of near-vertical sandy banks. The teneral stage is short, and may last for only two days.

Flight periods

C. splendens is on the wing from late May to the end of August, and is often found with species such as *Platycnemis pennipes*, *Ischnura elegans* and, occasionally, *C. virgo*.

Status and distribution

C. splendens is widely distributed in lowland areas of both southern Britain and Ireland, thinning out westward to the extent that it is scarce or absent throughout much of Cornwall and Caernarvon in Britain, and Co Mayo, western Co Galway and Co Kerry in Ireland. It is absent from most of northern England, although a small population has been present on the Solway Plain in Cumbria for many years, and it has recently been discovered on the Rivers Wansbeck and Blyth in Northumberland, the latter record in 1991, too late to include on the map. *C. splendens* is absent from Scotland, unless perhaps a small colony awaits discovery somewhere in lowland Border country. Sélys-Longchamps (1846) recorded it as Scottish, having seen it in the collection of a Mr Wilson in Edinburgh in 1845. *C. splendens* was recorded as being abundant at Fyvie, Aberdeenshire, by Trail (1878), but this record was doubted by Evans (1911), who thought it must be *C. virgo*, noting the tendency for the latter species in Scotland to be 'more or less hyaline at the base and tip of the wings in the male'. Whichever of the two species it was, it has not been mapped, because of the uncertainty.

European and world distribution

C. splendens is found throughout most of Europe, though not the Iberian peninsula, and its range extends east to China. There are several subspecies.

Calopteryx splendens (Harris)   **Banded demoiselle**

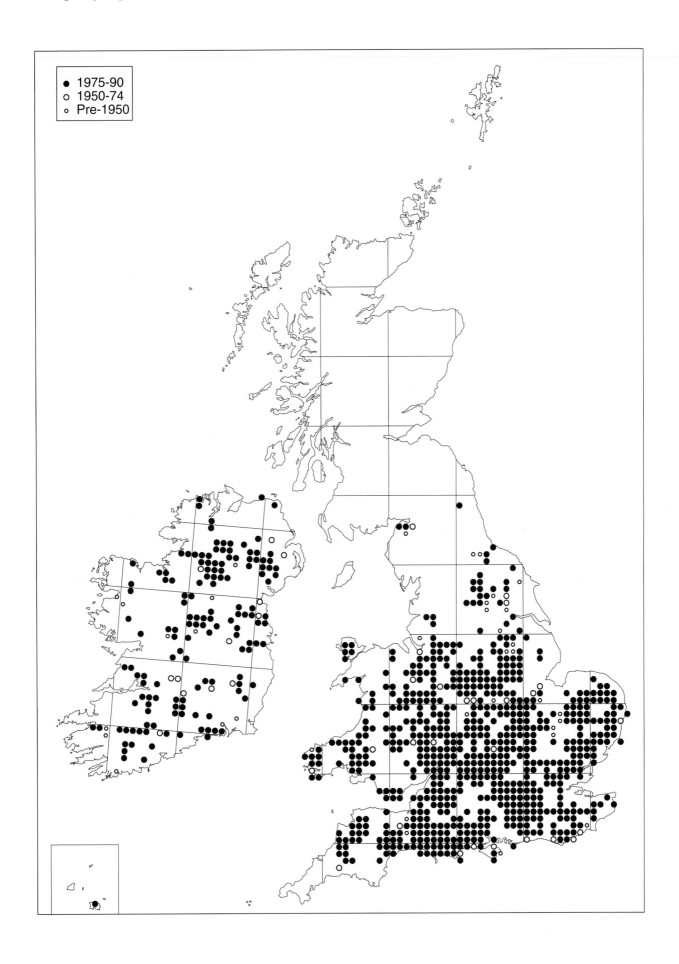

- ● 1975-90
- ○ 1950-74
- ○ Pre-1950

Lestes sponsa (Hansemann)   **Emerald damselfly**

Description

This is one of the two metallic green damselfly species with clear wings found in Britain and Ireland. Like the very much rarer *L. dryas*, it usually perches with its wings half open – a position intermediate between most damselflies and true dragonflies. In males, a pale blue pruinescence develops with age and, in mature individuals, it extends over the dorsal surface of abdominal segments 1 and 2, and the posterior abdominal segments, and also the sides of the thorax from below. The eyes are blue. Females are a duller green with areas of pink or beige on the sides of the thorax and abdomen. It is advisable to examine the anal appendages of males (and check whether the inferior appendages are almost straight or club-shaped, when viewed dorsally) and the ovipositor valves of females (and check whether or not they project beyond the apex of abdominal segment 10) in order to separate this species from *L. dryas*.

Habitat

L. sponsa breeds in a very wide range of habitats from eutrophic ditches in the lowlands to bog pools in mountain areas. It breeds also in canals, ponds, lakes and other static water bodies, and, occasionally, may be found amongst dense vegetation by slow-flowing streams. It prefers shallow water with an abundance of tall emergent and marginal vegetation such as rushes, sedges or horsetails, though it has been recorded breeding in ponds devoid of both submerged and emergent plants, if suitable marginal vegetation is present. In coastal areas, *L. sponsa* can tolerate quite brackish conditions.

Breeding biology

L. sponsa males are territorial, their density rarely exceeding 110 per 100 m of water's edge. Copulation takes place near or by water, and is of long duration (28–69 minutes). The eggs are inserted into water plants by the female, often in tandem, usually selecting the stem of an emergent macrophyte above water level and working her way down until completely submerged, sometimes remaining so for up to 30 minutes. Oviposition sometimes occurs in rank marginal vegetation away from the water's edge. The eggs pass the winter in diapause, a physiological device which delays hatching until the following spring, when water temperatures are more favourable. The larvae, which live amongst submerged water weeds, can complete their development remarkably quickly, in as little as two months (although last instar larvae occasionally overwinter). The species can thus survive the drying out of the habitat in late summer drought. The adults spend an unusually long time reaching maturity (16–30 days).

Flight periods

L. sponsa is on the wing from late June to the end of September. Unlike some other damselfly species, it sometimes roosts at the water's edge. In many northern and western bogs it occurs with *Sympetrum danae*. Elsewhere, it can be found with nearly all the other British and Irish species that breed in static water.

Status and distribution

L. sponsa occurs widely throughout Britain and Ireland, including many of the Scottish islands. Although it is quite common in many areas, in some counties it is a very local damselfly, less common than several other species of damselfly, reflecting the lack of suitable water bodies in which to breed.

European and world distribution

L. sponsa is a Palaearctic species. Its range extends from the Pyrenees to southern Norway and eastwards to Japan. It is absent or very local in several Mediterranean countries.

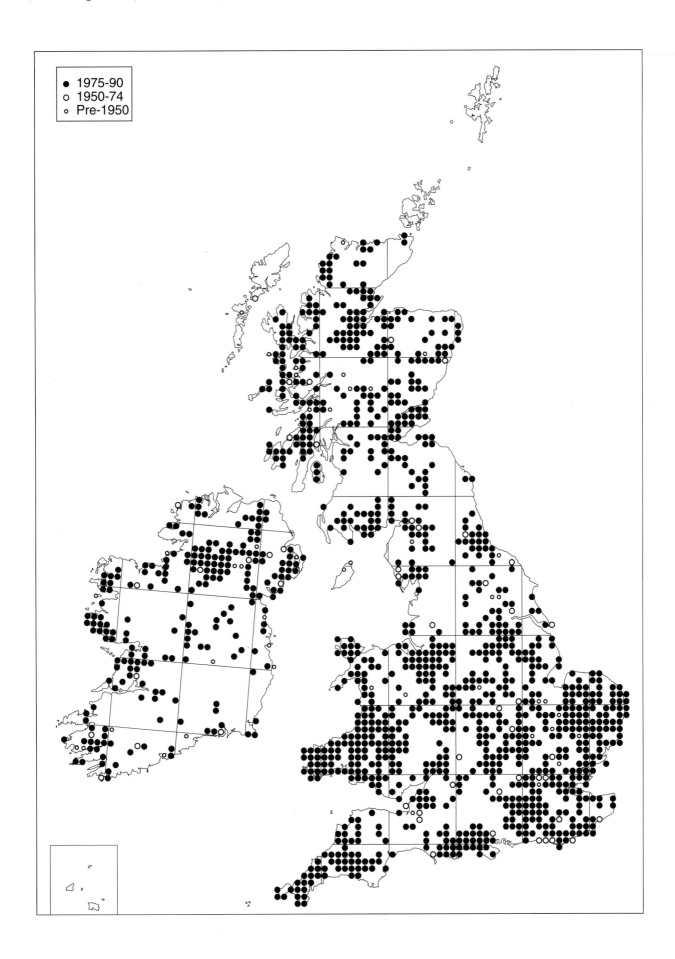

- ● 1975-90
- ○ 1950-74
- ○ Pre-1950

Lestes dryas Kirby   Scarce emerald damselfly

Description

This is one of the two metallic green damselfly species with clear wings found in Britain and Ireland. Like the much commoner *L. sponsa*, it usually perches with its wings held half open. In males, a pale blue pruinescence develops with age and, in mature individuals, it extends over the dorsal surface of the posterior abdominal segments, also segment 1 and part of segment 2 of the abdomen, and the sides of the thorax from below. The eyes are bright pale blue. The metallic green coloration in males is brighter than that of *L. sponsa*. Females of *L. dryas* are bronze-green, and the sides of the thorax and abdomen are very pale yellowish green. There is a pair of green rectangular spots on abdominal segment 1, unlike those of *L. sponsa* which are rounded. The female *L. dryas* is a much more robust damselfly than her *sponsa* counterpart. Despite these differences between the two species, it is advisable to examine the anal appendages of males and the ovipositor valves of females to provide certain proof of identity.

Habitat

L. dryas breeds in shallow ponds and lakes, overgrown canals and ditches and temporary pools, generally neutral to slightly alkaline and where there is an abundance of tall emergent plants such as common club-rush, rushes, sedges and horsetails. In coastal grazing marshes, it can tolerate brackish conditions and may be found where sea club-rush predominates. In the Breckland of Norfolk, it is sometimes found breeding in shaded ponds in dense woodland plantations as well as on open pingos. In Ireland, it is also found on a number of turloughs in limestone regions.

Breeding biology

L. dryas is probably territorial like other *Lestes*. It has a long copulation time (51–145 minutes). The eggs are inserted into the stems of emergent plants by the female, usually in tandem, above the water level, sometimes extending below the surface. Females will also oviposit in vegetation at temporary 'pools' which have dried up in summer. The eggs pass the winter in diapause, and development is completed within the following season. Details of larval habitats are given by Drake (1990, 1991).

Flight periods

L. dryas is on the wing from late June to early September. It is often found with *Sympetrum sanguineum* and *Coenagrion pulchellum* and with *L. sponsa*.

Status and distribution

L. dryas was always very local in England, and was confined to eastern counties from East Sussex to Yorkshire. It was known from the London marshes in the early 19th century (Stephens 1835–37), but its presence was not confirmed in Ireland until 1894, when it was discovered near Athlone, Co Westmeath. During the 1950s and 1960s, *L. dryas* was lost from many of its known sites in England, and there were no records at all for a period in the 1970s and it was feared extinct. It was rediscovered in Essex in 1983 (Benton & Payne 1983). It had probably been overlooked, and since then it has been found at other sites in Essex, Kent and Norfolk. The causes of the contraction of its breeding range in England have been described in detail, and were due mainly to agricultural improvements which resulted in lower water tables and destruction of marshy habitat (Moore 1980). At its shallow water sites, *L. dryas* is particularly susceptible to the effects of seral change, aggravated by prolonged periods of drought. In Ireland, *L. dryas* has not suffered so much, perhaps owing to its presence on a higher proportion of natural sites than in England. However, it is threatened by drainage at several localities. Although rare, further fieldwork in Ireland will probably reveal more sites in central and mid-western counties.

European and world distribution

L. dryas has one of the widest distributions of any British and Irish dragonfly. It is an holarctic species which is found from Portugal to southern Finland and eastwards to Japan, and in North America. However, it is declining rapidly in parts of Europe due to agricultural pressures, and it is in danger of extinction in several countries.

Lestes dryas Kirby   **Scarce emerald damselfly**

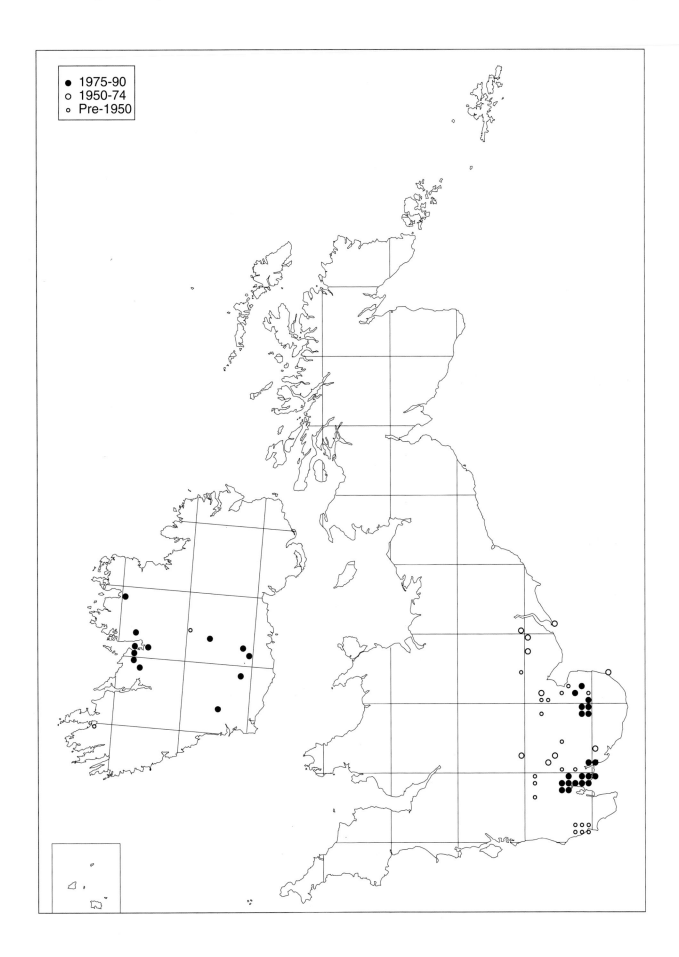

Platycnemis pennipes (Pallas)   **White-legged damselfly**

Description Both sexes of this species can be identified easily, whilst settled, by the broad, feather-like white tibia of the mid- and hind-legs. The male is a much paler blue than any other blue damselfly found in Britain, and there is a thin black longitudinal line running the length of the dorsal surface of the abdomen, becoming thicker posteriorly. The eyes of males are pale blue also. Mature females are pale green with the black median abdominal line slightly thinner than in males. The creamy white form known as var. *lactea* is a teneral phase in both sexes, though it occasionally persists to maturity. It is unlike any other British damselfly, although inexperienced observers should note that newly emerged damselflies of most species can appear a pale translucent greyish colour. Examination of the tibia will quickly settle the question.

Habitat *P. pennipes* breeds along unshaded sections of unpolluted larger streams and rivers with moderately slow to very sluggish flow, and also canals. Occasionally it has been found in large numbers at the sheltered margins of large lakes in the Weald and a few ponds elsewhere, and breeding has been proven at one such site. Its favoured habitats are fringed with thick herbage, amongst which *P. pennipes* flies with a slow weak flight, frequently settling. It may often be found, with other damselflies, sheltering amongst tall grass in nearby meadows.

Breeding biology *P. pennipes* appears not to be territorial and can occur in high densities. The males dangle their white legs in a courtship display, and use them also in a threat display. Copulation takes 13–27 minutes. The female inserts her eggs into the underside of floating leaves, and the stems, of water plants, in tandem with the male which holds its body upright to ward off other males. Larval development probably takes two years. Emergence usually occurs on the stems and leaves of tall emergent and bankside plants.

Flight periods *P. pennipes* is on the wing from the beginning of June, sometimes earlier, to mid-August. It is often found with *Calopteryx splendens* and the commoner damselflies such as *Ischnura elegans* and *Coenagrion puella*. At several localities it occurs with *Gomphus vulgatissimus* and *Libellula fulva*.

Status and distribution In Britain it is confined to suitable habitat south of the Wash. The linear nature of many of the records on the distribution map illustrates the preference of *P. pennipes* for the larger rivers and their tributaries. There is evidence that the species has declined in the eastern part of its range in England, possibly due to pollution and the intensive management of riverside vegetation by water authorities. It has not been recorded from Ireland, though there is plenty of apparently suitable habitat in the south.

European and world distribution The genus *Platycnemis* is one of the few confined to the Palaearctic region. *P. pennipes* occurs throughout Europe except Ireland, the Iberian peninsula, and most of northern Scandinavia. It is found east to Asia Minor and Siberia.

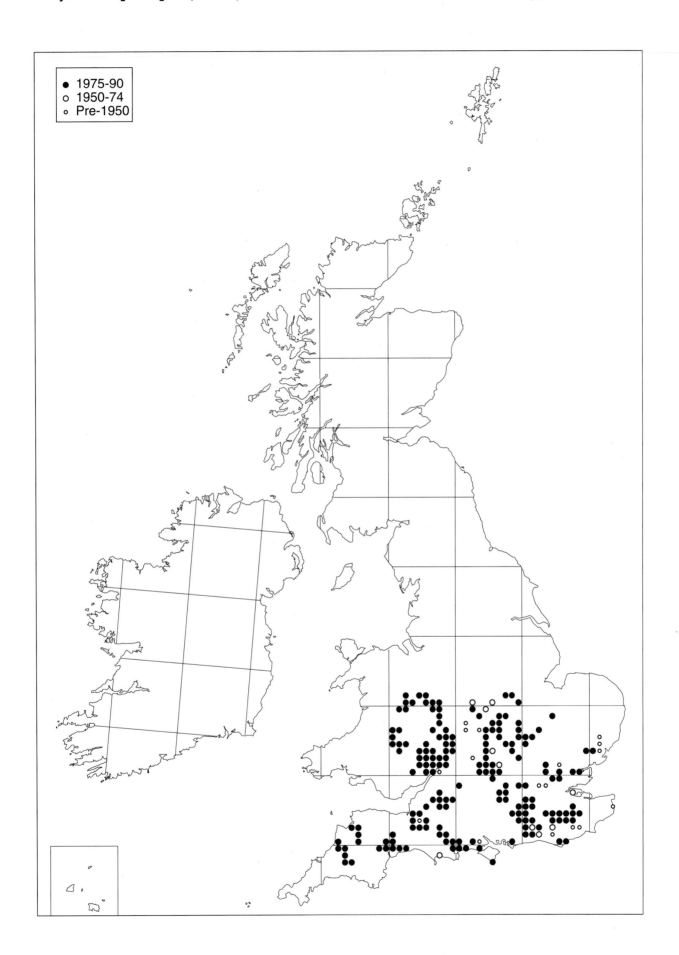

● 1975-90
○ 1950-74
○ Pre-1950

Pyrrhosoma nymphula (Sulzer)   **Large red damselfly**

Description This is one of the two red damselflies found in Britain, and the only one to occur in Ireland. It is much the commoner of the two species and can readily be distinguished from *Ceriagrion tenellum*, the other red damselfly, by the prominent red or yellow antehumeral stripes, and black legs. It is also a much more robust damselfly. In males, the deep red and black coloration of the thorax and abdomen makes the species an attractive sight. The eyes of both sexes are also red, duller in females. The female occurs in three colour forms: in one the abdomen is mainly black, and the other two vary in the extent of black on the red abdomen.

Habitat *P. nymphula* is found in a very wide range of habitats in Britain and Ireland, including acid bogs, the quieter stretches of quite fast streams and rivers, and also in well-vegetated ponds, canals and ditches. It can occur in slightly brackish water (Longfield 1937).

Breeding biology The adults of *P. nymphula* are very territorial. Their highest steady density is about 30 per 100 m of water's edge. Copulation takes about 15 minutes and the eggs are inserted into the tissues of submerged plants or the underside of floating leaves of plants, such as pondweed, with the male in tandem. The larvae, which live amongst roots and bottom debris, usually take two years to develop, but can take one year, or, at high larval densities, three years (Macan 1974). It is one of the few species known to be territorial in the larval stage. Successful territorial behaviour results in larger larvae and hence greater reproductive success as adults (Harvey & Corbet 1985).

Flight periods *P. nymphula* has a synchronised emergence and is one of the first dragonflies on the wing, from late April onwards in south-western counties. There is a second, smaller, unsynchronised emergence in the summer, and a few adults may be on the wing until early September. Adults take 6–15 days to mature (Corbet & Harvey 1989). Reproductively mature adults may then live about a week on average, some surviving 35–45 days.

Status and distribution In some small peat pools and acid seepages in upland areas, *P. nymphula* may be the only dragonfly present. Elsewhere, it can be found with almost all our other dragonfly species, including *C. tenellum* in southern England and Wales. *P. nymphula* is widespread as a breeding species in Britain and Ireland, occurring as far north as the Orkneys. However, in some chalk counties, notably Wiltshire, it is a scarce species and is absent from many sites which support other dragonflies. It has declined in the intensively cultivated areas of eastern England, such as the Fens, except where there is very clean, unpolluted water.

European and world distribution *Pyrrhosoma* is one of the few genera that is confined to the Palaearctic region. *P. nymphula* is widespread throughout most of Europe, although thinning out towards the south in some Mediterranean countries, and absent from several larger Mediterranean islands. Its range extends into Asia, and Morocco in North Africa.

Pyrrhosoma nymphula (Sulzer)

Large red damselfly

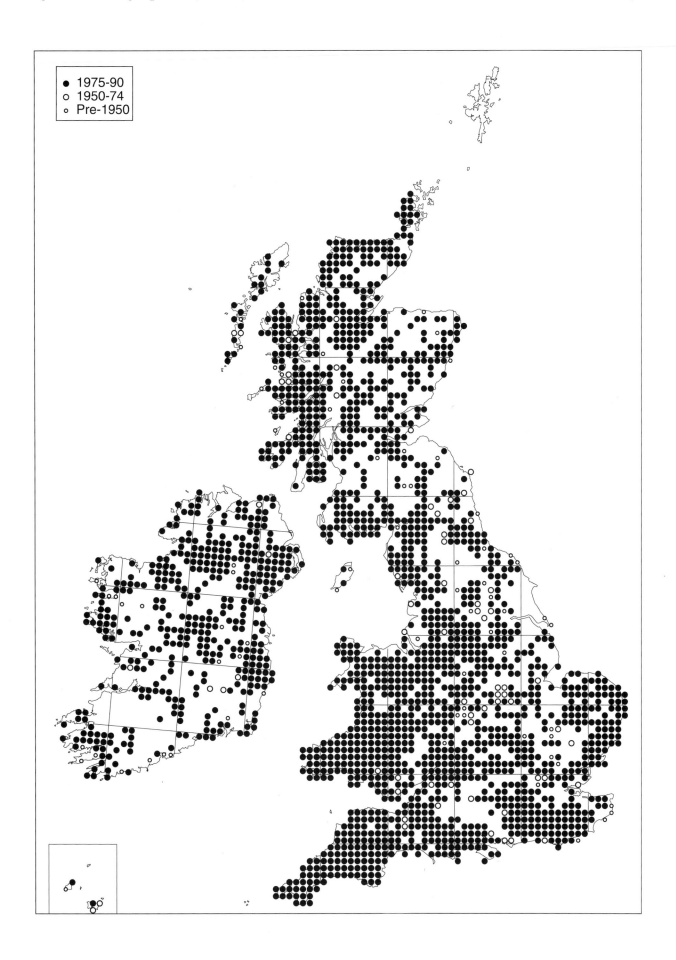

Erythromma najas (Hansemann)   **Red-eyed damselfly**

Description

This is a robust damselfly in which males are mostly black with blue markings and bright red eyes, and so cannot be confused with any of our other resident species. The dorsal surface of the thorax is bronze-black, with no antehumeral stripes. The sides of the thorax are blue, as is the dorsal surface of abdominal segments 1, 9 and 10. In the similar *Ischnura elegans*, only abdominal segment 8 is blue dorsally. In mature females the eyes are not as bright as in males, and the blue markings on the abdomen are lacking, apart from a thin blue ring dorsally between several posterior segments. The sides of the thorax and abdomen are yellowish green.

Habitat

E. najas is most often recorded from those mesotrophic lakes, large ponds, canals and dykes where there is plenty of aquatic vegetation with floating leaves, such as water-lilies, broad-leaved pondweed or amphibious bistort. It also breeds in sluggish rivers, provided the current is sufficiently slow not to prevent the growth of the above-mentioned plants.

Breeding biology

The males are aggressive and fly purposefully and low over the water surface in search of females. Both sexes frequently settle on floating leaves, though in males seldom on the same leaf. Winsland (1983) and Benton (1988) record interspecific competition between *E. najas* and *Enallagma cyathigerum*. Oviposition occurs in tandem, the eggs being inserted into the stems of aquatic plants. Winsland (1983) noted that a pair of *E. najas* in tandem remain submerged for 28 minutes. The larvae, which live amongst submerged water plants, generally take two years to complete their development, but can take one year.

Flight periods

E. najas is on the wing from mid-May to the end of August. In south-eastern Britain it may be found with many other dragonfly species, such as *Anax imperator*, *Aeshna grandis*, *Libellula depressa* and the commoner damselflies.

Status and distribution

E. najas is numerous in the Weald, and fairly common in some other south-eastern and midland counties. It extends north to the Pocklington and Leven Canals in Yorkshire, and has a toe-hold in Wales along the Montgomery Canal. It is a very rare breeding species in the south-western peninsula of England. A single female specimen, apparently taken at Bridge of Weir (presumably Renfrewshire, Scotland) on 13 June 1885, is in the J J F X King collection (O'Farrell 1950). This record, and those of several other species in the collection, has not been mapped (see **Vetting of records** section in **Description of data set**). It was recorded as Irish by Haliday in the 19th century, but its status was regarded with scepticism by King and Halbert (1910) and Nelson (1986).

European and world distribution

Erythromma is one of the few genera which is confined to the Palaearctic region. *E. najas* is widespread throughout central and northern Europe, but is absent from most of the Mediterranean area. Its range extends east to Siberia and Japan.

Erythromma najas (Hansemann)   Red-eyed damselfly

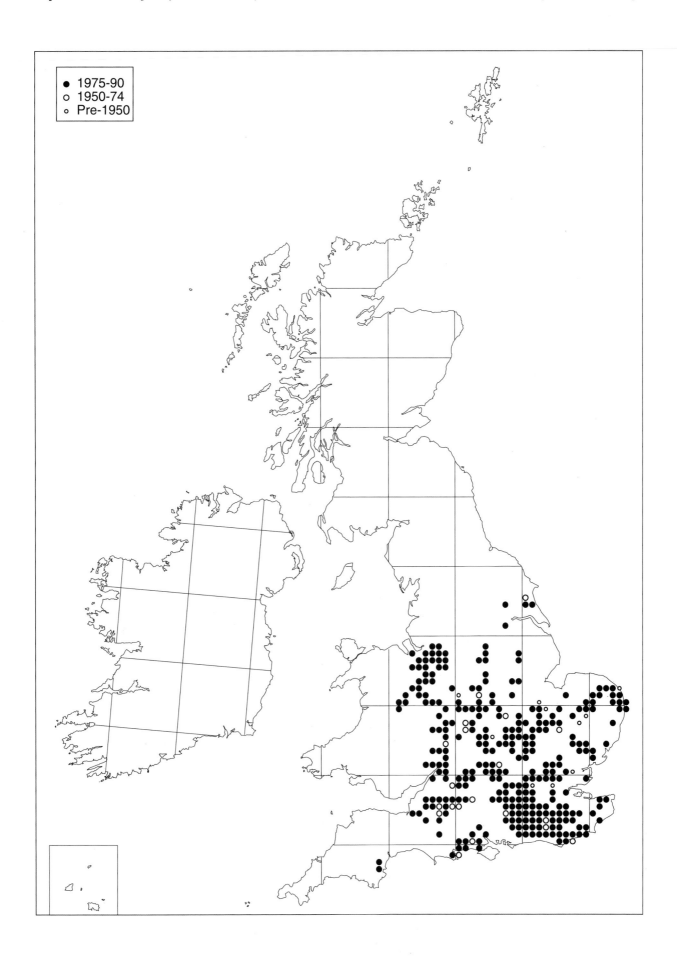

Coenagrion mercuriale (Charpentier)   **Southern damselfly**

Description

The males of this small and dainty damselfly are predominantly blue and black, in common with other species in this genus. Typically they possess a 'mercury' sign on segment 2 of the abdomen, but this mark is subject to some variation and may superficially resemble *C. pulchellum* and *C. scitulum*. The pattern of black markings on the dorsal surface of the abdomen is usually quite distinctive, however. The shape of the anal appendages is diagnostic. Females are dark with pale olive-green or blue sides to the thorax and abdomen, extending to the dorsal abdominal surface as thin inter-segmental rings. Females of *C. mercuriale* can be distinguished from *C. puella* and *Enallagma cyathigerum*, with which they may be found, by the markings on the sides of the thorax and on the head (Welstead & Welstead 1983b), and from female *C. pulchellum* by the almost straight hind margin of the pronotum.

Habitat

C. mercuriale breeds in base-rich runnels and streams, often in heathland areas but it is not confined to these (Merritt 1983a). Mayo and Welstead (1983) discuss its occurrence on water-meadow ditches on the floodplains of two chalk rivers. Colley (1983) describes its presence on a spring flush in a calcareous valley mire on Anglesey. Winsland (1985) discusses its habitat requirements on the New Forest heathlands. Water at breeding sites is usually shallow and slow-flowing over a gravel or marl bed overlaid in places with organic detritus.

Breeding biology

The males are not territorial. Populations are usually small but densities of 250 per 100 m of stream can occur. Jenkins (1991) reviews a population study at a site in the New Forest. Oviposition occurs in tandem. The eggs are inserted into the tissues of aquatic and emergent plants such as marsh St John's-wort, black bog-rush, bog pondweed, and fool's water-cress. Larvae usually take two years to develop. Details of larval development are given by Corbet (1957).

Flight periods

C. mercuriale has a relatively short flying season from early June to mid-August. It has a slow, weak flight, low down amongst emergent vegetation. In heathland localities, it may be seen with or near colonies of *Ceriagrion tenellum*, *Ischnura pumilio*, and *Orthetrum coerulescens*. On water meadows it may be found settled amongst lush vegetation with *Calopteryx splendens*, *Coenagrion puella* and *I. elegans*.

Status and distribution

C. mercuriale is confined to a few southern and western counties in England and Wales. It has not been recorded from Ireland. Its strongholds are the New Forest heathlands and Mynydd Preseli in Pembrokeshire. Elsewhere it breeds at a few sites on the Dorset heaths, east Devon pebble-bed commons, Gower peninsula, Anglesey, and the floodplains of the River Itchen and River Test in Hampshire. In July 1991, a single adult male was captured at Cothill Fen, Oxfordshire (too late to be included in the maps). *C. mercuriale* is subject to many threats, principally the cessation of grazing by stock animals (Evans 1989) resulting in the smaller runnels and streams becoming completely overgrown with rank vegetation such as purple moor-grass. Other threats include excessive nutrient enrichment from the runoff of nitrogenous fertilizers from adjacent agricultural land, drainage due to agricultural and forestry pressures and, in the case of water meadows, over-extraction of water by water companies resulting in lowering of the water table. *C. mercuriale* has become extinct in Cornwall, having last been seen at its site at Trevorgans near St Buryan in 1957, and has been lost from several of its former sites in Devon during the 1950s and 1960s. It has also declined in Dorset. The species does not wander far from its breeding sites, and this apparent lack of dispersal ability could hinder its spread to suitable habitat in neighbouring areas. It needs rigorous protection.

European and world distribution

C. mercuriale has a restricted range on the continent, centred on south-west Europe and North Africa, becoming rare further north and east. It is threatened throughout most of its range, and is the only British resident dragonfly species to

Coenagrion mercuriale (Charpentier)   **Southern damselfly**

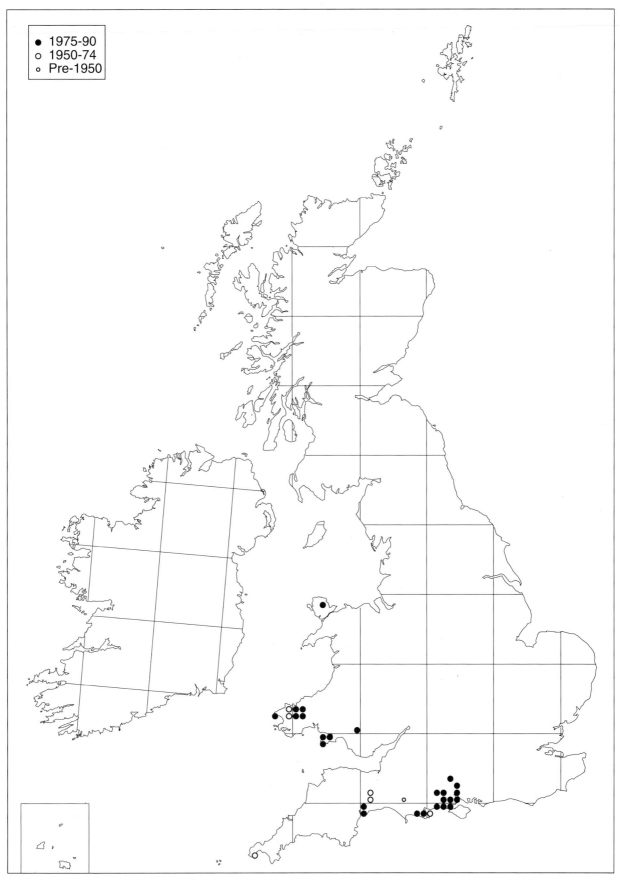

be listed in the European Communities 'Habitats and Species' Directive, and in the Appendices to the Berne Convention. It occurs on several National Nature Reserves (NNRs) and one Royal Society for the Protection of Birds (RSPB) reserve.

Description

Like other *Coenagrion* species, the males of *C. scitulum* are blue with black markings. The black mark on segment 2 of the abdomen is 'typically' a thick-stalked U-shape, but this is subject to such variation that it is probably incorrect to refer to it as typical. This mark may be much reduced in size to the extent that the individual can superficially resemble a small *Enallagma cyathigerum*. Females are dull blue-green with black abdominal markings. A pointer in the direction of a captured individual being something special is the shape of the pterostigma, which is elongated in both sexes, being nearly twice as long as broad and unlike all other coenagrionids likely to be encountered in Britain, in which the pterostigma is roughly square.

Breeding biology

Territorial behaviour has not been recorded. Oviposition takes place in tandem with the male, with the male sloping forward, unlike the near-vertical posture which is usual for other *Coenagrion* males. The eggs are inserted into the tissues of aquatic plants. The larvae probably take one year to develop.

Flight period

The recorded flight period of *C. scitulum* in Britain is from late May to the end of July.

Status, distribution and history

It has only ever been known from Essex and was first discovered near Benfleet on 21 July 1946 by E B Pinniger whilst leading a London Natural History Society meeting, in the company of Cynthia Longfield, to look for *Lestes dryas* (Pinniger 1947). The ditches in this area were stagnant, and some brackish, and overgrown with spiked water-milfoil and sea club-rush. First a male was found, of a species unknown to either of them, and then two females a short distance away. These were taken by Longfield and subsequently identified as *C. scitulum*. The area was searched thoroughly the following year, and C O Hammond found a pair on 22 May at the known locality. Later, the main breeding site was found to be a few miles to the east, near Hadleigh, at a pond containing common water-crowfoot. In 1951, A E Gardner counted over 250 individuals at this site. *C. scitulum* was last seen on 22 June 1952, again by Gardner. Early in 1953, much of the east coast of England was disastrously flooded, including Canvey Island and the marshes at Hadleigh. Despite many searches, *C. scitulum* was never found again. A fuller account of this species' residence in Essex is given by Benton (1988). *C. scitulum* has been recorded from Guernsey and Jersey in the Channel Islands. It almost certainly bred on Guernsey, having been recorded at Chouet on 29 June, 2 July and 28 July 1956 by J Cowley. Ten males and two females, taken during the latter two visits, are in the Natural History Museum, London. Belle (1980) could find no trace of the species on Guernsey in 1978, and believed it to be extinct. Le Quesne found three individuals on Jersey in 1940 and 1941, at St Peter's Reservoir and Grands Vaux (Le Quesne 1951), but proof of breeding was not established.

European and world distribution

C. scitulum is a Mediterranean species with isolated populations in several countries of central Europe.

Coenagrion scitulum (Rambur)   **Dainty damselfly**

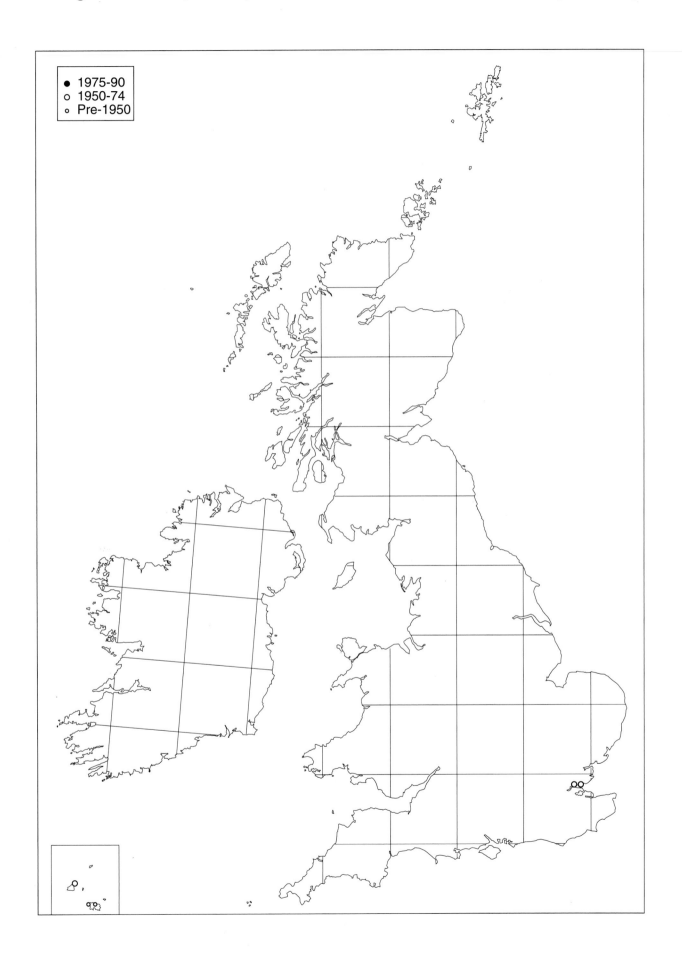

Coenagrion hastulatum (Charpentier)　　**Northern damselfly**

Description

Males of *C. hastulatum* are mostly pale blue with black markings. The sides of the thorax are pale greenish blue, and in this respect may superficially resemble *C. lunulatum*, though these two species differ in the extent of blue on the abdomen, which is more prevalent in *C. hastulatum*. Males of both species typically have a short black bar on either side of segment 2 of the abdomen, but they usually differ in the shape of the central mark on this segment which is typically arrow-shaped in *C. hastulatum*. However, this mark is variable and may be reduced to a stalked spot as in *Enallagma cyathigerum*, or a transverse bar as in *C. lunulatum*. The latter species also differs from *C. hastulatum* in the shape of the posterior margin of the pronotum and the anal appendages. Females are dark with green sides to the thorax and abdomen, and superficially resemble female *E. cyathigerum*, with which they sometimes coexist, but lack the vulvar spine on the ventral surface of abdominal segment 8 of that species.

Habitat

C. hastulatum breeds in sheltered pools and boggy lochans with abundant emergent vegetation, and with an optimum depth of perhaps 50 cm. It also breeds in the shallow sheltered margins of medium-sized lochs, where *C. hastulatum* flies slowly amongst tall emergent common reed and sedges, frequently settling. Its favoured sites are usually mesotrophic, and often contain white water-lily, bogbean and narrow-leaved sedges such as slender sedge, as well as marginal *Sphagnum* lawns with bog-myrtle and common cottongrass. This species can survive the temporary drying out of its habitat (Valtonen 1986).

Breeding biology

Territorial behaviour has not been recorded, and males can exist at high population densities. The females oviposit in aquatic plants in tandem. Oviposition has been observed in bog pondweed and water horsetail. Larval development probably takes one or two years in Scotland.

Flight periods

C. hastulatum is on the wing from the beginning of June to early August. It often flies with *E. cyathigerum* (which is more robust and, in males, is brighter blue and lacks the greenish tint to the thorax – quite distinctive when the two species are seen together), and may also be seen with *Lestes sponsa*, *Pyrrhosoma nymphula*, *Libellula quadrimaculata*, and other species.

Status and distribution

C. hastulatum was first added to the British list in 1900, a specimen being taken near Aviemore, Inverness-shire, by J W Yerbury (McLachlan 1900a, b, c). Subsequently, a specimen apparently taken in Sutherland in 1842, by Richard Weaver, came to light (Lucas 1904, 1909). These and other records are discussed by Marren and Merritt (1983). *C. hastulatum* is confined to three small areas of central–northern Scotland: Speyside (Inverness-shire), Deeside (Aberdeenshire) and near Pitlochry (Perthshire). In each of these areas it is found at a number of sites, usually in small numbers, though occasionally it can be relatively plentiful. However, although the majority of its haunts seem reasonably safe from drainage operations and pollution, it remains a very rare dragonfly and its breeding sites require protection. Several already occur within nature reserves, including two NNRs and one RSPB reserve.

European and world distribution

C. hastulatum is found throughout most of northern Europe. Relict populations occur in the Pyrenees, Massif Central and the Alps.

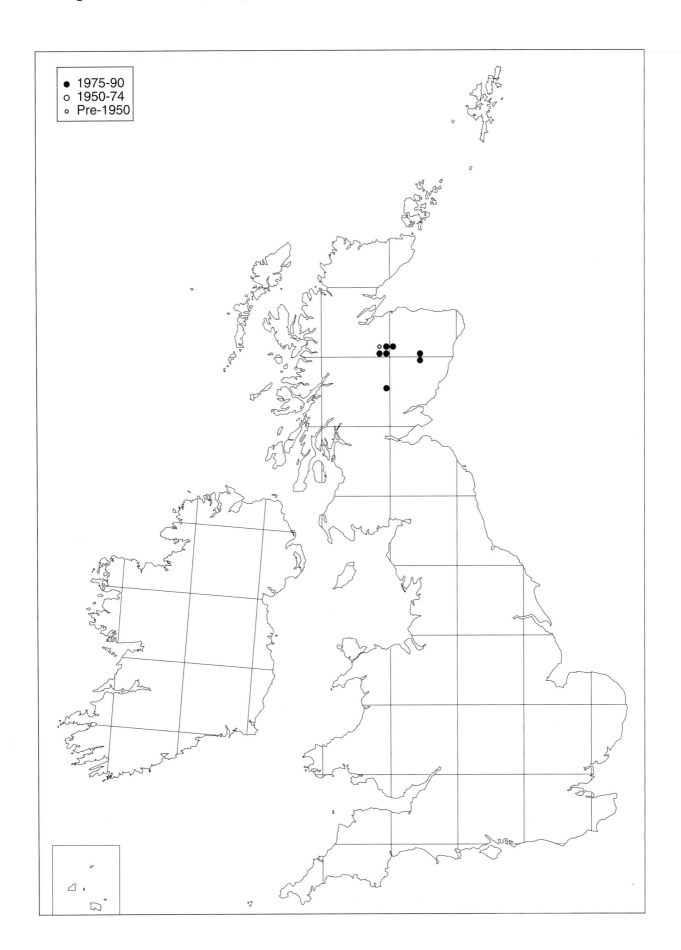

- ● 1975-90
- ○ 1950-74
- ○ Pre-1950

Coenagrion lunulatum (Charpentier)   **Irish damselfly**

Description

Male *C. lunulatum* are predominantly blue and black, and are quite distinctive – unlike any other resident damselfly in Ireland. The sides of the thorax shade from blue dorsally to apple-green ventrally. The sides of the abdomen are apple-green, as are the eyes. The abdomen is blue and black dorsally, with much more black than is present on male *C. hastulatum*, which it superficially resembles. There are two small black bars on the sides of abdominal segment 2, and a transverse crescent mark anterior to the junction with segment 3. Females are dark with greenish sides to the thorax and abdomen, and can be distinguished from females of other species with which they may be found by the shape of the hind margin of the pronotum, which has a distinct median lobe.

Habitat

In the Irish midlands, *C. lunulatum* breeds on several slightly alkaline mesotrophic lakes and a valley fen. The lakes possess lush marginal vegetation, including common club-rush, common reed, bogbean and slender sedge/bottle sedge swamp, as well as floating macrophytes such as white water-lily and pondweeds. At the valley fen site, *C. lunulatum* is confined to several open pools bordered by bogbean and slender sedge swamp (Speight & Legrand 1984). In northern Ireland, *C. lunulatum* occurs on small peaty mesotrophic lakes, some of which are probably mildly acidic, in marginal hill country with similar, though sparser, vegetation to the midland sites; and in the Lough Neagh area, it is found on several sheltered, well-vegetated pools in cut-over bogs (Nelson 1986; Rippey & Nelson 1988).

Breeding biology

C. lunulatum appears to be non-territorial and can occur at high densities, although in Ireland most of the populations appear to be fairly small (Rippey & Nelson 1988). Females insert their eggs into the tissues of aquatic plants, in tandem. The life history of this species in Ireland has been studied only partially to date.

Flight periods

C. lunulatum is on the wing from late May to late July. It can be found with *C. pulchellum*, *Aeshna juncea*, *Brachytron pratense* and other species of lakes, fens and cut-over bogs.

Status and distribution

C. lunulatum has not been found in Britain, and is a recent addition to the Irish list: it was discovered in Co Sligo on 28 June 1981 by P Archer and D C F Cotton (Cotton 1982). Since then, many sites have been discovered, mostly in the north of Ireland. Much speculation has centred on why this species was not found earlier, in view of the fieldwork that had been done in Ireland in previous decades. However, much of Ulster, where most of the newly discovered sites have occurred, had never received a great deal of attention in the past, and it could easily have been overlooked further south. It is almost certainly still under-recorded in the midlands. In Britain, similar habitat occurs in Galloway, Cumbria, Anglesey and elsewhere, but, as yet, *C. lunulatum* has not been found.

European and world distribution

C. lunulatum is a northern European species found on the continent from The Netherlands and Scandinavia eastwards to Siberia and Japan. Outlying populations occur in the Massif Central and the French Alps.

Coenagrion lunulatum (Charpentier)   **Irish damselfly**

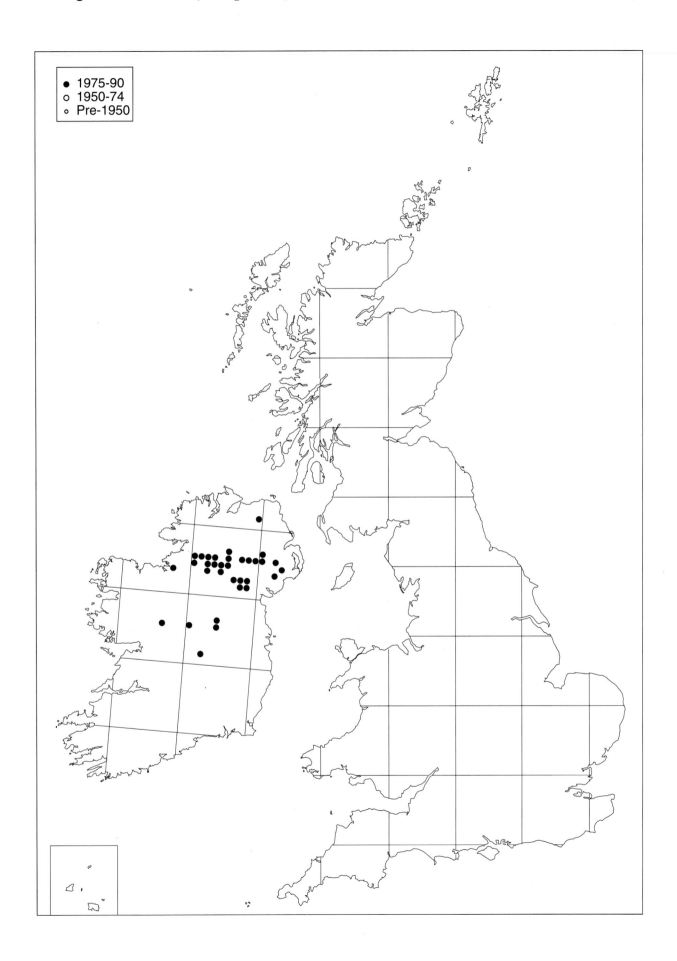

Coenagrion armatum (Charpentier)   **Norfolk damselfly**

Description

The male of *C. armatum* is almost entirely black with dull greyish blue coloration on several segments at either extremity of the dorsal surface of the abdomen, though not segment 10 which is black. Unlike other species of this genus, there are no antehumeral stripes on the male thorax, although four spots may occur. The black marking on segment 2 of the abdomen typically has a lateral, sometimes isolated, arm extending along either side of the segment. The most notable feature of male *C. armatum*, however, is the anal appendages, in which the inferior pair of appendages is very elongated. Females are mostly dull black with greenish markings, but they are unique in that the black on the dorsal surface of segment 2 does not extend the whole length of the segment – the anterior half is greenish. Of the female, Porritt (1910) wrote 'when flying in the sun, the mature insect is a very striking *Agrion* and cannot be mistaken for any other British species; the green on the front and posterior segments of the abdomen shines like emeralds...'.

Habitat and breeding biology

C. armatum favours mesotrophic ponds and ditches with an abundance of common reed and sedges, amongst which they fly. Females have been observed to oviposit into the tissues of frogbit.

Flight periods

The flight period in Britain is not well recorded, but is likely to have been from late May to at least mid-July.

Status and distribution

C. armatum was first recorded in Britain at Stalham, Norfolk in May 1903 by Balfour-Browne (Balfour-Browne 1904). A Mr Edelston subsequently informed Balfour-Browne that he had found it there in 1902. The site, at Sutton Broad, Stalham, appears to have been the stronghold of the species, it being seen there regularly until the 1950s. Porritt (1912) recorded *C. armatum* 'on both Sutton and Stalham Broads, and over a fairly wide area'. A few *C. armatum* of both sexes were also recorded from a ditch at Hickling Broad by T A Coward on 24 May 1919. Cynthia Longfield (1954) wrote that A E Gardner had reported that *C. armatum* still occurred in fair numbers, but she went on to say that 'it is, however, very disturbing that the latter's restricted habitat is rapidly drying out and the nature of the vegetation changing completely... and it is sincerely to be hoped that some remedy will be found in time to save the extinction of *C. armatum*'. It was not, and the species was last reported in 1957 (Hammond 1977). Surveys by the NCC in the mid-1970s found the area of its former site to be thoroughly overgrown with common reed, sallow and alder carr, and mostly dried up.

European and world distribution

C. armatum is a boreal species which occurs from the Baltic area eastwards through Poland and Russia to Mongolia. It was last recorded in The Netherlands in 1924 (Geijskes & van Tol 1983), and was lost from sites in northern Germany in the mid-1970s owing to the drying up of its habitat (Schmidt 1978).

Coenagrion armatum (Charpentier)   **Norfolk damselfly**

Coenagrion puella (Linnaeus)   Azure damselfly

Description

C. puella males are pale sky-blue with black markings. The blue antehumeral stripes on the thorax are narrower than those on *Enallagma cyathigerum*, the other common blue damselfly, and the black marking on segment 2 of the abdomen is quite different, being typically a thin unstalked U-shape. Like other *Coenagrion* species, *C. puella* has two short, thick black lines on the side of the thorax in both sexes, whereas the similar *E. cyathigerum* has only one (Longfield 1949a; Welstead & Welstead 1983b). Females can occur in one of several forms: one is dark with greenish markings on the thorax and abdomen, and the other forms have blue markings which can be quite extensive and closely resemble *C. pulchellum* females, from which they can be distinguished by the shape of the hind margin of the pronotum, which is not tri-lobed as in *C. pulchellum*.

Habitat

C. puella is found in a very wide range of habitats in Britain and Ireland, including garden ponds, lakes, streams and rivers, peaty pools and ditches. It is often seen in large numbers in early summer, frequently settling on floating weed or algae, and in nearby glades and meadows.

Breeding biology

C. puella is not territorial, but there is evidence that its density is regulated to some extent by its behaviour, which includes threat displays (Moore 1995). Copulation is prolonged and only occurs on warm sunny days. The mating success of females depends on their length of life: the rate of egg laying and clutch size are of lesser importance in *C. puella*. Oviposition takes place in tandem, with the female inserting her eggs into the tissues of floating and submerged plants, and sometimes becoming completely submerged. Larval development usually takes one year, but can take two (Parr 1970). Emergence occurs in the morning on emergent vegetation, including the flower spikes of pondweeds in the centre of ponds, with the females emerging a day or two earlier than males and being less likely to return to their emergence sites than males (Banks & Thompson 1985). The mean lifespan of mature adults is between five and six days (Banks & Thompson 1985). Grazing animals around ponds can reduce breeding success greatly, because they reduce the numbers of emergence sites and make those which are left more vulnerable to predation by birds. Adult *C. puella* roost on rather broader stems than *Ischnura elegans*, but less broad ones than *E. cyathigerum* (Askew 1982), with just their eyes visible on either side, from the front. This is a defence mechanism: they will move round the stem as danger approaches.

Flight periods

C. puella is on the wing from mid-May to the end of August, but is most common in early summer. It can be seen with almost all other British and Irish species that share its geographical range.

Status and distribution

C. puella breeds widely and extremely commonly throughout England and Wales, the lowlands of central and southern Scotland, and most of Ireland. Its absence from parts of central-southern England and from parts of the Fens is due to the lack of water bodies in these areas because of, respectively, the porous chalk substrate and the loss of wetlands through agricultural pressures. *C. puella* is seldom found at moderate to high altitudes, and is absent from the uplands of north Wales, the northern Pennines, and much of Scotland.

European and world distribution

C. puella is found commonly throughout much of Europe, though it is absent from most of Scandinavia. Its range extends east to the Caspian Sea.

Coenagrion puella (Linnaeus)

Azure damselfly

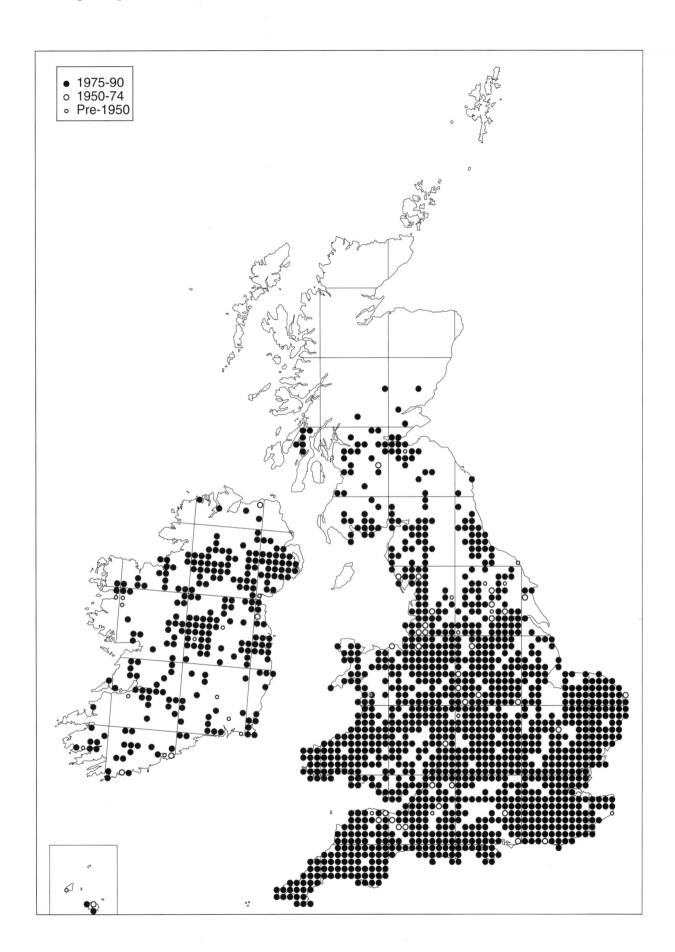

Coenagrion pulchellum (Vander Linden)   **Variable damselfly**

Description

The identification of *C. pulchellum*, as with most other species in this genus, requires careful examination. Males are blue with black markings. The blue antehumeral stripes are narrow and often reduced to a pair of ! marks. The black mark on segment 2 of the abdomen is typically stalked and usually much thicker than in male *C. puella*, which this species resembles. Sometimes, however, this stalk is absent. The black mark on the dorsal surface of segment 9 is nearly always more extensive than on *C. puella*. The shape of the anal appendages is diagnostic. There are two female forms: one is dark with greenish yellow markings on the sides of the thorax and abdomen, and the other is a blue form in which the black markings on the dorsal surface of the abdomen are more extensive than in the male, and in which the black mark on abdominal segment 2 superficially resembles male *C. mercuriale*, being thistle-shaped. This form is almost identical to a blue female form of *C. puella*, but female *C. pulchellum* can be separated from both these species by the tri-lobed posterior margin of the pronotum.

Habitat

C. pulchellum breeds in fens, mesotrophic ponds and lakes, slow-flowing dykes in coastal levels, canals and peaty pools and ditches in cut-over bogs. It is probably more dependent on emergent vegetation than *C. puella*.

Breeding biology

C. pulchellum does not appear to be territorial and it can occur at high densities. Copulation takes 10–15 minutes, and the eggs are inserted into the stems or leaves of aquatic plants such as pondweeds, water-lilies or the floating remains of rushes and common reed, while in tandem. The larvae probably take one year to develop.

Flight periods

Adults are on the wing from mid-May to the beginning of August. In Britain and Ireland they are often seen with dragonflies such as *Brachytron pratense* and *Sympetrum sanguineum*, as well as the commoner damselflies including *C. puella*. However, in Ireland, *C. pulchellum* appears to be more tolerant of acidic conditions and can be found with *Aeshna juncea* and *Lestes sponsa* on peaty moorland pools at moderately low altitudes. Where *C. pulchellum* and *C. puella* co-exist in Ireland, *C. pulchellum* is usually much the commoner.

Status and distribution

In Britain, *C. pulchellum* is found most commonly on the coastal marshes and levels of Somerset, Sussex and Kent, in Norfolk and the Fens, in the fens of Anglesey and in south Galloway. Elsewhere it is quite a scarce damselfly, and has declined in many areas of eastern England due to intensive agricultural pressures. In areas such as Romney Marsh, Kent, and in the Fens, this decline has been caused mainly by the conversion of grazing marshes to arable land, with the consequent lowering of the water table and loss of traditional dyke management techniques. *C. pulchellum* was recently rediscovered at several locations in west Scotland along with, appropriately, *B. pratense* (Smith & Smith 1984). *C. pulchellum* occurs extensively throughout the fens and peatlands of the Irish midlands, and is commonly found in Co Fermanagh, south Tyrone and the Lough Neagh area. It is probable that future surveys will link these two distribution areas. *C. pulchellum* is not uncommon in western districts of Co Cork, Co Kerry and Co Galway. Elsewhere it has a scattered distribution that needs clarification by further fieldwork.

European and world distribution

C. pulchellum has a slightly more northerly distribution in Europe than *C. puella*, being absent from much of the Iberian peninsula and Mediterranean islands, and it is found further north in Scandinavia. Its range extends to west Asia.

Coenagrion pulchellum (Vander Linden)   **Variable damselfly**

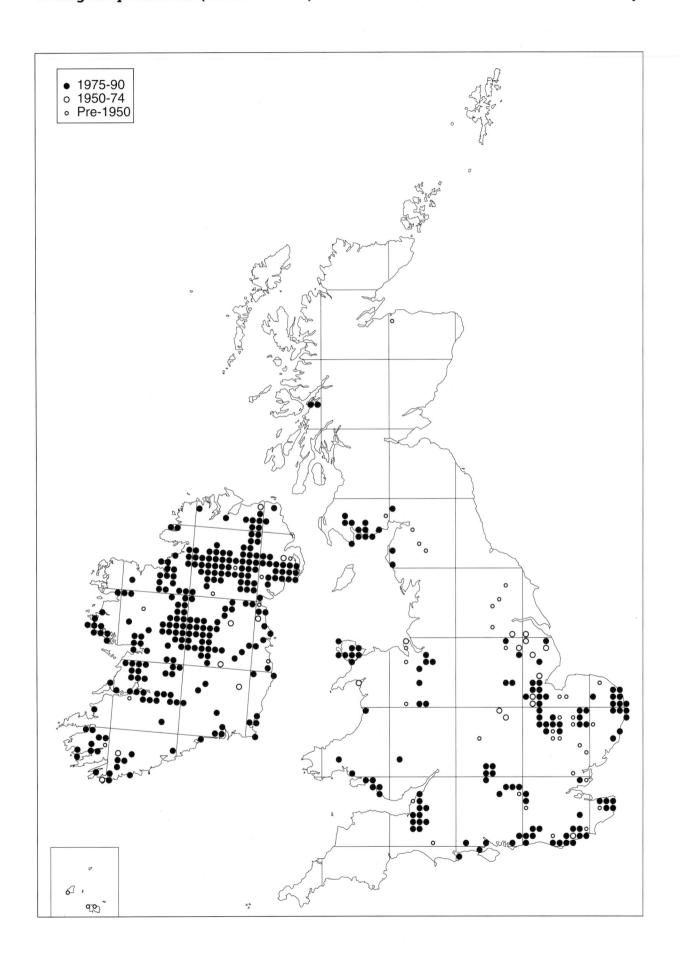

● 1975-90
○ 1950-74
○ Pre-1950

Enallagma cyathigerum (Charpentier) Common blue damselfly

Description

This species is the bluest of the blue and black damselflies, and the most widespread. In males, the blue antehumeral stripes are much broader than in *Coenagrion* species. The sides of the thorax are almost entirely blue and the black mark on segment 2 of the abdomen seldom varies beyond a median roundish spot, typically joined to the posterior inter-segmental ring by a short stalk. The female occurs in two colour forms: one is black with greenish antehumeral stripes, and greenish sides to the thorax and abdomen, and the other is black with bright blue markings, although these are less extensive abdominally than on the male. In both forms a vulvar spine is present on the ventral surface of abdominal segment 8, unlike *Coenagrion* species.

Habitat

E. cyathigerum breeds in ponds, lakes, canals, and rivers of moderate to slow flow. Unlike *C. puella*, it rarely breeds in very small ponds. It can be very abundant in the most oligotrophic and acidic conditions, sometimes at high altitudes, as well as being common and widespread in lowland and even eutrophic conditions elsewhere. *E. cyathigerum* can occur in very large numbers, and swarm low over the water surface often far from the margins, frequently settling on emergent flower-heads of aquatic plants such as pondweeds.

Breeding biology

Males are robust and aggressive. Winsland (1983) and Benton (1988) record interspecific competition between *E. cyathigerum* and *Erythromma najas*. Densities are usually less than 50 per 100 m of water's edge, but up to 363 per 100 m have been recorded (Parr 1976). Copulation lasts 20 minutes or more, and frequently occurs away from water. The eggs are inserted into the tissues of submerged and emergent vegetation. This usually occurs in tandem in the case of surface oviposition, but if the female submerges then the male will uncouple and await her reappearance, guarding her point of descent. Females can remain submerged for long periods. Larvae take from one to three, usually two, years to develop (Macan 1974), and live amongst submerged water weeds. *E. cyathigerum* is a summer species which can overwinter in the antepenultimate and earlier instars. Mature *E. cyathigerum* roost on broader stems than *Ischnura elegans* or *C. puella* (Askew 1982).

Flight periods

E. cyathigerum is on the wing from late May to late September. Mature adult life is about 12 days, but males can live for up to 39 days. It is found with many other dragonfly species that share similar habitats. In south-east England it will quickly colonise newly excavated gravel pits, with *Orthetrum cancellatum*.

Status and distribution

E. cyathigerum is widespread throughout Britain, including the Orkneys, Shetlands and Western Isles, and occurs widely in Ireland. On Scottish lochs, it is often the only species present. It breeds at higher altitudes than either *C. puella* or *I. elegans*.

European and world distribution

E. cyathigerum is found throughout most of Europe, thinning out in some Mediterranean areas. It is an holarctic species, occurring in Asia east to Mongolia, and in North America. It is found commonly north of the Arctic Circle. Amongst Zygoptera, only *E. cyathigerum* and *Lestes dryas* are found on both sides of the Atlantic. It is among the most wide-ranging and abundant Odonata species in the world.

Enallagma cyathigerum (Charpentier)

Common blue damselfly

- ● 1975-90
- ○ 1950-74
- ○ Pre-1950

Ischnura pumilio (Charpentier)   **Scarce blue-tailed damselfly**

Description

I. pumilio is one of two British and Irish damselflies in which the abdomen of males is entirely black dorsally apart from a blue mark towards the posterior end; the other species is the larger and much commoner *I. elegans*. In *I. pumilio* this pale blue marking occupies the posterior third of abdominal segment 8 and all of segment 9, which normally has a pair of tiny black spots dorsally, although these are sometimes enlarged (Welstead & Welstead 1983a). There is a pair of blue antehumeral stripes on the thorax, the sides of which are usually blue, sometimes blue-green, as are the sides of the first few abdominal segments. Mature females are dull black dorsally with pale green sides to the thorax and abdomen. In some females, the eyes, legs, sides of the thorax and the abdomen are a striking orange colour. This is known as var. *aurantiaca* Sélys-Longchamps, and is an immature form which matures into the typical adult female.

Habitat

I. pumilio favours mineral-enriched water in which to breed, usually as slow-flowing seepages, runnels and streams but also as static water in shallow ponds and lakes. It is found in suitable habitat often in heathland areas, but is not confined to these, being found also in chalk pits and in quarries. In Pembrokeshire, Fox (1987) recorded *I. pumilio* breeding on base-rich flushes and spring-lines on sites favoured also by *Coenagrion mercuriale*, and on mesotrophic dew ponds and stock pools on mineral soils in marginal hill country. Such ponds, which are often disturbed by cattle trampling, are characterised by the presence of emergent soft rush and compact rush, floating sweet-grass and lesser spearwort. In central southern England, *I. pumilio* occurs on seepages resulting from disturbed spring-lines in chalk pits, gravel pits and a limestone quarry (Cham 1991). Similar habitats are occupied in the china clay areas of west Devon and Cornwall. In west Cornwall, *I. pumilio* is found on former tin-streaming sites. In the north of Ireland it has recently been discovered from a number of disused quarries in the north (Rippey & Nelson 1988) and from natural spring flushes.

Breeding biology

I. pumilio is a delicate damselfly and has a weak flight, low down amongst emergent vegetation. Populations can be quite dense. The eggs are inserted into the tissues of aquatic and emergent plants by the female, unattached to the male. Cham (1990, 1992) observed egg laying in hard rush, jointed rush, and stoneworts.

Flight periods

I. pumilio is on the wing from late May to early September. In heathland areas, it may occur with *C. mercuriale*, *Ceriagrion tenellum* and *Orthetrum coerulescens*, but in the upland sites of west Wales, at altitudes of up to 400 m, it can be the only dragonfly present. In chalk pits and gravel pits, it may be found at pools and seepages frequented also by *I. elegans*, *Libellula depressa* and *Sympetrum striolatum*.

Status and distribution

The distribution of *I. pumilio* is strongly influenced by its habitat requirements, but there is probably also a climatic factor involved which prevents its occurrence in northern England and beyond. It is found most commonly in south-west Britain from Anglesey to the New Forest, but, since its discovery at a chalk pit in Bedfordshire in 1987, it has been found at a number of other pits and quarries in that region, several of which have been created very recently, indicating recent colonisation. This species has clearly benefited from the extraction industries, and will probably continue to do so. Doubleday (1871) recorded it as 'rare' from old gravel pits in the Epping district of Essex, but this record, although plausible, has not been mapped (see **Vetting of records** in **Description of data set**). Elsewhere in East Anglia, *I. pumilio* has been recorded from Cambridge (Sélys-Longchamps 1846), from Gamlingay, Cambridgeshire (Imms 1938), and from near Cromer, Norfolk, in 1899 (O'Farrell 1950). In Ireland it has a scattered distribution, and further fieldwork may demonstrate that it occurs more widely and with greater frequency than existing records indicate. Cotton (1981) reviews early Irish records.

European and world distribution

In Europe, *I. pumilio* is found most commonly in the south. It occurs from Morocco and southern Spain to southern Scandinavia, where it was recently discovered, and east to southern Russia and Siberia. It has been recorded from the Azores and Madeira, indicating good powers of dispersal.

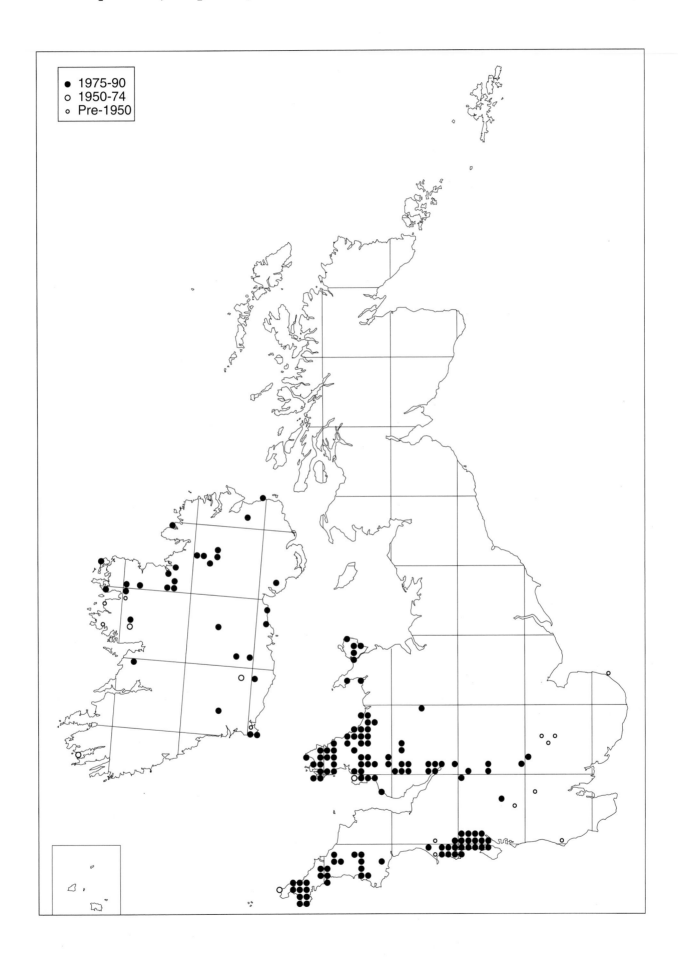

Ischnura elegans (Vander Linden)   **Blue-tailed damselfly**

Description
This species is one of the two damselflies found in Britain and Ireland in which the abdomen of males is entirely black dorsally except for a blue mark towards the posterior end. This blue mark occupies segment 8 only – not part of 8 and all of 9 as in the similar but much rarer *I. pumilio*. The general body coloration is also much brighter. In mature males, the dorsal surface of the thorax has a pair of blue antehumeral stripes, and the sides of both the thorax and the first few abdominal segments are also blue. In females the situation can be quite confusing as there are a number of colour forms, including one which resembles the male, and others which mature into yet other colour forms. Some are richly coloured, especially the rose-pink and the violet colour forms – others are various shades of greens and browns. This coloration occupies the sides of both the thorax and first few abdominal segments, as well as the antehumeral stripes. In several of these colour forms, segment 8 of the abdomen is blue, as in the male. High population density favours the male-like female form, and accelerates colour change in other forms (Hinnekint 1987). In both sexes, the pterostigma of the forewing is the same size as that of the hindwing, unlike *I. pumilio* in which that of the forewing is noticeably larger. *I. elegans* also possesses a median lobe (lacking in *I. pumilio*) on the posterior margin of the pronotum.

Habitat
I. elegans breeds in a wide range of habitats, including garden ponds, lakes, moderate- to slow-flowing streams and rivers, canals, ditches and peaty pools. It can live in quite brackish conditions, and can tolerate more pollution than any other resident dragonfly.

Breeding biology
I. elegans is territorial and has a threat display. Its highest steady density is about 30 males per 100 m of water's edge, although it may be seen in much larger numbers in nearby marginal vegetation. Copulation takes longer than in any other British or Irish dragonfly: from two to six hours, indicating prolonged sperm displacement on the part of the male (see **Introduction to the species accounts**). The female then oviposits, unattached to the male, inserting her eggs into the tissues of aquatic plants. Usually, ovipositing females are not interfered with much by males (Parr 1973). *I. elegans* is often present by water when bad weather keeps other species away. Unlike other species, its peak numbers are not always at noon. *I. elegans* develops in one or two years, depending on latitude (Parr 1969, 1970). *I. elegans* sometimes emerge with the exuviae pointing head-downwards (Thickett 1991; Mackenzie Dodds 1992). Unlike other damselflies, immatures are often found at the water's edge (Parr 1973). Mature adults choose narrow stems on which to roost, and this is related to the dimensions of the head (Askew 1982): therefore, they are often found where rushes grow. Mature insects often roost by water.

Flight periods
I. elegans has a long flying season from mid-May to late September. Being catholic in its habitat requirements, it can be found with most other dragonfly species in Britain and Ireland, including *I. pumilio*. However, owing to its tolerance both of brackish conditions and of quite high levels of pollution, it may be the only species present at some sites. It is a pioneer species on newly dug ponds.

Status and distribution
I. elegans is very common throughout lowland Britain and Ireland, including remote islands such as the Scillies and the Orkneys. Like *Coenagrion puella*, it does not occur in areas of moderate to high altitude and this explains its absence from the upland areas of north Wales, the Pennines, Scotland, and parts of Ireland. Its apparent absence from parts of central-southern England and parts of the Fens is real, and is the result of a lack of water bodies because of, respectively, the porous nature of the chalk soils and intensive agricultural pressures.

European and world distribution
I. elegans occurs widely in Europe, though it is absent from most of the Iberian peninsula and from northern Scandinavia. It is found in the Middle East, and Asia as far east as China. It has recently been recorded from the extreme south of Spain.

Ischnura elegans (Vander Linden)

Blue-tailed damselfly

- ● 1975-90
- ○ 1950-74
- ○ Pre-1950

Ceriagrion tenellum (Villers)   **Small red damselfly**

Description   *C. tenellum* is one of two British damselflies in which the male is predominantly red, but is smaller and daintier than the much more common *Pyrrhosoma nymphula*. The abdomen of the male, and one of the three female forms (var. *erythrogastrum* Sélys-Longchamps), is entirely crimson-red, unlike *P. nymphula*. Other distinguishing features are the red legs, red pterostigmata and the lack of antehumeral stripes on the bronze-black dorsal surface of the thorax. In one of the other two female colour forms (var. *intermedia* Sélys-Longchamps), the anterior three abdominal segments are mostly red dorsally, the remaining segments being black. In the third female colour form (var. *melanogastrum* Sélys-Longchamps) the abdomen is entirely black apart from thin yellow inter-segmental abdominal rings, but the dull reddish legs and red pterostigmata distinguish it from other species.

Habitat   *C. tenellum* typically breeds in shallow bog pools, fringed with *Sphagnum* moss, on lowland heaths. These pools often contain lesser bladderwort, marsh St John's-wort and marginal grasses, sedges and bog-myrtle through which the adults fly weakly, seldom wandering far. *C. tenellum* is also found in peaty ditches on a few cut-over bogs and poor fens, as well as the shallow well-vegetated margins of old ball-clay and china-clay ponds, and old marl pits. It is not restricted to static water, and can occur on slow-flowing water on heathlands, and on former tin-streaming sites in Cornwall. It is also found on a few calcareous valley mires where it occupies shallow, often tiny, peaty pools within areas dominated by plants such as blunt-flowered rush, black bog-rush, and often with a loose scattering of common reed.

Breeding biology   *C. tenellum* is territorial, but can occur at very high densities – approaching 150 per 100 m of water's edge. Copulation can take as long as 90 minutes. The female oviposits in tandem, inserting her eggs into the tissues of *Sphagnum* moss and other aquatic and emergent plants. The larvae live among the peaty detritus and plant roots, and usually take two years to develop.

Flight periods   *C. tenellum* is on the wing from early June to early September. In heathland areas it can be found by slow-flowing runnels with *Coenagrion mercuriale* and *Ischnura pumilio*, and on bog pools in valley mires with *Orthetrum coerulescens*. When *Sphagnum* bogs are marginal to larger heathland ponds, *C. tenellum* may occur with a much wider range of species, including *Aeshna juncea*, *Anax imperator*, *Sympetrum danae* and *Lestes sponsa*.

Status and distribution   The distribution of *C. tenellum* is strongly influenced by its habitat requirements. However, a climatic factor is probably involved as well, limiting its range to the southern half of Britain. It has not been reliably recorded from Ireland, though apparently suitable habitat is present in some central and southern counties. In Britain, it is most commonly found in the heathland areas of the Surrey/Hampshire border, the New Forest, Dorset, Cornwall and Pembrokeshire. It occurs on several calcareous valley mires in Anglesey, the Lleyn peninsula, and at Cothill Fen in Oxfordshire and one locality in Norfolk. Its last Suffolk records were from Redgrave Fen in the 1940s and from heathland at Fritton Warren in the 1950s. It became extinct at Wicken Fen, Chippenham Fen and Gamlingay Bog in Cambridgeshire in the latter part of the 19th century. Its Norfolk site is currently threatened by excessive extraction of water from underground aquifers, and by plans to widen an adjacent road. *C. tenellum* is vulnerable to seral changes in habitat. It bred regularly at a few sites on the Somerset Moors until the early 1970s, but became extinct as a result of the drying out of its habitat due to the lowering of the water table caused by adjacent peat extraction operations.

European and world distribution   *C. tenellum* is essentially a species of south-west Europe and the Mediterranean area, with isolated pockets further north as far as Britain and Germany, where it is probably at the limits of its ecological tolerance (Parr & Parr 1979). It also occurs in northern Morocco and Algeria.

Ceriagrion tenellum (Villers)

Small red damselfly

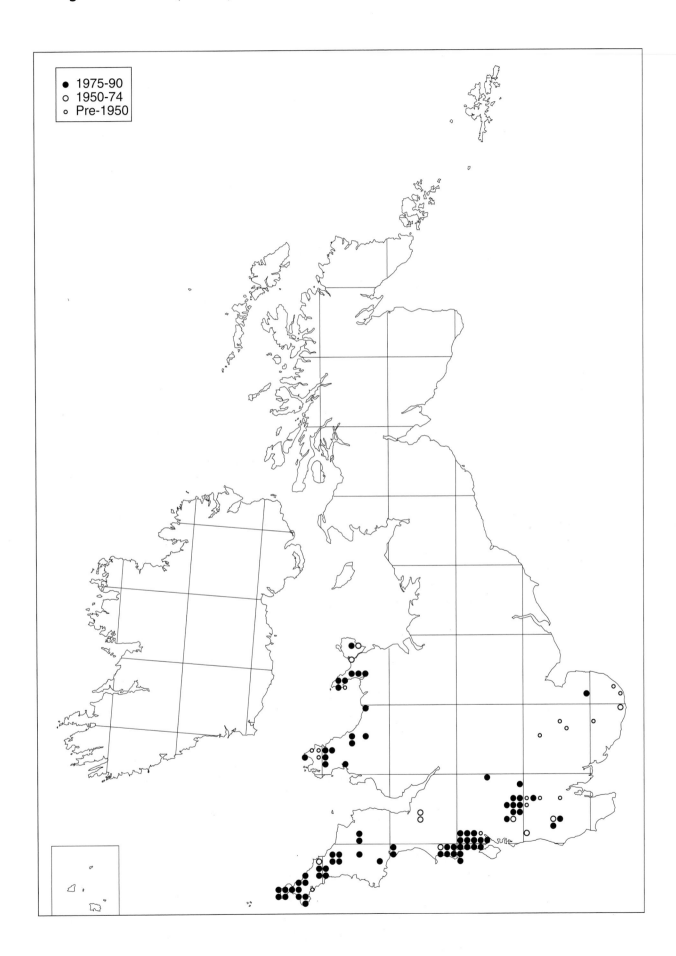

Aeshna caerulea (Ström)   **Azure hawker**

Description   This is a medium-size hawker dragonfly, similar in body length to *A. mixta*. In the mature male, the abdomen is black with an extensive pattern of mostly paired blue markings on the dorsal surface of the abdomen. Unlike other blue-spotted aeshnids, there are no green or yellow abdominal markings; thus, *A. caerulea* can be distinguished from the larger, and much commoner, *A. juncea* which can occur in the same localities (however, close examination is necessary as this difference is not obvious in flight). The antehumeral stripes on the brownish black thorax are thin or absent, and there are a pair of narrow pale stripes on the sides of the thorax. Females are browner, and also have a pattern of paired markings along the abdomen, but these vary from dull beige to lavender-blue, as in immature males, and, exceptionally, are pale whitish or bright blue (D J Clarke, pers. comm.).

Habitat   *A. caerulea* breeds within large open moorland areas in shallow bog pools with at least some marginal *Sphagnum* moss, at altitudes ranging from near sea level to 550 m (Clarke *et al.* 1990). Males of *A. caerulea* often sun themselves on whitish boulders, the white trunks of birch trees or on pale moss hummocks of *Racomitrium lanuginosum*. The close proximity of woodland areas is not an essential feature of *A. caerulea* breeding sites.

Breeding biology   There is doubt about whether this species is territorial. Eggs are laid into soft peat or *Sphagnum* moss in shallow bog pools of up to 30 m^2 surface area, and water depth of 20 cm over a further 20 cm of peaty mud, although smaller pools are usually selected (Clarke *et al.* 1990). Oviposition lasts up to three minutes at any one place, and occurs only during periods of sunshine. The eggs pass the winter in diapause, and the larvae probably take three years to develop, but captive breeding experiments suggest that there may be considerable variability (Clarke 1994). Emergence has been observed on the stems of common cottongrass and of over-hanging heather.

Flight periods   *A. caerulea* is on the wing from the beginning of June, occasionally earlier, to mid-August. Other species which are known to breed in the same general area are *Pyrrhosoma nymphula*, *A. juncea*, *Somatochlora arctica*, *Leucorrhinia dubia*, and *Libellula quadrimaculata*.

Status and distribution   The first appearance of *A. caerulea* on the British list stems from a specimen taken in northern Scotland and given to Sélys-Longchamps by a Mr Wilson in 1845 (Corbet *et al.* 1960). Its position as a British species was enhanced by R McLachlan's discovery of it at Rannoch, Perthshire, in June 1865 (McLachlan 1865). It is a scarce dragonfly in Britain, restricted to northern Scotland and Galloway. It seems to have been recorded more frequently in the past, and has probably suffered in some areas from the increase in conifer planting and the drainage which that entails. However, it may easily be overlooked. It has not been recorded from Ireland, although there appears to be suitable habitat.

European and world distribution   *A. caerulea* is a boreo-montane species, and is found from north Scotland and north Scandinavia to arctic Russia. There are relict populations in the Alps and other mountain areas of central Europe and the Caucasus.

Aeshna caerulea (Ström)

Azure hawker

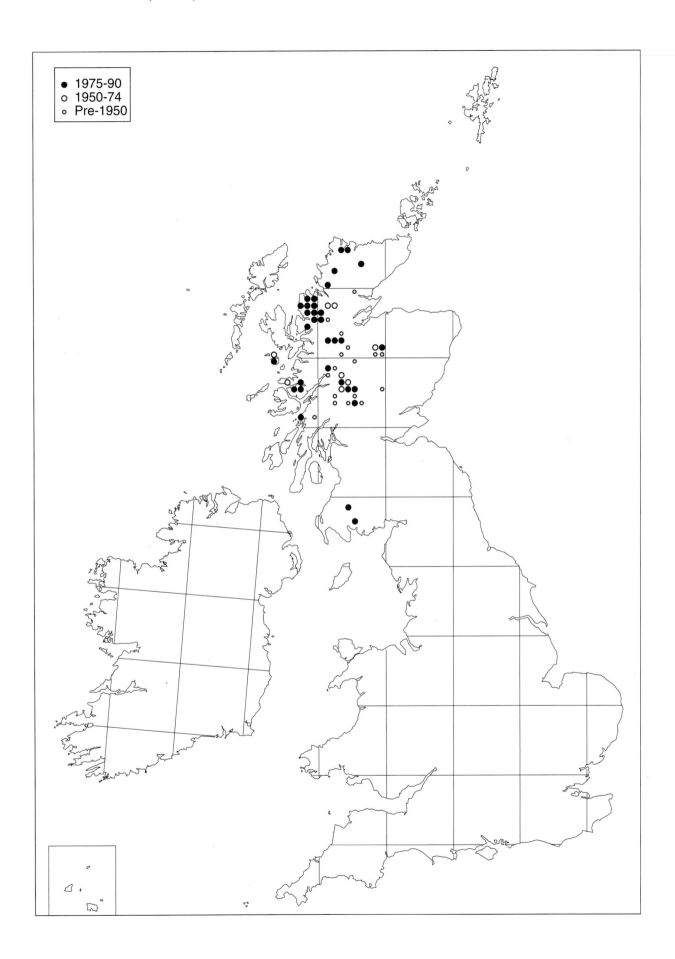

Aeshna juncea (Linnaeus)   **Common hawker**

Description

A. juncea is a large hawker dragonfly, males of which have blue spots and yellow markings on a dark brown-black body, and are thus similar to *A. cyanea*, *A. mixta* and *Brachytron pratense*. In males, the paired blue spots on the dorsal surface of abdominal segments 9 and 10 are separated, unlike those of *A. cyanea* in which they are joined into two broad blue bands. The yellow antehumeral stripes are much thinner than those of *A. cyanea*, but are more extensive than those of *A. mixta*. The costa is bright yellow, distinguishing *A. juncea* from the other three species, in which it is brown. Both male and female *A. juncea* lack the very hairy thorax of *B. pratense*; also, their pterostigmata are not as elongated, and they are much larger. In female *A. juncea*, yellow to green usually replaces the blue coloration on males, and the antehumeral stripes are reduced to two thin lines.

Habitat

A. juncea typically breeds in bog pools, the margins of ponds and lakes in moorland and heathland areas, and occasionally in slow-flowing sections of upland streams. Such sites are generally of an acidic nature and range from oligotrophic to slightly mesotrophic. Less commonly, *A. juncea* may breed in peaty fens, more often in Ireland than in Britain.

Breeding biology

Males are territorial; highest steady density being about 2 per 100 m of water's edge. Where they occur with *A. cyanea* on small ponds, *A. cyanea* generally drives them out (Moore 1964). Copulation takes place amongst heather, bushes and trees, and lasts for 60–75 minutes. Females oviposit alone, inserting their eggs into submerged tissues of plants such as pondweeds and rushes or, occasionally, into soft peaty mud. This may take place in quite dull weather, and the rustling of wings low down amongst emergent vegetation may be the first indication to an observer that a dragonfly is present. Such rustling is the result of wing-whirring, which is a means of gaining and maintaining body heat in low temperatures, and is a device practised by many of the larger dragonfly species. The eggs pass the winter in diapause, and larvae take two or more years to develop. As in other aeshnids, the larvae live amongst submerged vegetation, or plant remains, and catch their prey by remaining motionless and concealed, striking out when an item of food comes within range. Occasionally, they will actively pursue their prey over very short distances. Emergence often occurs on the stems of common cottongrass and rushes.

Flight periods

A. juncea is on the wing from early July to early October. The males spend much time feeding over moorland or along rides in conifer plantations, often far from water. *A. juncea* is often found with other species which can tolerate oligotrophic, acidic conditions, such as *Sympetrum danae*, *Libellula quadrimaculata*, *Lestes sponsa* and *Pyrrhosoma nymphula*.

Status and distribution

A. juncea occurs most commonly in upland areas of Britain and Ireland, and on lowland heaths and moors. It is absent or very scarce in the English east midlands, East Anglia, Kent and Sussex, owing to a lack of suitable habitat, and has probably declined in some areas in recent years as a result of the reclamation of lowland heaths for agriculture, forestry and urban development.

European and world distribution

A. juncea is an holarctic species found throughout northern and central Europe, with southern outposts in mountain areas. It occurs east to Siberia and Japan, and in Alaska, Canada and northern USA.

Aeshna juncea (Linnaeus)

Common hawker

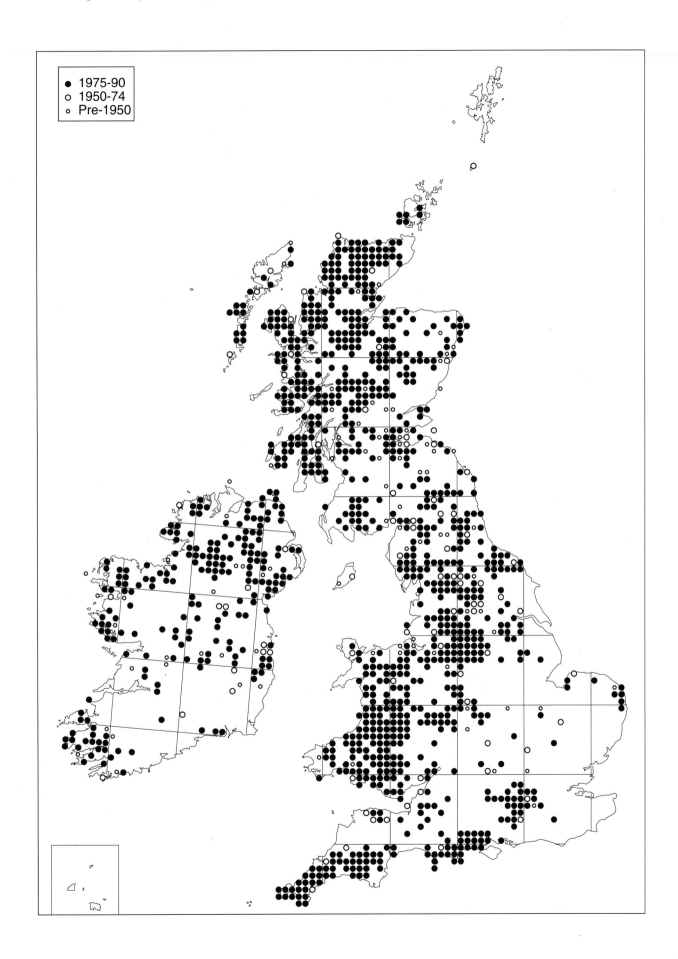

Aeshna mixta Latreille   **Migrant hawker**

Description *A. mixta* is a medium-size hawker dragonfly, similar in pattern and coloration to *A. cyanea*, *A. juncea*, and *Brachytron pratense*. In males, the antehumeral stripes are much reduced or absent, thus separating *A. mixta* from the other three species. The costa is dark brown, distinguishing it from *A. juncea* in which it is bright yellow. The abdominal spots on the dorsal surface of segments 9 and 10 are paired, not joined together to form two broad bands as in *A. cyanea*. *A. mixta* is much smaller than both *A. juncea* and *A. cyanea*, though it is of similar size to *B. pratense*. However, *A. mixta* lacks the very hairy thorax of that species, and its pterostigmata are not as elongated, neither do their flying seasons overlap. In female *A. mixta*, the body markings are similar to those of the male, but the coloration is much duller and the abdominal spots are a pale yellowish green. The anal appendages of the female are the longest of all our resident aeshnids, excluding *B. pratense*, being more than the combined length of abdominal segments 9 and 10.

Habitat *A. mixta* breeds in ponds and lakes, including flooded sand and gravel pits, with well-vegetated margins. It also breeds in canals, ditches, which in coastal areas may be quite brackish, and, occasionally, sluggish rivers and streams. On heathlands, *A. mixta* appears to avoid the more acidic waters tolerated by *A. juncea*.

Breeding biology *A. mixta* is usually only weakly territorial and occurs at higher densities than larger aeshnids. It is not uncommon to see three or four males flying together in a confined area without aggression. Even more than other *Aeshna* species, *A. mixta* is frequently seen hawking at the edges of woods, along woodland rides and glades, and beside tall hedges away from water, sometimes in large numbers. Copulation time is lengthy and usually takes place in marginal vegetation near the water's edge. Females insert their eggs into the tissues of emergent plants, such as bulrush, often above water level, and will occasionally oviposit into bare mud. Diapause is spent in the egg stage. Larval development is rapid, being completed in one season.

Flight periods *A. mixta* has a late flying season, from late July to late October. It can be seen with many other late summer species, such as *A. cyanea*, *A. grandis*, *Sympetrum striolatum* and the commoner damselflies.

Status and distribution *A. mixta* has not yet been recorded from Ireland. In Britain it breeds from Cornwall and south Wales to the Humber, but is most common in south-eastern and midland counties. It has clearly extended its range in Britain during this century. Lucas (1900) wrote, 'This dragonfly seems to be almost confined to the south-eastern corner of England and the Channel Islands, and even from there but few captures have been recorded'. Longfield (1949c) reported that *A. mixta* was most commonly found in southern and eastern counties below the Severn/Wash line, and cites a few instances of its being found further north. Benton (1988) records the spread of *A. mixta* into Essex in the 1930s and 1940s. In Bedfordshire, it was described in 1947 as being by no means common, but it is now ubiquitous (Dawson 1988). Holland (1983) records the spread of this species in Gloucestershire since the 1970s, as does Allport (1985) in Yorkshire. In Cornwall, breeding was confirmed for the first time in 1991. It was first recorded in Cheshire in 1993. The population of *A. mixta* is sometimes increased greatly in late summer by influxes from the continent. On 17 August 1982, in excess of a thousand were seen by K D Wilson in a wood near Brighton, Sussex, many of which were teneral. Three days later he found a similar number in a wood near Eastbourne, up to 25 settled on a single branch.

European and world distribution *A. mixta* is common throughout most of south and central Europe, being found as far north as Denmark. It occurs in North Africa, the Caucasus, and east to China and Japan.

Lough Gealain near Mullagh More, The Burren, Co Clare.
May 1989

Altitude *c.* 60 m. Turlough (see Glossary) in area of limestone pavement, with mostly bare shoreline and some stands of marginal common reed and rushes, with hazel scrub nearby. Lake bed covered by deposit of marl. Site for *Orthetrum cancellatum*, *Brachytron pratense* and *Coenagrion pulchellum*.

PHOTOGRAPH: R THOMPSON

Montiaghs Moss, near Aghalee, Co Antrim.
June 1991

Altitude 15 m. Cut-over bog in Lough Neagh basin, with many small sedge-filled pools formed from peat cuttings, containing broadleaved pondweed. Adjacent willow, alder and birch scrub in heathland dominated by purple moor-grass. Site for *Coenagrion lunulatum, C. pulchellum, Brachytron pratense, Aeshna juncea* and *Sympetrum danae*.

PHOTOGRAPH: R THOMPSON

Loch Bran, Glen Mor, Inverness-shire
July 1991

Altitude 195 m. Shallow peaty mesotrophic lake with sheltered bays, adjacent to birch and Scots pine woodland. Open water contains white water-lily, with emergent common reed and beds of slender sedge and bottle sedge. Lake margin also has *Sphagnum* lawns with bog-myrtle and heather. Site for *Somatochlora metallica, Libellula quadrimaculata, Sympetrum danae, S. striolatum* and *Lestes sponsa*.

PHOTOGRAPH: R THOMPSON

Silver Flowe NNR, Kirkcudbrightshire (Galloway)
June 1986

Altitude 260 m. Series of shallow pools and channels, with emergent bogbean and marginal and submerged *Sphagnum* species, in an area of blanket bog containing deergrass, common cottongrass, purple moor-grass, heather and hummocks of *Sphagnum*.
Site for *Aeshna caerulea, A. juncea, Libellula quadrimaculata, Pyrrhosoma nymphula* and *Enallagma cyathigerum*.

PHOTOGRAPH: D J CLARKE

Scaleby Moss, near Carlisle, Cumbria
June 1985

Altitude 30 m. Cut-over bog with small peaty pools, formed from flooded peat cuttings, containing floating *Sphagnum* and emergent common cottongrass, in an area dominated by heather, bog-myrtle, birch scrub and Scots pine woodland. Site for *Leucorrhinia dubia*, *Aeshna juncea*, *Sympetrum danae* and *Pyrrhosoma nymphula*.

PHOTOGRAPH: R MERRITT

Gull Pool, Delamere Forest, Cheshire
May 1988

Altitude 75 m. Sheltered acidic lake in area of glacial sands, fringed with Scots pine, birch and sallow, and with marginal soft rush and *Sphagnum* lawns containing marsh cinquefoil and common cottongrass. The shallow lake, overlying soft peat, contains an abundance of the submerged moss *Drepanocladus fluitans*. Site for *Cordulia aenea*, *Leucorrhinia dubia*, *Libellula quadrimaculata*, *Sympetrum danae* and *Lestes sponsa*.

PHOTOGRAPH: R MERRITT

River Dee, near Holt, Denbighshire/Cheshire border
July 1988

Altitude 7 m. Slow-flowing river over a sandy bed in an area of cattle-grazed pasture. The sandy banks support closely cropped reed canary-grass, with amphibious bistort, common nettle and willow. Site for *Gomphus vulgatissimus* and *Calopteryx splendens*.

PHOTOGRAPH: R MERRITT

Shipmeadow Marsh, near Beccles, Suffolk
July 1988

Altitude 1 m. Grazing marsh on the alluvial floodplain of the River Waveney. Dyke vegetation includes yellow water-lily and amphibious bistort, with marginal rushes and sedges. Site for *Libellula fulva*, *Brachytron pratense*, *Coenagrion pulchellum* and *C. puella*.

PHOTOGRAPH: R MERRITT

River Stour, Stoke by Clare, Suffolk
August 1988

Altitude 54 m. Slow-moving river with rich aquatic vegetation including yellow water-lily and pondweed species, emergent common club-rush and branched bur-reed, and marginal reed canary-grass, common nettle and willows. Site typical for *Platycnemis pennipes*, *Calopteryx splendens*, *Erythromma najas* and *Ischnura elegans*.

PHOTOGRAPH: H MENDEL

Sundon Springs chalk quarry, near Luton, Bedfordshire
June 1990

Altitude 140 m. Seepages from disturbed spring lines, forming shallow, sludgy pools in ruts and depressions, dominated by hard rush, with jointed rush, common spike-rush and stoneworts. Site for *Ischnura pumilio*, *I. elegans*, *Libellula depressa* and *Sympetrum striolatum*.

PHOTOGRAPH: S A CHAM

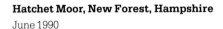

Pett Level, near Winchelsea, Sussex
August 1988

Altitude 2 m. Sheep-stocked coastal grazing marsh, with a network of ditches which contain bulrush, frogbit, duckweeds, flowering-rush and hard rush. Site for *Brachytron pratense*, *Aeshna mixta*, *Sympetrum sanguineum*, *Coenagrion pulchellum*, *Lestes sponsa* and, formerly, *L. dryas* (last recorded 1941).

PHOTOGRAPH: R MERRITT

Hatchet Moor, New Forest, Hampshire
June 1990

Altitude 35 m. Shallow mesotrophic pond with bare gravelly banks in area of heathland. The open water contains beds of white water-lily, with water-plantain and marsh St. John's-wort at the margins. Site for *Anax imperator*, *Libellula depressa*, *Orthetrum cancellatum* and *Sympetrum striolatum*.

PHOTOGRAPH: R THOMPSON

Cadover Bridge, near Lee Moor, Devon
June 1988

Altitude 216 m. Shallow pool in old china clay workings, resulting from the silting up of a settling pond, with emergent common cottongrass, soft rush, unbranched bur-reed, floating sweet-grass and lesser spearwort. Site for *Ischnura pumilio, I. elegans, Lestes sponsa, Libellula quadrimaculata* and *L. depressa*.

PHOTOGRAPH: R MERRITT

Furze Hill, near Pirbright Common, Surrey
August 1988

Altitude 54 m. Peaty, mesotrophic pond with white water-lily and broadleaved pondweed, and marginal bulrush, rushes, bog-myrtle and *Sphagnum*, surrounded by Scots pine, birch and sallow. Site for *Ceriagrion tenellum, Erythromma najas, Aeshna grandis, A. cyanea, Cordulia aenea* and *Somatochlora metallica*.

PHOTOGRAPH: R MERRITT

◄

Colaton Raleigh Common, Devon
August 1987

Altitude 90 m. Shallow spring-fed gravelly runnel emanating from underlying calcareous sandstone in heathland dominated by heather and western gorse, with scattered Scots pine and birch. The margins support black bog-rush, purple moor-grass and rushes, and boggy areas contain *Sphagnum* and round-leaved sundews. This and the following locality are sites for *Coenagrion mercuriale, Pyrrhosoma nymphula, Cordulegaster boltonii* and *Orthetrum coerulescens*.

PHOTOGRAPH: R MERRITT

Mynydd Preseli, near ►
Brynberian, Pembrokeshire
May 1985

Altitude 145 m. Spring-fed runnel over marl, containing marsh St John's-wort, bog pondweed and marginal *Sphagnum* species, in an area of sheep-grazed heath dominated by purple moor-grass, heather and bilberry.

PHOTOGRAPH: R MERRITT

PLATE 1 *Calopteryx virgo* adult   PHOTOGRAPH: R THOMPSON

PLATE 2 *Pyrrhosoma nymphula* adult   PHOTOGRAPH: R THOMPSON

PLATE 3 *Coenagrion lunulatum* adult   PHOTOGRAPH: R THOMPSON

PLATE 4 *Platycnemis pennipes* adult   PHOTOGRAPH: R THOMPSON

PLATE 5 *Coenagrion hastulatum* adult   PHOTOGRAPH: R THOMPSON

PLATE 6 *Ischnura pumilio* adult   PHOTOGRAPH: R THOMPSON

PLATE 7 *Aeshna caerulea* adult   PHOTOGRAPH: R THOMPSON

PLATE 8 *Aeshna isosceles* adult   PHOTOGRAPH: R THOMPSON

PLATE 9 *Gomphus vulgatissimus* adult   PHOTOGRAPH: R THOMPSON

PLATE 10 *Aeshna mixta* adult   PHOTOGRAPH: R THOMPSON

PLATE 11 *Anax imperator* adult   PHOTOGRAPH: R THOMPSON

PLATE 12 *Cordulegaster boltonii* adult   PHOTOGRAPH: R THOMPSON

PLATE 13 *Libellula fulva* adult   PHOTOGRAPH: R THOMPSON

PLATE 16 *Orthetrum coerulescens* adult   PHOTOGRAPH: R THOMPSON

PLATE 14 *Sympetrum danae* adult   PHOTOGRAPH: R THOMPSON

PLATE 17 *Leucorrhinia dubia* adult   PHOTOGRAPH: R THOMPSON

PLATE 15 *Calopteryx virgo* larva   PHOTOGRAPH: R THOMPSON

PLATE 18 *Platycnemis pennipes* larva   PHOTOGRAPH: R THOMPSON

PLATE 19 *Pyrrhosoma nymphula* larva   PHOTOGRAPH: R THOMPSON

PLATE 22 *Enallagma cyathigerum* larva   PHOTOGRAPH: R THOMPSON

PLATE 20 *Aeshna caerulea* larva   PHOTOGRAPH: R THOMPSON

PLATE 23 *Anax imperator* larva   PHOTOGRAPH: R THOMPSON

PLATE 21 *Cordulia aenea* larva   PHOTOGRAPH: R THOMPSON

PLATE 24 *Leucorrhinia dubia* larva   PHOTOGRAPH: R THOMPSON

Aeshna mixta Latreille   **Migrant hawker**

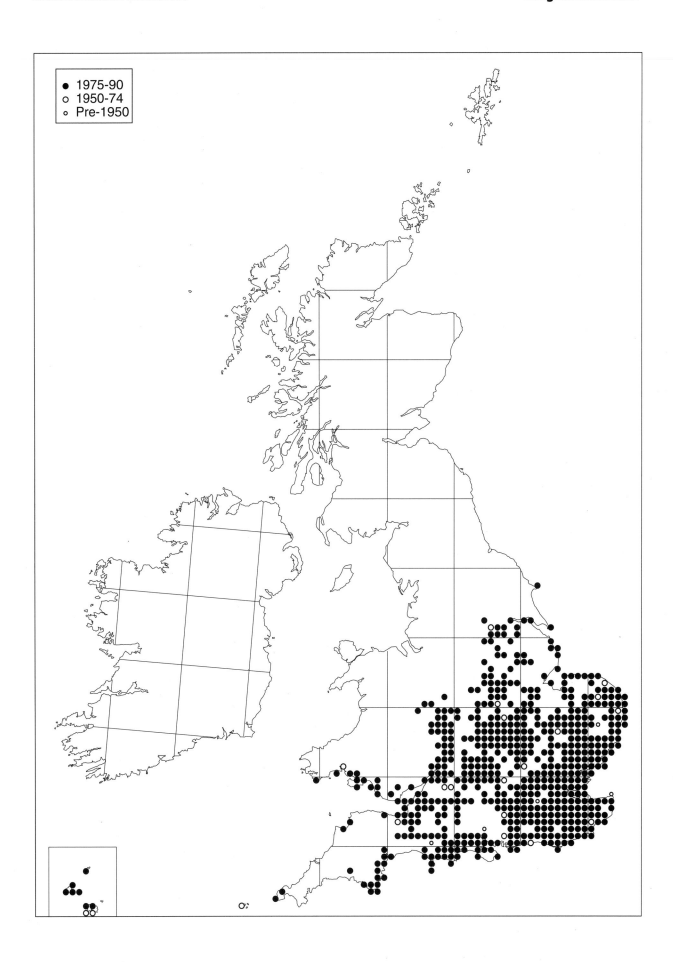

Aeshna cyanea (Müller)   **Southern hawker**

Description

A. cyanea is a large hawker dragonfly in which the coloration and pattern of body markings are similar to *A. juncea*, *A. mixta* and *Brachytron pratense*. Both sexes of *A. cyanea* can be distinguished from the other three species by the presence of two broad bands on the dorsal surface of abdominal segments 9 and 10 – blue in males, green in females. The antehumeral stripes are broad, unlike those of *A. juncea* and *A. mixta* in which they are thinner or absent altogether. These stripes and the two broad bands on either side of the thorax are also much greener than in *A. juncea* and *A. mixta*, in which they are yellow. The larger paired spots on the dorsal surface of abdominal segments 2–7 are green in mature males, but blue in the other three species. *A. cyanea* lacks the very hairy thorax of *B. pratense*, and its pterostigmata are not as elongated. It is also much larger. In female *A. cyanea*, yellowish green replaces the blue coloration of males.

Habitat

A. cyanea breeds in mesotrophic ponds, lakes, canals and ditches. It is a frequent visitor to garden ponds in southern Britain. It is restricted to lower altitudes than *A. juncea*.

Breeding biology

Males of *A. cyanea* are territorial. In Britain the highest steady density is about 2 per 100 m of water's edge but, elsewhere in Europe, higher densities have been recorded (Poethke 1988). Small ponds may have only a single male at any one time, but dozens, even hundreds, of larvae may emerge from it (Merritt 1983b; Gaunt 1984). A succession of different males will occupy the same pond in the course of the same day. The length of each visit depends on the number present in the area: the more there are, the more frequent and shorter will be their visits. The total amount of time spent by the pond depends on air temperature (Kaiser 1974). Unlike most other British dragonflies, it hunts quite late in the evening, and even when it is raining. Copulation takes place away from water and lasts for up to two hours. Females insert their eggs into vegetation by the water's edge, including dead wood, and also into moss and bare soil. Females often oviposit in the evening and in poor weather. Diapause occurs in the egg stage, and the larvae usually take two or three years to develop. Emergence sites vary from tall marginal vegetation to wooden posts, trunks of bushes and even the vertical concrete walls of small reservoir tanks.

Flight periods

A. cyanea is on the wing from early July to early October. It may be seen with many other species such as *A. grandis*, *Anax imperator*, *Libellula depressa*, *Sympetrum striolatum*, and the common damselflies.

Status and distribution

A. cyanea is found commonly in southern Britain, less so in northern England. Sélys-Longchamps (1846) listed it from Scotland, but its first fully documented record was in 1886 when it was discovered at Tayvallich, Kintyre. It still breeds near there today. Its rarity in Scotland is probably due partly to a climatic factor in view of the species' European distribution. Its absence from the uplands of north Wales can probably be explained by a lack of suitable habitat, and this may have blocked its spread into Anglesey and the Lleyn peninsula. The only known record from Ireland is of a single female found in Cork city on 17 October 1988 by K G M Bond. It was picked up dead, after a night in which Saharan dust fell on the city (Bond 1989). It has been deposited in the National Museum, Dublin.

European and world distribution

A. cyanea is found from the Iberian peninsula and the western Mediterranean to southern Scandinavia and east to the Caucasus. It is absent from the southern Balkans.

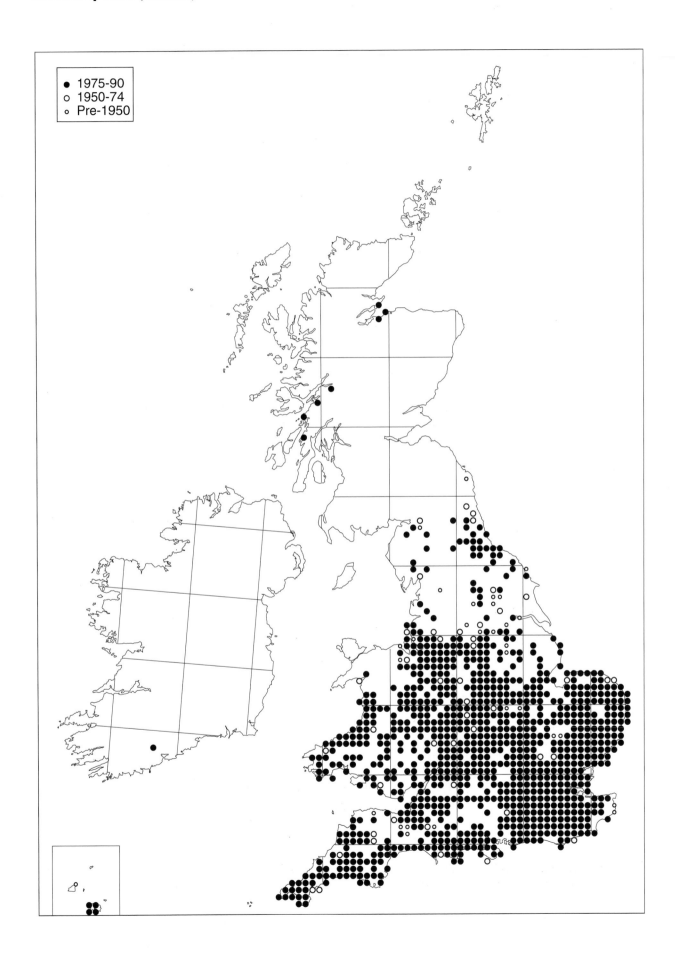

● 1975-90
○ 1950-74
○ Pre-1950

Aeshna grandis (Linnaeus)   **Brown hawker**

Description

Both sexes of this species are unmistakable in having a dark brown body with wings suffused all over with an orange-brown tint. The sides of the thorax possess two broad yellow bands. In males, there are a pair of large blue spots on the dorsal surface of abdominal segment 2, a large blue mark laterally on segment 3, and smaller blue marks along the sides of segments 4–8. There are also tiny paired yellow markings dorsally on abdominal segments 2–8. The eyes are brownish blue. In females, the blue spots on segment 2 are absent, and the marks along the sides of the abdomen are yellow.

Habitat

A. grandis occurs on ponds, lakes, slow-moving rivers, canals and ditches. It is one of the most frequently encountered large dragonflies in south-eastern and midland counties of Britain, often visiting garden ponds and flying late into the evening.

Breeding biology

A. grandis is territorial and adult male densities rarely exceed 2 per 100 m of water's edge. It is unusual also in defending territories away from water. After a lengthy copulation, the female lays her eggs singly into the tissues of emergent plants just below the water surface, or into floating aquatic vegetation provided there is sufficient support for her not to become completely immersed. Sometimes several females will settle on a small floating log and oviposit close together into the wood, whilst at other times they will show aggressive behaviour towards each other. The eggs pass the winter in diapause. The larvae take from two to four years to complete development, and live amongst submerged water plants. As with several other weed-dwelling aeshnid species, such as *A. cyanea* and *Anax imperator*, a proportion of first-year larvae are cryptically coloured, often with a banded pattern. This may help reduce cannibalism and interspecific predation from older larvae.

Flight periods

A. grandis is on the wing from early July to early October. It occurs with the many other species of dragonfly which breed in well-vegetated ponds and waterways within its geographical range.

Status and distribution

In Britain, *A. grandis* is widespread throughout the lowland areas of the south-east, the midlands and as far north as Lancashire, Yorkshire, and the southern fringe of Cumbria, with a few isolated records further north. There is a single record from Scotland: from Colvend in Dumfries-shire in the mid-19th century. *A. grandis* occurs in Wales along the arm of the Montgomery canal, and near the border with Cheshire. It is absent from Devon and Cornwall. In Ireland, *A. grandis* is probably more common in the central midlands and the south-east than the records suggest – most of the fieldwork there having been done in the early summer – but it does appear to be rare in some western districts, notably western Co Cork and Co Kerry.

European and world distribution

On the continent *A. grandis* is found from France to eastern Siberia. It occurs at quite high latitudes in Scandinavia, but is absent from much of the Mediterranean area.

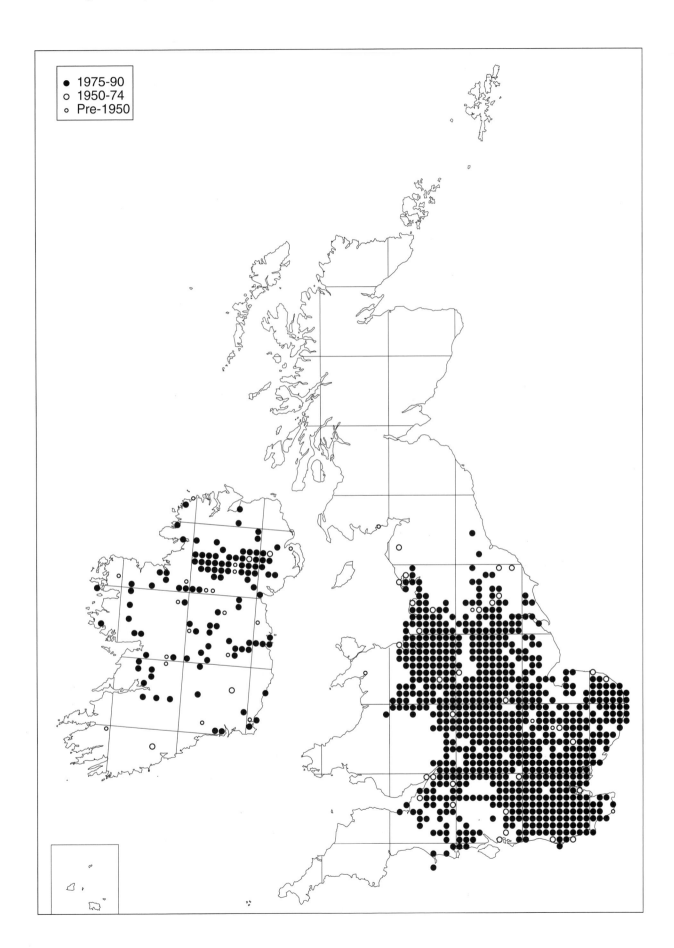

Aeshna grandis (Linnaeus)　　　　　　　　　　　　　　**Brown hawker**

● 1975-90
○ 1950-74
○ Pre-1950

Aeshna isosceles (Müller)   **Norfolk hawker**

Description

A. isosceles is one of the two predominantly brown hawker dragonflies resident in Britain. It can be distinguished easily from the much commoner *A. grandis* by the clear untinted wings (although there is a small, and diagnostic, amber-coloured area at the base of the hind wing), and the green eyes. The coloration of the thorax and abdomen of *A. isosceles* is a paler brown than *A. grandis* and, in mature males, the abdominal coloration is rich amber-brown. Both sexes possess two short yellow bands on either side of the thorax, and a yellow mark on the dorsal surface of abdominal segment 2. This mark superficially resembles a narrow triangle – hence the name *isosceles*. There is a thin black mid-dorsal line along the length of abdominal segments 3–9, thickening on segments 8–9, and also a number of thin transverse bars.

Habitat

A. isosceles breeds in unpolluted grazing marsh dykes which contain the aquatic plant water-soldier in areas where the water table is maintained at a high level. Other plants often present are frogbit, pondweeds and greater bladderwort. The reason why *A. isosceles* is confined to dykes with water-soldier in Britain, while it is not so confined on the continent, is unknown (Leyshon & Moore 1993).

Breeding biology

The males defend rather small territories. The highest steady density is about 9 per 100 m of water's edge. After copulation near water, the females oviposit into the submerged tissues of aquatic plants, favouring water-soldier, an indicator species of unpolluted water. On occasions, female *A. isosceles* have been observed to select the white flower-head on which to settle during oviposition. This projects about 2 cm above the water surface and provides sufficient support for the dragonfly as it lays its eggs into the flower stalk and submerged leaves. Egg laying lasts for 4–5 minutes, often with only a brief period of flight of 10–15 seconds' duration before the process is repeated. The larvae probably take two years to develop. Emergence usually occurs on water-soldier, but also on bankside vegetation.

Flight periods

A. isosceles has a very short flying period, being on the wing from early June to the end of July. It is often seen with *Coenagrion pulchellum*, *Brachytron pratense* and *Libellula quadrimaculata*.

Status and distribution

A. isosceles was taken by J C Dale at Whittlesey Mere, in Cambridgeshire, on 22 June 1818, and at Horning, Norfolk, by J Sparshall on 5 August 1824 (Dale 1901). It was recorded again at Whittlesey Mere in June 1845, a female being taken and subsequently illustrated in *British Libellulinae* by W F Evans (Evans 1845), but this mere was drained in 1850. There is an undated 19th century record from Swaffham Fen, Cambridgeshire (Imms 1938), and an unlocalised record from the Fens in 1893 (Lucas 1900). Today, it is largely restricted to the Broadland area of Norfolk and Suffolk. The eutrophication of the rivers and broads from the leaching of agricultural fertilizers and from sewage effluent has degraded much of Broadland. Disturbance and pollution from pleasure boats have contributed to the problem. *A. isosceles* is now restricted to a few grazing marshes which are relatively isolated from polluted water. But here the pressures continue with the conversion of pasture to arable farming. This results in the loss of traditional benign dyke management techniques, the lowering of the water table and the reduction of water quality owing to nutrient enrichment from agricultural runoff. Breeding has been proved recently from the dyke systems associated with seven grazing marshes, and is suspected at six others. Important new records from north Suffolk are given by Mendel (1992). The species occurs on several nature reserves and is given special protection under the Wildlife and Countryside Act 1981. It was found regularly at a site on Jersey in the 1940s (Le Quesne 1946), but is now extinct there due to habitat changes.

European and world distribution

A. isosceles is widely distributed in Mediterranean areas, including North Africa, and in central Europe. It is absent from Scandinavia apart from Gotland.

Aeshna isosceles (Müller)   **Norfolk hawker**

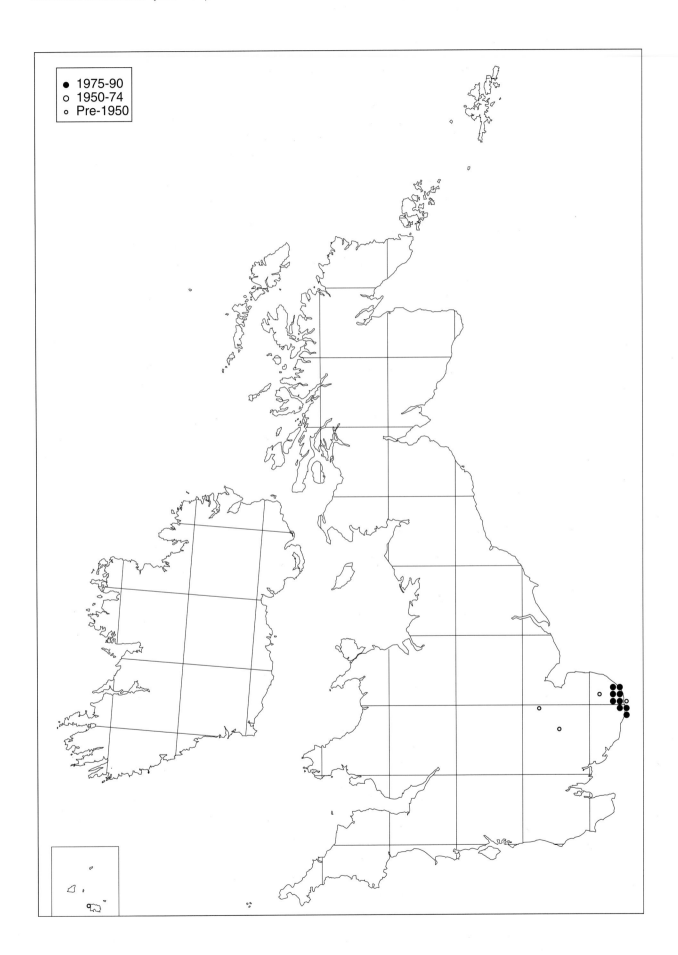

Anax imperator Leach   **Emperor dragonfly**

Description

The predominantly sky-blue abdomen and apple-green thorax of mature males make this large robust hawker dragonfly unmistakable. The thoracic coloration extends to segment 1 of the abdomen and to the sides of segment 2. A broad black mid-dorsal line, of uneven width, runs from segment 2 to the end of the abdomen. The eyes are greenish blue. Females are similarly patterned, but the mid-dorsal line is broader. The thorax and sides of the first 2 abdominal segments are apple-green as in the male, but the blue abdominal coloration is usually replaced by dull green.

Habitat

A. imperator breeds in ponds and lakes, including flooded sand and gravel pits where there is rich marginal vegetation, and in dykes, canals and slow-flowing rivers. Unlike some other aeshnids, they rarely breed in garden ponds – these usually being too small. Adults can often be seen flying along a regular beat over a lake, patrolling their territory, 2–3 m above the surface. They are seldom seen far from water.

Breeding biology

A. imperator males are very territorial. There are rarely more than 5 per 100 m of water's edge, and a small pond is never likely to have more than one male at any one time, although many larvae may emerge from it (Moore 1964). Copulation takes place away from water, sometimes in the tops of trees, and lasts about 10 minutes. The female inserts her eggs into the tissues of submerged plants. When flying from one oviposition site to another she often bends the end of her abdomen downwards – a posture which usually prevents males from attempting to mate. Most larvae emerge in their second year, having spent their second winter in diapause in the last larval instar. They have a synchronised emergence, sometimes in such large numbers that, if there is a lack of unoccupied emergence sites (tall emergent vegetation, bushes, etc), some larvae will emerge on top of others. However, some larvae develop within one year; on occasion, these may make up the entire population (Holmes & Randolph 1994). Under warm conditions, they emerge in the evening, and usually make their maiden flight away from water in the morning. Corbet (in Corbet *et al.* 1960) records predation of newly emerged adults by blackbirds (*Turdus merula*), whilst Khan (1983) records predation by wood-mice (*Apodemus sylvaticus*).

Flight periods

A. imperator is on the wing from early June to late August. It can be seen with many other southern species of well-vegetated ponds, gravel pits and canals, such as *Aeshna grandis*, *Aeshna mixta*, *Libellula depressa* and *Orthetrum cancellatum*.

Status and distribution

A. imperator is widespread in southern England and south Wales, though it is absent from the uplands of Dartmoor and the Brecon Beacons, and from the chalk downland areas of Wiltshire and Hampshire. It has increased in numbers in the northern part of its range in recent years. It has been found at several new sites in Derbyshire created by local authorities in the 1980s as a result of recreation and amenity schemes on former colliery sites. The recent increase in records from Cheshire has culminated in breeding being proven in 1993 for the first time. *A. imperator* is not reliably recorded from Ireland.

European and world distribution

A. imperator has a very wide world distribution. Not only does it occur from Portugal to Germany and east to the Middle East, Pakistan and central Asia, but it is also found in much of northern and southern Africa and Madagascar. It is absent from Scandinavia except for southern Sweden.

Anax imperator Leach   **Emperor dragonfly**

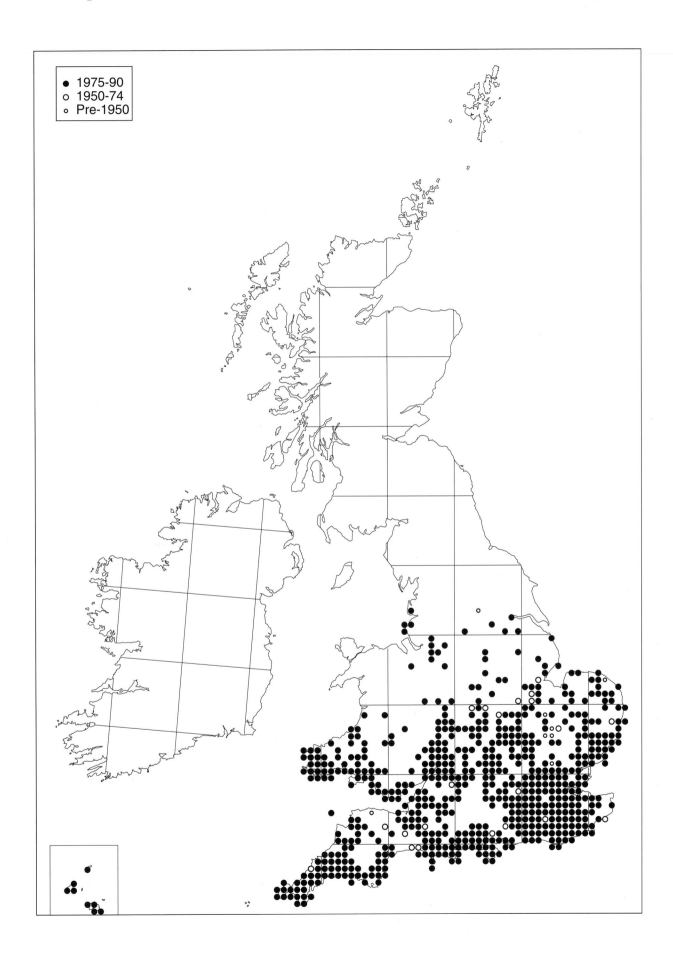

Brachytron pratense (Müller)   Hairy dragonfly

Description   *B. pratense* is a medium-size hawker dragonfly which, from its general dark coloration with greenish yellow markings on the thorax and a pattern of paired blue or yellow spots on the abdomen, resembles *Aeshna cyanea*, *A. juncea* and *A. mixta*. It can easily be separated from *A. cyanea* by virtue of the paired spots on abdominal segments 9 and 10 not being joined into two broad bands, and from *A. juncea* by its brown costa, which is bright yellow in *A. juncea*. Male *B. pratense* differ from *A. mixta* in having broad antehumeral stripes, unlike *A. mixta* in which they are much reduced or absent. *B. pratense* can be distinguished from all three of these *Aeshna* species by its very hairy thorax and anterior part of the abdomen, and its very elongated pterostigma. There are also differences in size and flight period.

Habitat   *B. pratense* breeds in mesotrophic ponds, lakes, including mature gravel pits, canals, ditches and marshy fens where there is plenty of tall emergent vegetation such as common club-rush, common reed, bulrush and great fen-sedge, amongst the margins of which males fly low down searching for ovipositing females. *B. pratense* may occasionally breed in slowly moving rivers. Individuals quickly settle on vegetation when the sun goes in, more readily than in other aeshnid species, a possible reason why the species may be overlooked.

Breeding biology   Males are territorial, the highest steady density being about 9 per 100 m of water's edge. After a lengthy copulation, the female oviposits in both living and dead vegetation, often in floating mats of the previous year's reeds. Being a spring species, non-diapause eggs are laid, which hatch after three to four weeks. The larvae usually take more than two years to develop, but can complete their development in one year in a small pond (Holmes 1984). If disturbed, the larvae may feign death for a short while, and be difficult to detect among the plant debris.

Flight periods   *B. pratense* has a short flying season from mid-May to mid-July. It can be found with species that favour unpolluted well-vegetated dykes and fens, such as *Coenagrion pulchellum*, *Libellula quadrimaculata*, and *Sympetrum sanguineum*, although its flight period overlaps only slightly with the latter.

Status and distribution   *B. pratense* is most commonly found in Britain on the coastal levels and grazing marshes of Somerset, Sussex, Kent and Norfolk. It also occurs in the fens of Anglesey, the Cheshire meres and on the wetlands along the coast of south Wales and Suffolk. It was recently discovered breeding at a few isolated sites in south and west Scotland by Bob and Betty Smith (Smith & Smith 1984), and, since then, new breeding sites have been found in Kintyre. It is possible that the species had been overlooked in the past. It was listed as Scottish by Sélys-Longchamps (1846). In many parts of the English midlands, including the Fens, and in other areas such as Romney Marsh in Kent, *B. pratense* declined considerably in the post-war period, as a result of changes in agricultural land use from grassland to arable. These changes resulted in an increase in pollution, the eutrophication of many wetland sites and, additionally, in the case of grazing marshes, the implementation of adverse dyke management schemes, including lowering of the water table. Despite these factors, *B. pratense* appears to have increased in recent years in unpolluted dykes and mature gravel pits in Cambridgeshire. In Ireland, *B. pratense* is fairly widespread in the fens and peatlands of the midlands, in Co Fermanagh and around Lough Neagh. But some of these areas are subject to drainage operations and agricultural pollution, and the position may deteriorate.

European and world distribution   The genus *Brachytron* occurs only in the Palaearctic region. Its only species, *B. pratense*, is found on the continent from France to southern Scandinavia and east to the Caucasus and the Caspian Sea. It is rare in the Mediterranean region.

Brachytron pratense (Müller)　　　　Hairy dragonfly

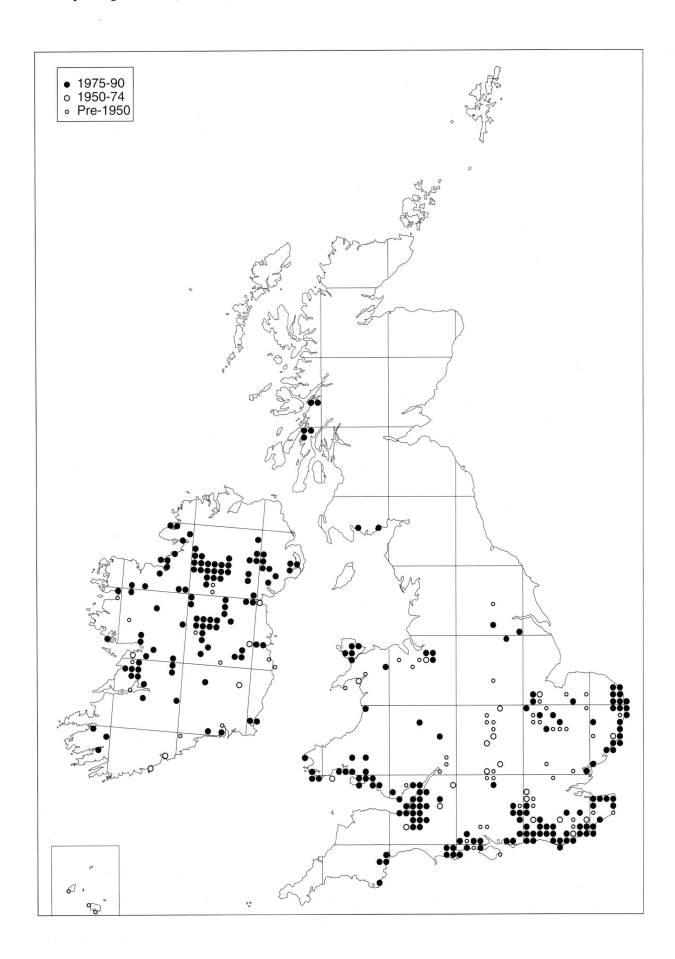

- ● 1975-90
- ○ 1950-74
- ○ Pre-1950

Gomphus vulgatissimus (Linnaeus) Club-tailed dragonfly

Description

G. vulgatissimus is a medium-size dragonfly in which the coloration is black with areas of pale lime-green and yellow. It bears a superficial resemblance, amongst British dragonflies, to *Cordulegaster boltonii* but is much smaller and the pattern of pale markings is quite different. G. vulgatissimus differs from all other British Anisoptera in that its pale greenish eyes are not contiguous dorsally. In both sexes, the thorax and anterior segments of the abdomen are extensively marked with pale lime-green to yellow markings. The posterior abdominal segments are not so heavily marked dorsally, but do possess a bright yellow mark laterally on each of the expanded segments 8 and 9, which is very distinctive. This lateral expansion, especially noticeable in males, gives the body a clubbed appearance – hence the vernacular name.

Habitat

G. vulgatissimus breeds in unpolluted rivers of moderate to slow flow, the depositional nature of which provides the silt or mud in which the larvae live. On the continent, G. vulgatissimus breeds also in static water of ponds and lakes, and Kemp (1988) records an example of this in Shropshire.

Breeding biology

There is some doubt about the extent to which G. vulgatissimus is territorial. Mating can take place far away from water (Moore 1991b). On the River Severn, it exhibits a preference for sheltered 'mill-pond'-like stretches of river where the water is slow flowing and in close proximity to woodland or scrub (Kemp & Vick 1983). During oviposition, the females fly very low over these quieter reaches of river, unaccompanied by males, and drop their eggs into the water while in flight, sometimes just touching the surface with the tip of their abdomens. The larvae live in the bottom silt and mud, and probably take three or more years to develop. G. vulgatissimus is a spring species with a synchronous emergence. As a result, its presence on a river can often be noted because of the numerous exuviae on riverside herbage, the trunks of trees or directly on the soil of the river's bank. Unlike other Anisoptera, they can emerge in a horizontal position. Locating exuviae is most easily accomplished in areas of river that flow through pasture rather than arable land. This is because the cattle trample the bankside vegetation while drinking, thus creating open sandy areas over which the larvae crawl to emerge on the bank or amongst the loose vegetation. Dispersal is invariably away from the river, and adults can be seen flying in woodland rides or along hedgerows several kilometres from the river.

Flight periods

G. vulgatissimus has a short flying season from mid-May to early July. It is commonly found with *Platycnemis pennipes* and *Calopteryx splendens*.

Status and distribution

G. vulgatissimus is confined to seven river systems in southern Britain, namely: the Rivers Thames, Arun, Dee, Severn, Wye, Tywi, and Teifi and their tributaries. It formerly bred on several rivers in the New Forest area including the River Oberwater and the Moors River, but has not been seen there since 1970. A male and a female, now in the Natural History Museum, London, were captured at Castor Hanglands, Cambridgeshire, on 1 June 1951, but a search of the nearby River Nene has not so far proved successful. Several G. vulgatissimus were seen, and one taken, in June 1939 at an unnamed location about a mile from the River Darent in Kent (Longfield 1949b). G. vulgatissimus has not been recorded authentically from Ireland. However, a specimen marked as Irish exists in the Trinity College Museum, Dublin (King & Halbert 1910). According to King and Halbert, this was probably taken by Miss Ball (a celebrated Irish entomologist of the early 19th century) who had no doubt that the species occurred in Ireland. They speculate that the specimen may have come from the Youghal district in the south, where Miss Ball spent some time collecting dragonflies. Certainly, the River Blackwater near Youghal looks suitable for this species, which can easily be overlooked. G. vulgatissimus is vulnerable to pollution, and to the increased use of rivers by pleasure boats, the wash from which can dislodge and drown large numbers of emerging adults in May.

European and world distribution

On the continent, it occurs in many central and northern countries from France and northern Italy to southern Scandinavia and east to Russia. It is scarce in the Mediterranean region.

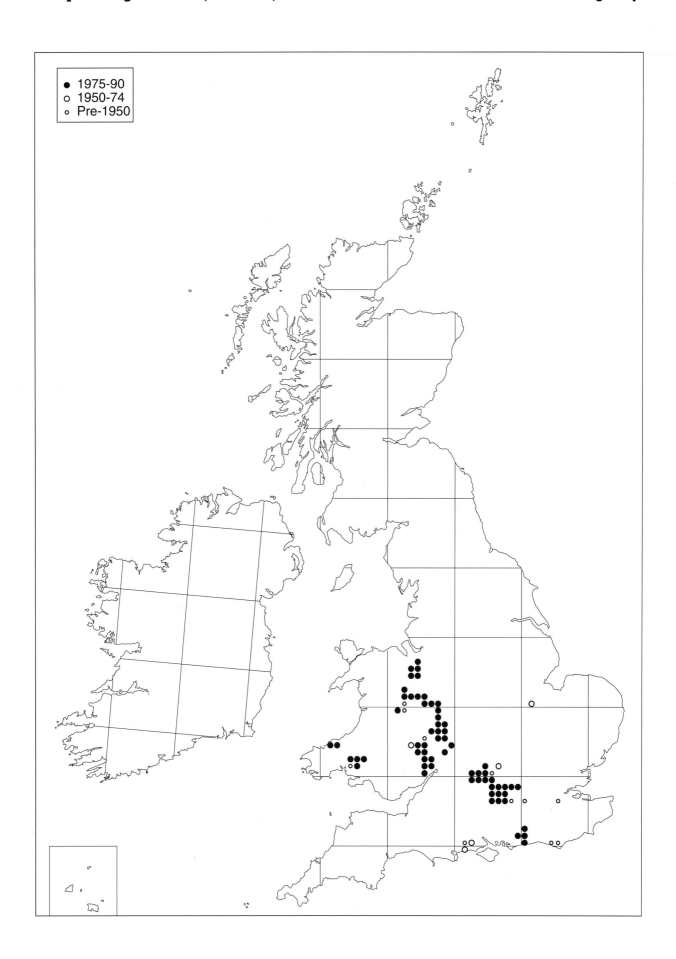

Cordulegaster boltonii (Donovan)   Golden-ringed dragonfly

Description

C. boltonii is a large hawker dragonfly with a very striking appearance, having a black and yellow body and green eyes. The abdomen of males widens towards the posterior end giving it a club-shape similar to the much smaller *Gomphus vulgatissimus*, but the pattern of yellow markings is quite different. *C. boltonii* owes its vernacular name to the series of paired yellow markings on the dorsal surface of the abdomen which extend to the sides and give the appearance of rings. Female coloration is similar to the male.

Habitat

C. boltonii breeds in boggy runnels and moderate- to fast-flowing rivulets, streams and rivers with a silt, gravel or stony bed, usually in western and upland areas but also on lowland heaths.

Breeding biology

Males patrol long lengths of stream flying very low, usually less than 50 cm from the surface and much lower than *Aeshna juncea* which can occupy similar habitat. They are very aggressive but do not defend particular territories. After a lengthy copulation away from water, the female, unaccompanied by the male, hovers by the edge of the stream and thrusts her abdomen down in a stabbing motion pushing her eggs into sediment with her long ovipositor. In fast-flowing stony streams, quiet backwaters are selected where silt has been deposited. The larvae usually take more than two years to develop, and have been known to take four or five years. They live partially concealed in the silt with just their eyes and the end of their abdomen protruding and they prey on passing organisms. In boggy runnels, the larvae may also be found in peaty detritus along with larvae of *Orthetrum coerulescens*.

Flight periods

C. boltonii is on the wing from early June to early September. It may be seen with *Calopteryx virgo* and *Pyrrhosoma nymphula* on streams, and with the latter species and *O. coerulescens* near bogs.

Status and distribution

In Britain, *C. boltonii* is widespread in western and upland districts from Cornwall to the extreme north of Scotland, and on the southern lowland heaths of Dorset, the New Forest, Surrey/Hampshire border and Ashdown Forest in Sussex. It is absent from much of central and eastern England. In Ireland, despite an abundance of apparently suitable habitat, *C. boltonii* has not been recorded authentically. Sélys-Longchamps (1846) listed *C. boltonii* as Irish from 'Northern Lakes', on the basis of information gained from the eminent Irish entomologist, Haliday, during the former's visit to Ireland in 1845. A specimen, apparently taken by Haliday in Ireland, is in the National Museum, Dublin (King & Halbert 1910). On 24 August 1986, an individual of the genus *Cordulegaster* was observed closely, while settled, by R Thorpe, at Firkeel in Co Cork, at the mouth of Bantry Bay. As this would represent beyond doubt an addition to the Irish List, absolute proof of specific identity is necessary, and, as a result, the record has not been mapped in this *Atlas*.

European and world distribution

C. boltonii is found widely in Europe from Portugal to southern Scandinavia and east to Russia. It is rare or absent in lowland areas bordering the North Sea, and absent from the eastern Mediterranean. There are several European subspecies.

Cordulegaster boltonii (Donovan)   **Golden-ringed dragonfly**

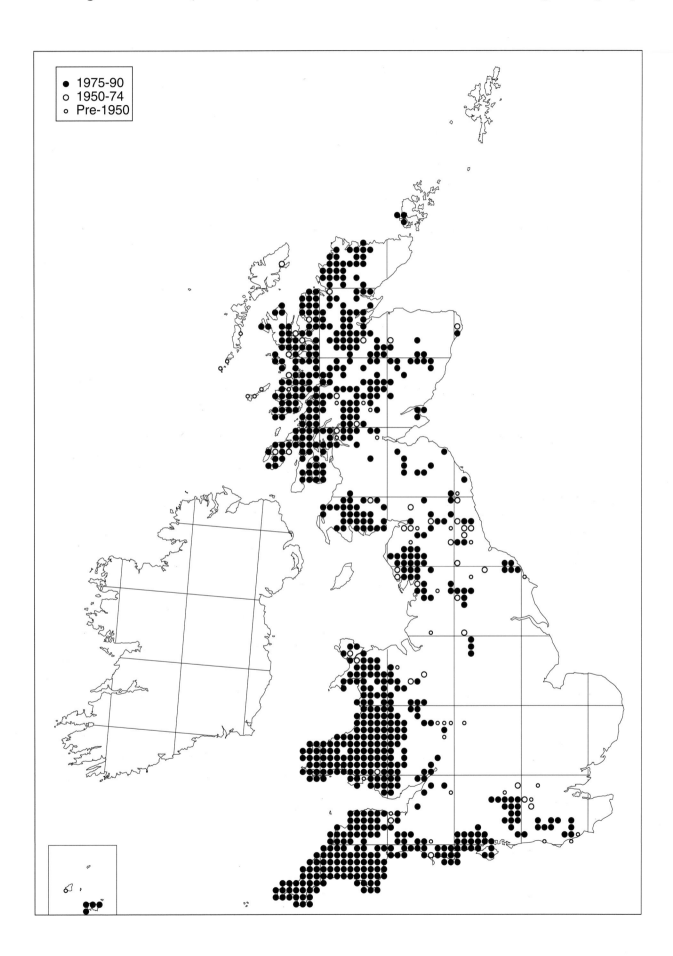

- ● 1975-90
- ○ 1950-74
- ○ Pre-1950

Cordulia aenea (Linnaeus)   Downy emerald

Description   C. aenea is one of three surviving corduliids found in Britain, and one of two from Ireland. They are dark medium-size dragonflies with a metallic sheen to their bodies. In C. aenea, the thorax is metallic bronze-green with a dense covering of buff-coloured downy hairs. The abdomen is dark greenish black with bronze reflections, and is slightly club-shaped in males. There are pale yellow markings on abdominal segments 2 and 3 laterally and ventrally. The eyes are green, and there is a small amber area at the base of the wings. C. aenea resembles both Somatochlora arctica and S. metallica, but there are distinctive differences in the yellow facial markings and in the shape of the anal appendages.

Habitat   C. aenea breeds on well-vegetated mesotrophic, neutral to mildly acidic ponds, lakes and canals often where there are shallow, sheltered bays with trees and bushes overhanging the water margin. In Hampshire and Surrey it has also been recorded from slow-flowing streams and small rivers. In the Scottish Highlands and in Ireland, the breeding sites are relatively open along the water margin, although woodland is often in close proximity (Caledonian pinewoods or Killarney oakwoods, respectively). These sites are small peaty lakes in low heather moorland containing white water-lily, bogbean and additionally, in the Highlands, marginal Sphagnum and sedges (slender sedge, bottle sedge and bog-sedge) and, in Ireland, marginal great fen sedge.

Breeding biology   C. aenea patrol the edges of water bodies with a characteristic rapid flight interspersed with short periods of hovering. They hold the end of their abdomen slightly higher than the thorax in flight, giving a distinctive appearance. They are aggressive, and the length of a beat depends on the number of males present. The theoretical optimal length of the patrol beat has been calculated by Ubukata (1986) and corresponds with field data for C. aenea amurensis (8–10 m when other males are present, 20–60 m when they are not) (Ubukata 1975). After copulation, usually in nearby trees and bushes, the female oviposits, unaccompanied by the male, by repeatedly dipping the tip of her abdomen into the water while in flight, often in the shadier parts. About ten eggs are released with each dip. These are gelatinous and stick to submerged vegetation. They soon hatch, and the larvae, which live amongst bottom debris, probably take two to three years to develop.

Flight periods   C. aenea is on the wing from late May to late July. In the Highlands, it may be seen with S. metallica, Aeshna juncea, and Libellula quadrimaculata, whilst further south, in Argyllshire, it occurs with Brachytron pratense and Aeshna cyanea. In southern England, its breeding sites may contain all these species plus Erythromma najas, Anax imperator, Libellula depressa, and others.

Status and distribution   The earliest record appears to be from Hampstead, Surrey, where Donovan took it in 1805 (Longfield 1949b). Today it is widespread in suitable habitat in the Weald and on the heaths on the Surrey/Hampshire border. It is not uncommon in the New Forest area and the Dorset heaths, but elsewhere it has a very scattered distribution – from Newton Abbot in Devon to Glen Affric in the Highlands. The presence of C. aenea at isolated sites probably represents relict populations from an earlier period. In Ireland, C. aenea was first recorded by a Mr Hely, in a letter to Haliday in 1838, at Killarney, Co Kerry (King & Halbert 1910), but it appears that this record was disbelieved. It was found again in the Killarney area by E Bullock in 1923 (Graves 1947), and still breeds at a few sites there today. These are within the Killarney National Park and so receive some protection. Elsewhere in Ireland, several individuals were found in the forest at Glengarriff, Co Cork, on 14 July 1978 (Goyvaerts 1979), but a breeding population has yet to be located. On 23 May 1992, several C. aenea were discovered at a site near Ballinaboy, West Galway, by M Tickner (B Nelson, pers. comm.).

European and world distribution   On the continent, C. aenea occurs from France through central and northern Europe to Siberia and Japan. It is absent from the Iberian peninsula, most of the Mediterranean area, and much of northern Scandinavia.

Cordulia aenea (Linnaeus)

Downy emerald

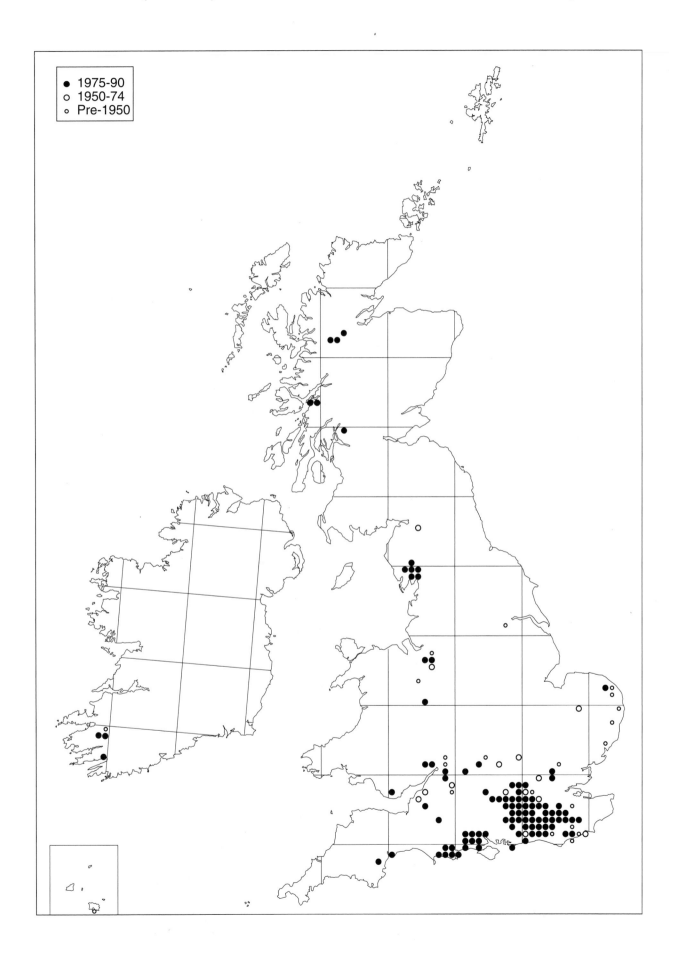

Somatochlora metallica (Vander Linden) **Brilliant emerald**

Description

S. metallica is slightly larger than the other two resident corduliid species, and has a greener appearance. It is readily distinguished from *S. arctica* and *Cordulia aenea*, which it resembles, by the distinctive pattern of yellow facial markings and the shape of the anal appendages. Also, in females, there is a very prominent spike-like vulvar scale which projects almost perpendicularly to the body on the ventral abdominal surface between segments 8 and 9, and is almost as long as those two segments. The eyes are green. The thorax is bright bronze-green and not so heavily downy as *C. aenea*. The abdomen, which is slightly club-shaped in males, is dark metallic green with a bronze sheen. There are pale yellow markings on abdominal segments 2 and 3, both laterally and ventrally and, in females, two small spots on segment 3 dorsally. There is a small amber area at the base of the wings which, in mature females, are entirely suffused with a pale amber tint.

Habitat

In south-east England, *S. metallica* breeds on mesotrophic, neutral to mildly acidic, ponds, lakes and canals, often where there are sheltered bays overhung with trees and bushes. It also occurs on small slow-flowing rivers. In the Scottish Highlands, *S. metallica* often breeds in similar habitat to *C. aenea*, namely: ancient peaty lochs which usually contain white water-lily, bogbean and marginal *Sphagnum*.

Breeding biology

On finding a female, copulation takes place away from water in trees or amongst low bushes and scrub. The female oviposits while hovering very low down, repeatedly tapping her abdomen, two to three times per second, into either wet *Sphagnum* moss or peat (both under and away from the water), or directly into shallow water amongst tree roots or common reed. Oviposition in *S. metallica* is discussed by Smith (1984) and Fox (1991). The larvae live amongst peaty detritus and leaf litter, and probably take two or more years to develop.

Flight periods

S. metallica is on the wing from mid-June (occasionally earlier) to mid-August. In Scotland it can be seen with *C. aenea*, *Aeshna juncea*, *Libellula quadrimaculata* and the commoner northern damselflies. In south-east England the list includes most of the species to be found on mesotrophic ponds and lakes. On slow-flowing rivers, it can be seen with *Calopteryx splendens* and *Platycnemis pennipes*.

Status and distribution

In Britain, *S. metallica* is divided into two distinct populations. One, in the Highlands, is centred on Glen Affric and Glen Mor. The other, in England, is much larger and includes the Weald of Sussex and west Kent, and the heaths of Surrey, north Hampshire and Berkshire. The first fully documented record of *S. metallica* in Britain was from Strathglass in 1869 by Dr Buchanan White (McLachlan 1870). At the turn of the century it was still thought to be solely a Scottish species by many leading entomologists (Lucas 1900), despite the fact that Stephens (1835–37) had recorded it as 'rare in England: it has been found in the metropolitan district in June'. It was first (re)discovered in England on 4 August 1908 at The Warren, near Crowborough in Sussex, by E R Speyer (Speyer 1909). Considering that many of the entomologists of that period were based in south-east England, perhaps *S. metallica* was indeed absent, but one wonders whether, for example, the *C. aenea* recorded by C A Briggs on 13 September 1891 at Bookham, Surrey, was in fact *S. metallica*, in view of the exceptional late date. In 1922, *S. metallica* was found at Loch a' Chrion Dîore in Argyllshire by K J Morton (specimen in the Royal Scottish Museum), and was refound there by E M and R W J Smith on 27 June 1995.

European and world distribution

S. metallica occurs in central and northern Europe and east to the Volga and Asia Minor. In the south of its range it is restricted to higher altitudes, such as the Pyrenees and the Alps.

Somatochlora metallica (Vander Linden)　　　　　**Brilliant emerald**

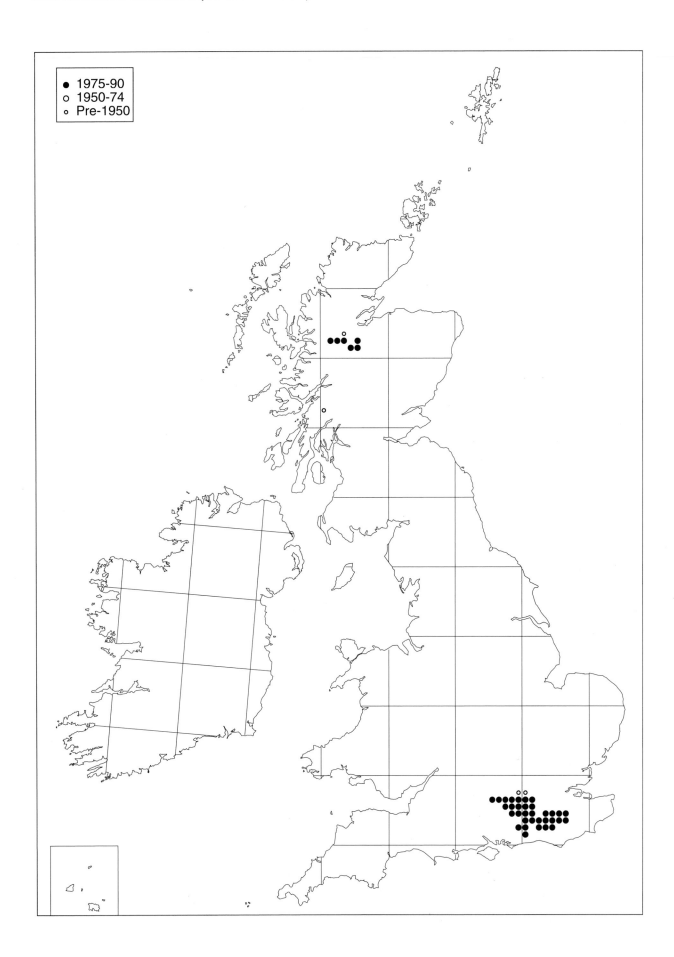

Description   *S. arctica* is a dark medium-size dragonfly with a metallic sheen to its body, and a blacker appearance than both *S. metallica* and *Cordulia aenea* which it resembles. The thorax is dark metallic green with bronze reflections and has a covering of fine hairs, though these are not as dense as in *C. aenea*. The abdomen, pinched at the waist, is black with a bronze sheen. The eyes are green. There are yellowish markings laterally and ventrally on abdominal segments 2 and 3, and two large spots, especially pronounced in the female, on segment 3 dorsally, much larger than those on female *S. metallica*, and also a smaller pair of dots dorsally on segment 2. *S. arctica* can be most readily distinguished from *S. metallica* and *C. aenea* by the pattern of yellow facial markings and the shape of the anal appendages. The vulvar scale of females is much shorter and blunter than that of *S. metallica*.

Habitat   *S. arctica* breeds in small shallow bog pools in moorland areas at altitudes ranging from near sea level to 400 m, and often in close proximity to trees, although not always so. The pools which *S. arctica* favours usually have a water depth of less than 7 cm over deep peat-detritus substrate, and contain much *Sphagnum* moss, sundews, and emergent plants such as white beak-sedge, common cottongrass and bog-myrtle. Breeding requirements are discussed by Butler (1983) and, in Switzerland, by Wildermuth (1986).

Breeding biology   Males patrol areas of peat bog with a characteristic rapid flight, usually 1–3 m high, interspersed with periods of hovering. Copulation takes place in scrub or amongst heather. The female oviposits by dipping the tip of her abdomen into shallow water or exposed wet peat whilst in flight. The larvae live in the peaty detritus soup, and probably take two or more years to develop. Emergence occurs on low vegetation, usually 10–15 cm above the water surface.

Flight periods   *S. arctica* is on the wing from early June to early August. In Scotland, it may be found with *Leucorrhinia dubia, Aeshna caerulea, A. juncea,* and other moorland dragonflies and damselflies. In Ireland, the known breeding area is in close proximity to that of *C. aenea,* and the two species may be seen hawking together or sheltering in heather, away from water.

Status and distribution   In Britain, *S. arctica* is confined to the western and central Highlands of Scotland, where it was first recorded in July 1844 at the Black Forest of Rannoch, Perthshire, by a Mr Weaver (Sélys-Longchamps 1846). It appears to have declined in some areas, possibly as a result of afforestation and the drainage which that entails. In Ireland, it has so far only been recorded near Killarney, Co Kerry, where it was first discovered in 1862, a specimen being given by a Mr Birchall to R McLachlan, and where it still breeds at a few sites today. These are situated within the Killarney National Park, and so receive some protection.

European and world distribution   On the continent, *S. arctica* is found from the Ardennes in Belgium to Scandinavia and east to Siberia and Japan. In the south of its European range, it is restricted to mountain areas such as the Pyrenees, Massif Central, and the Alps.

Somatochlora arctica (Zetterstedt)   **Northern emerald**

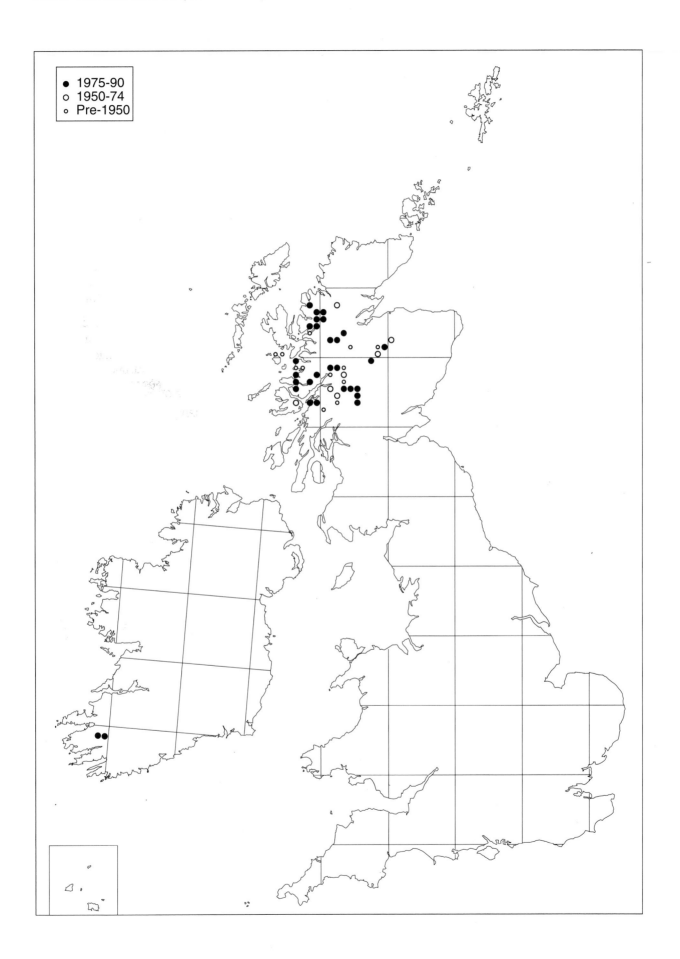

- 1975-90
- 1950-74
- Pre-1950

Oxygastra curtisii (Dale)   Orange-spotted emerald

Description
This corduliid dragonfly is believed to be extinct in Britain. It can be distinguished from the three resident corduliids, namely *Somatochlora metallica*, *S. arctica* and *Cordulia aenea*, by the slender abdomen, on the mid-dorsal surface of which is a series of elongated yellow markings usually on all segments except 8 and 9. Some individuals, usually females, have much reduced markings with only a few spots on the anterior segments (Chelmick 1983). The general body coloration is metallic green with bronze reflections. In common with other corduliids, *O. curtisii* can appear quite dark in flight, the yellow spots being inconspicuous. Other distinguishing features are the pattern of yellow facial markings and the shape of the anal appendages. There is a small amber area at the base of each wing which, in immature individuals, may suffuse the entire wing with a pale tint. The eyes are greenish.

Habitat
On the continent, *O. curtisii* breeds on moderate- to slow-flowing tree-lined rivers and canals with little or no emergent vegetation, and with a silt or mud bottom in which the larvae live. The only known breeding sites in Britain were such riverine habitat.

Breeding biology
Observations on the ecology and distribution of *O. curtisii* have been made by Fraser (1940), Chelmick (1983) and Moore (1991a). The males are aggressive and fly low over the water chasing off other males and searching for females. Territories appear to be ill-defined, though, on the shadier parts of rivers, males may vigorously defend small sunlit areas against other males. Oviposition takes place close to the river bank amongst the tangle of tree roots where the female dips the tip of her abdomen into the water so releasing her eggs. The larvae live in the bottom silt and mud, and probably take two or more years to develop. Emergence occurs on exposed bankside tree roots, and on the trunks and branches of overhanging trees at heights of up to 3 m (Chelmick 1983).

Flight periods
In Britain, the recorded flying times were from mid-June to the end of July. Whilst hawking for insects, *O. curtisii* will often circle quite high up in a clearing or woodland glade, disappearing as soon as the sun goes in. Other species which occurred on the same river as *O. curtisii* were *Platycnemis pennipes*, *Calopteryx splendens*, *Libellula fulva* and *Gomphus vulgatissimus*.

Status and distribution
O. curtisii has the distinction of having been first discovered and described in Britain. It was found at Parley Heath near Hurn in Hampshire (now Dorset) on 29 June 1820 by J C Dale. It continued to be recorded intermittently on the River Stour and the Moors River between Pokesdown and Parley Heath for many years. By the 1950s, however, suitable habitat on the West Moors River, its sole location, had been much reduced by excessive shading of the river bank by trees (Moore 1991a). In July 1957, Moore estimated that suitable habitat along the 1.2 km of river that he visited (which represented about a third of the total available habitat) was sufficient for only about six male territories. Such changes must have contributed to its decline, and over-collecting cannot have helped either, but the cause of extinction is believed to be the accidental pollution caused by a large sewage works constructed upstream to serve a new housing estate. The last record of *O. curtisii* in Britain was 19 July 1963 when a male was captured by B P Moore at Hurn (specimen in the Natural History Museum, London). In July 1946, one female and two males were picked up from vegetation in a marshy area by the River Tamar, north of Gunnislake Bridge, Devon, by O G Watkins (pers. comm.), and one was despatched to Cynthia Longfield at the Natural History Museum, London. Despite searches at the time, and in the 1970s by R Merritt, N W Moore and H P K Robinson, no further individuals could be located. Nevertheless, it could have been overlooked. There is an unauthenticated record of *O. curtisii* from Braunton Burrows in north Devon, *c* 1830 (Fraser 1940).

European and world distribution
Oxygastra is one of the few genera that is virtually confined to western Europe. It is found most commonly in Portugal, Spain and southern France, with small outlying populations in neighbouring countries.

Oxygastra curtisii (Dale)   **Orange-spotted emerald**

- ● 1975-90
- ○ 1950-74
- ○ Pre-1950

Libellula quadrimaculata Linnaeus   **Four-spotted chaser**

Description

This libellulid is predominantly brown in both sexes, but with striking wing coloration when observed closely. It takes its name from the dark mark at the node of each wing. There is also a black patch at the base of the hindwings, crossed by yellow veins, and a deep saffron suffusion on the basal area of each wing which extends towards the node. The thorax is brownish and covered in dense pale hairs. The abdomen, which tapers posteriorly, is brownish except for the posterior third, comprising segments 7–10 and part of 6, which is black dorsally. Also, there are narrow yellow markings laterally on segments 4–8, sometimes also 9. A variety known as f. *praenubila* Newman occurs not uncommonly. It is characterised by a dark patch towards the end of each wing near the pterostigma.

Habitat

L. quadrimaculata breeds in a wide range of mainly still water habitats: from the dykes of coastal levels to bog pools and lochans in mountain areas. It is also found in ponds, lakes and canals.

Breeding biology

The males are very territorial. They make their sallies from sticks and tall emergent plants on which they perch, and also patrol the water's edge. Their highest steady density is about 15 males per 100 m of water margin but, when exceptional numbers are present in the vicinity of a pond, the territorial system breaks down for a period. Warren (1964) observed territorial behaviour in *L. quadrimaculata* at a bog pool that was occupied also by *Leucorrhinia dubia*. He noticed that the two species hunted over the same area but at different levels. Provided the *L. dubia* remained low, it would not be molested, but if it flew up to the level at which the *L. quadrimaculata* was perched, about 70 cm from the ground, it would be attacked, and the *L. dubia* individual would be chased away over the trees, only to return a few minutes later. Copulation takes place in flight, and lasts only 5–20 seconds. The female hovers, often where there is vegetation not far below the water surface, and drops her eggs into the water by flicking her abdomen downwards. The eggs sink and adhere to the vegetation. The male usually keeps guard nearby and wards off intruders. However, females also oviposit alone. The larvae live amongst the bottom debris, and probably take two years to develop. Emergence often occurs on marginal rushes such as soft rush.

Flight periods

L. quadrimaculata is on the wing from late May to early August, and can be seen with the many other species that favour static water sites.

Status and distribution

It is widespread throughout Britain and Ireland, including the Orkneys and the Outer Hebrides, but is absent from many apparently suitable sites in the Pennines and north-east England.

European and world distribution

L. quadrimaculata is an holarctic species that occurs throughout most of Europe, though local in the extreme north and south. Its range extends east to Japan, and to North America. On the continent, vast migrations are known to occur, which tend to have a cycle of ten years or so. Mass migrations rarely take place in Britain or Ireland, although they have been recorded from Essex and Kent in the past. Immigration in small numbers may occur more frequently, however.

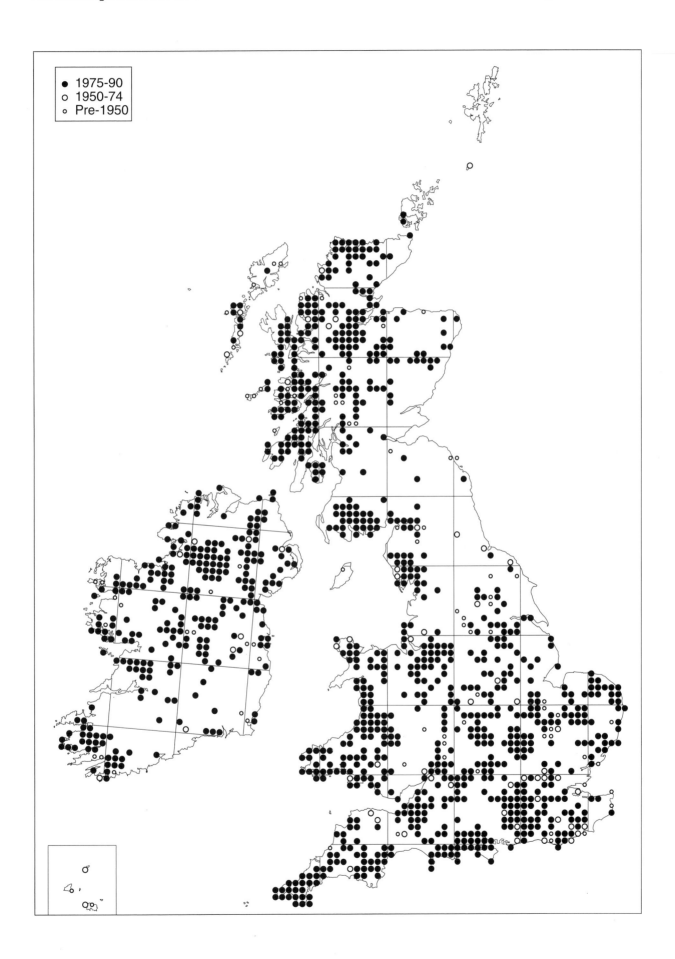

●	1975-90
○	1950-74
○	Pre-1950

Libellula fulva Müller
Scarce chaser

Description
L. fulva is one of the four libellulids in which mature males possess a pale blue pruinescence on the abdomen. In *L. fulva* this extends over abdominal segments 3–7, leaving the anterior two and posterior three segments black. This black tip to the abdomen is noticeable in flight and helps distinguish it from mature male *Orthetrum coerulescens* and from *L. depressa* (segment 10 in *L. depressa* is dark but so small as to be scarcely noticeable in flight, and its abdomen is much broader than that of *L. fulva*). At the base of the wings is a dark black-brown patch, much reduced in the forewings, which distinguishes *L. fulva* from *O. coerulescens* and *O. cancellatum*, in which the wings are clear. The thorax is dark brown and hairy, and the eyes are blue-grey. Females and immature males lack the blue pruinescence. They have a rich orange-amber-coloured abdomen with black triangular marks mid-dorsally on segments 4–10. The wings possess a black basal patch and bright orange veins which extend towards and sometimes beyond the nodes, but lack the black nodal marks of *L. quadrimaculata*. However, female *L. fulva* do possess a dark patch at the apex of each wing, sometimes much reduced; this is sometimes apparent in males. It should not be confused with *L. quadrimaculata* f. *praenubila*. The thorax is amber-brown and the eyes are grey-brown.

Habitat
L. fulva breeds on unpolluted rivers and dykes with slight to moderate flow, and occasionally in static water habitats such as mature gravel pits which are at least 20 years old (Milne 1984). It prefers stretches of riverbank which contain patches of tall emergent vegetation such as common club-rush, reed sweet-grass and branched bur-reed, as well as small areas of yellow water-lily.

Breeding biology
The male is territorial. Its highest steady density is about 9 per 100 m of water's edge when males are active, but in late evening several may perch in close proximity. Copulation occurs amongst riverside vegetation, and can take over 15 minutes. The female oviposits whilst hovering, and strikes the water every few seconds with the tip of her abdomen so releasing the eggs, often staying over the same spot for several minutes. The male usually hovers nearby to ward off intruding males. The larvae, which probably take two years to develop, live in the bottom silt and mud. Emergence is synchronous.

Flight periods
L. fulva has a short flying season from the end of May to mid-July. It may be seen with *Platycnemis pennipes*, *Calopteryx splendens* and *Gomphus vulgatissimus* on rivers, and with *Coenagrion pulchellum* and *Brachytron pratense* on grazing marsh dykes.

Status and distribution
L. fulva is a scarce dragonfly in Britain. It breeds on a few scattered river systems and nearby still-water sites. It occurs on the River Avon in Wiltshire and in Somerset; the Rivers Stour, Frome, Moors River, and Avon in Dorset (and Hampshire border in the latter river); the River Arun in Sussex; the North Stream and associated ditches near Sandwich, Kent; the Rivers Nene and Ouse and nearby gravel pits and fen dykes in Cambridgeshire; and grazing marsh dykes associated with the River Waveney in Suffolk and the River Yare in Norfolk. *L. fulva* bred for many years at Shirley Pool near Askern in Yorkshire, but has not been seen there since 1911. There are old records from Deptford and Bermondsey marshes, 'east of London', from the early 19th century. *L. fulva* has been recorded from Ireland only once. A male taken at Dingle, Co Kerry, in 1849 by 'R W' (probably Richard Weaver) is in the Dale Collection in Oxford (Lucas 1908). *L. fulva* is vulnerable to pollution of the rivers and drainage channel systems in which it breeds. It occurs on several NNRs and RSPB reserves.

European and world distribution
On the continent, *L. fulva* is widely but locally distributed from the south of France to north Germany, and east through central Europe to Russia. It is rare in Spain and has been reported only from the extreme south of Scandinavia.

Libellula fulva **Müller**   **Scarce chaser**

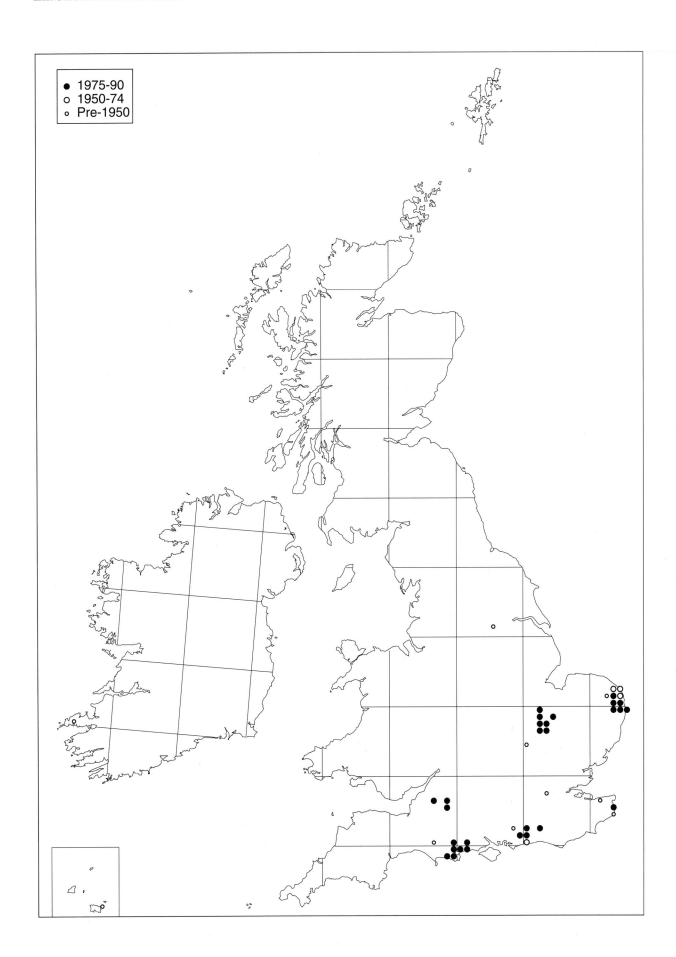

95

Libellula depressa Linnaeus   **Broad-bodied chaser**

Description

The very broad, flattened and pale blue abdomen of mature male *L. depressa*, and the large black-brown patch at the base of each wing distinguish this species from the three other male libellulids that possess a blue abdomen. In immature males and in females, the abdomen is yellowish brown with yellow markings laterally which are most prominent on segments 4–7. In males, a blue pruinescence develops with age and covers the abdomen, except for segments 1, 2 and 10 which remain dark, and the lateral yellow markings which may be slightly reduced in size. The pattern of markings on the wings is the same in both sexes although, in the female, the dark basal patches are more heavily marked with yellow veins than in males. These wing markings and the very broad short abdomen distinguish females from those of other libellulids. The thorax is dark brown in both sexes, with two pale whitish stripes dorsally. The eyes are dark brown.

Habitat

L. depressa breeds in well-vegetated ponds, lakes, canals and ditches. However, it is also one of the first dragonflies to colonise a newly created water body and will breed in small garden ponds, and in farm ponds that are mildly polluted. In south-west Britain, it occasionally breeds in peaty bog pools.

Breeding biology

The male is territorial and very aggressive. The population density of males rarely exceeds 8 per 100 m of water's edge. Therefore, small ponds will seldom if ever hold more than one male. As with other large libellulids, males perch on stems of tall emergent plants or on exposed sticks and make frequent flights to chase off intruding males, returning to the same perch. Copulation occurs in flight and only takes a few seconds. During oviposition, the female flies very low in and out of the vegetation at the water margin and thrusts her eggs into the water by flicking her abdomen downwards. Males sometimes guard females during this process, but females frequently oviposit alone and when no male is present at a pond. The eggs hatch after two to three weeks and the larvae, which live amongst the plant debris or silt at the bottom of the pond, probably take two or three years to develop in most circumstances, but can complete their life cycle in one year (Holmes & Randolph 1994). Emergence is usually synchronous, and takes place on marginal and emergent vegetation.

Flight periods

L. depressa is on the wing from mid-May to early August. On larger ponds and lakes it may be seen with species such as *Anax imperator*, *Aeshna grandis*, *Orthetrum cancellatum* and the common damselflies.

Status and distribution

L. depressa is found widely in southern Britain, thinning out in the north midlands. It has conspicuously declined in eastern England from the Fens to Yorkshire, having been lost from many former sites owing to agricultural pressures, especially the loss of farm ponds. However, there are some signs of a recovery in recent years. There is a single record from Ireland. Miss Ball, a celebrated entomologist, recorded it from Glendine, Co Waterford, in July 1834. It is unlikely that a mistake could have been made in the identification of this distinctive species as the specimen was identified by Sélys-Longchamps (1846). An Irish specimen, possibly that of Miss Ball, is in Trinity College Museum, Dublin (King & Halbert 1910).

European and world distribution

L. depressa occurs throughout Europe as far north as southern Scandinavia, and east to the Middle East and western Asia. It is absent from North Africa.

Libellula depressa Linnaeus

Broad-bodied chaser

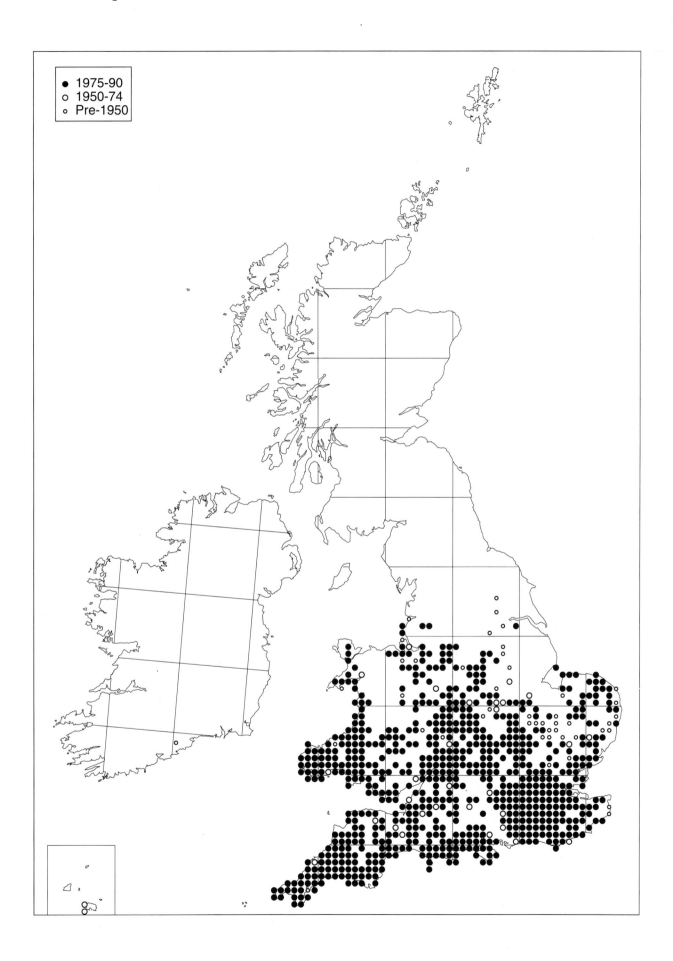

- ● 1975-90
- ○ 1950-74
- ○ Pre-1950

Orthetrum cancellatum (Linnaeus)   **Black-tailed skimmer**

Description Mature male *O. cancellatum* can be readily distinguished from the other large libellulids that have a blue abdomen by the lack of dark basal wing patches, which separates it from *Libellula fulva* and *L. depressa* (which also has a much broader abdomen), and by the dark posterior end of its abdomen which gives the species its vernacular name and separates it from *O. coerulescens*, in which the abdomen is all blue. In immature males and in females, the abdomen is yellowish brown with a pair of slightly zigzag black lines along either side of the dorsal surface, thus distinguishing them from other libellulid species. As males mature, they develop a blue pruinescence which covers the abdomen, except for segments 1–2 and 7–10. Faint yellowish lateral spots are visible on segments 3–6. Sometimes very old females develop faint pruinescence. The thorax and eyes are brown in both sexes.

Habitat *O. cancellatum* breeds in ponds, lakes, slow-moving rivers and in dykes which can be quite brackish. It is often one of the first species to colonise newly created gravel pits, sand pits and chalk quarries after they have become flooded. Its favoured sites often have an open aspect with areas of bare ground on which it frequently settles with downswept wings, sunning itself. In Ireland it breeds especially on marl lakes in limestone areas, those on The Burren often lacking tree cover and having a bare limestone shore.

Breeding biology Males are territorial, and defend their territories by making sorties from perches on robust vegetation or from the ground, and by patrolling the water margin. The highest steady density is about 10 males per 100 m of shoreline. Copulation may take a few seconds in flight, or 10–15 minutes when settled, but the time taken depends on the amount of sperm from previous matings which the male has to remove before inserting his own (Siva-Jothy 1987). During oviposition the female flies low along the water margin dipping the tip of her abdomen into the water every few seconds, so releasing the eggs. The male is often in attendance nearby. The eggs hatch after 5–6 weeks and the larvae, which live partially concealed in bottom silt, probably take two years to develop. At a recently excavated heathland lagoon in Dorset, B P Pickess recorded emergence of *O. cancellatum* most commonly on vegetation 1–4 m away from the water margin, occasionally over 10 m, and at a maximum distance of 17 m (Pickess 1987).

Flight periods *O. cancellatum* is on the wing from late May to early/mid-August. It can be seen with *Coenagrion pulchellum* and *Brachytron pratense* on coastal dykes (and on marl lakes in Ireland), and with a host of species on lakes and gravel pits in southern England, including *Anax imperator* and *Aeshna mixta*.

Status and distribution *O. cancellatum* has increased considerably in southern England during this century. Lucas (1900) refers to the small number of records that had come to his notice. It was first recorded in Essex in 1934 (Benton 1988), in Bedfordshire in 1950 (Dawson 1988), whilst in Gloucestershire Holland (1983) records its increase since the 1950s. It was first recorded in Lincolnshire in 1985, in Derbyshire in 1986, and in south Yorkshire in 1992. The most northerly British record to date is from Messingham sand pits in north Lincolnshire. This species has benefited greatly from the extraction industries, and has often spread to new areas by first colonising newly flooded gravel pits and sand pits with shallow margins, and then other water bodies. In Ireland, King and Halbert (1910) doubted that *O. cancellatum* had ever occurred and referred to contradictory remarks by Sélys-Longchamps and Hagen (1850). Longfield (1937) stated that 'it has been reported recently in Ireland in counties Mayo, Galway and Laois, where it may be an occasional migrant'. Today, it breeds at a number of natural sites, principally marl lakes in central counties. It was discovered in 1984 at a shallow lake within an area of machair-type vegetation in Co Donegal, and was recorded from Co Kerry in 1992.

European and world distribution *O. cancellatum* is widespread in Europe from Spain to southern Scandinavia, and east to Kashmir and Mongolia. It occurs in North Africa.

Orthetrum cancellatum (Linnaeus)   **Black-tailed skimmer**

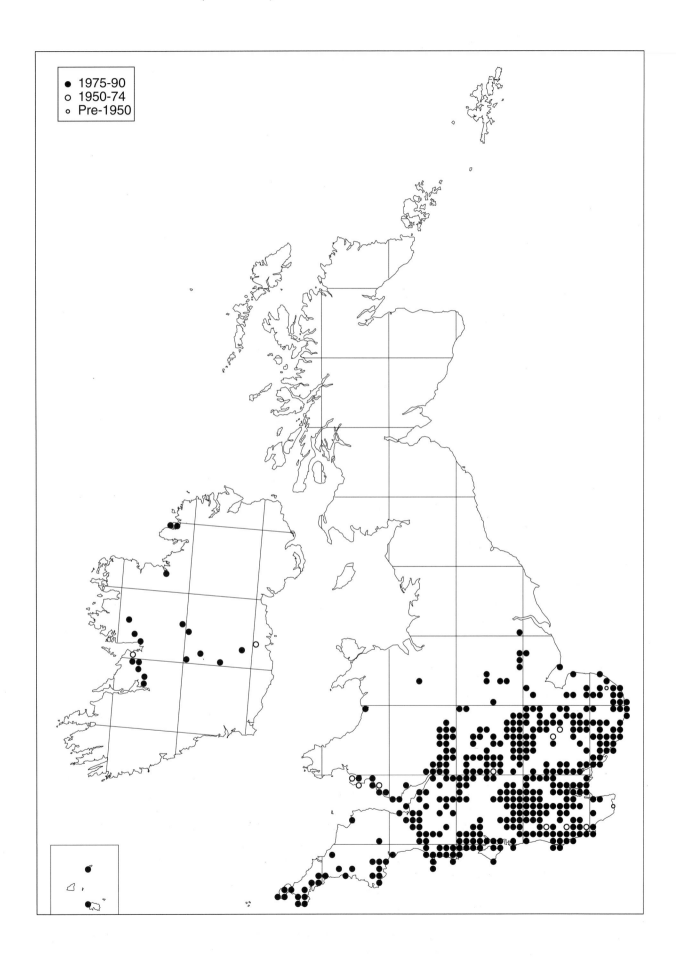

- ● 1975-90
- ○ 1950-74
- ○ Pre-1950

Orthetrum coerulescens (Fabricius)   **Keeled skimmer**

Description

O. coerulescens is the smallest of the four libellulids in which mature males possess a blue pruinescence on the abdomen. The lack of a dark tip to the abdomen distinguishes *O. coerulescens* from *O. cancellatum* and *Libellula fulva*. The lack of dark basal patches on the clear wings separates *O. coerulescens* from male and female *L. fulva* and *L. depressa* (this latter species also having a very much broader abdomen). The pterostigma is pale yellow-brown in both sexes, unlike the other large libellulids in which they are dark brown. In immature males and in females, the abdomen is yellowish brown with a thin longitudinal line running mid-dorsally along it, and has tiny transverse bars from segments 3–7. This line, and the pair of pale creamy stripes on the dorsal surface of the dark brown thorax distinguish *O. coerulescens* from females of *Sympetrum striolatum* which are similar in size and coloration. As males mature, a blue pruinescence develops over the entire abdomen. As with other blue libellulids, this may be rubbed off in places by the female during copulation, leaving dark marks dorsally. The base of the wings of females is suffused with saffron coloration which may extend faintly to the whole wing.

Habitat

O. coerulescens breeds in flushes, the boggy margins of runnels and streams, and bog pools in valley mires in areas of heath and moorland. They are characterised by the presence of plants such as *Sphagnum* moss, bog pondweed, bog asphodel, marsh St John's-wort and common cottongrass.

Breeding biology

O. coerulescens is territorial. Where territories lie along rivulets, highest steady density is 9 males per 100 m of watercourse. Males patrol their territories by flying low over the bog surface, often in an erratic manner. They also spend a lot of time perched on low vegetation, rocks or on the ground. Males and females will sometimes fly in tandem prior to copulation, the duration of which varies greatly and may take as long as 25 minutes. Usually the female rests for some time before ovipositing (Miller & Miller 1989), which she performs by dipping the tip of her abdomen in the water whilst in flight, and with the male in close attendance guarding her from other males. Larvae live in peaty detritus, or muddy silt of runnels, and probably take two years to develop.

Flight periods

O. coerulescens is on the wing from early June to early September. It can be seen with other species, depending on their geographical range, such as *Aeshna juncea*, *Cordulegaster boltonii*, *Coenagrion mercuriale*, *Pyrrhosoma nymphula* and *Ceriagrion tenellum*.

Status and distribution

O. coerulescens is restricted by its habitat requirements to lowland heathland in southern Britain and the moorlands of western districts from Cornwall to a few isolated locations in west Scotland, including several islands of the Inner Hebrides. In eastern England, where it is found very rarely, its few remaining sites are very small but have survived for many years (Moore 1986). It has become extinct at several sites as a result of land reclamation and lowering of the water table. The only site for *O. coerulescens* in eastern Scotland was at Methven Moss, near Perth, where it was recorded in 1908 with *Leucorrhinia dubia*. In Ireland, *O. coerulescens* is restricted mainly to peat bogs and seepages in the Mourne Mountains, the Wicklow Mountains, and the western moorlands of Co Kerry, Co Mayo and Connemara, plus a few sites elsewhere. There are few records from the lowland peatlands of the midlands.

European and world distribution

O. coerulescens is widespread in western and central Europe, including the Iberian peninsula, thinning out towards the north in Germany and southern Scandinavia and east towards Russia.

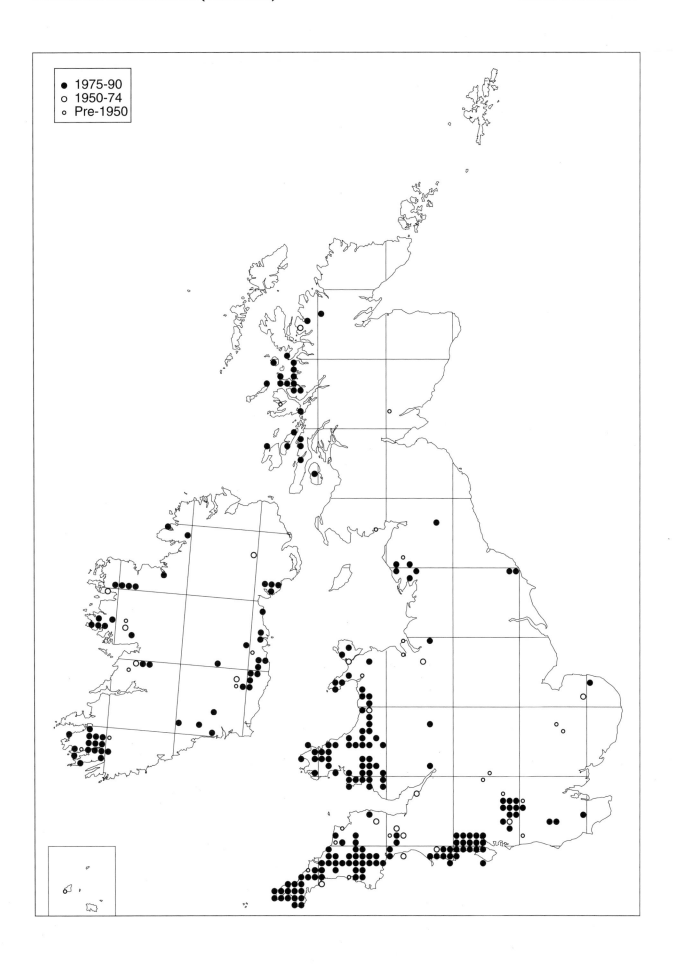

●	1975-90
○	1950-74
○	Pre-1950

Sympetrum striolatum (Charpentier)   Common darter
Sympetrum nigrescens Lucas   Highland darter

Description

Males of these small libellulids possess a predominantly reddish abdomen with black markings, and a brown thorax having areas of yellow and black laterally. Separation of *S. nigrescens* from *S. striolatum* has generally been based on the greater degree of black marking on the body, but this is not a reliable identification character. The distribution map for *S. striolatum* and *S. nigrescens* has been combined because of the uncertainty about the identification features used by recorders in making their original determinations. *S. nigrescens* was first described by Lucas (1912) as a new species, based mainly on coloration, though he appears later to have regarded it merely as a race of *S. striolatum*. Gardner (1955), in redescribing *S. nigrescens* as a separate species, stated that colour characters were variable where these species' ranges overlapped, and that only an examination of the genitalia of adults, and certain larval features, could separate them reliably. Almost none of the records held at BRC are based on such examinations. Doubts have since been expressed about the reliability of Gardner's findings, and hence the validity of the specific rank of *S. nigrescens* (Geijskes & van Tol 1983; Hämäläinen 1985; Merritt & Vick 1983). More detailed studies are required to resolve the question.

Males of *S. striolatum*/*S. nigrescens* can be separated from male *S. sanguineum* by the generally paler red, and less uniform, coloration of the abdomen, which is bright blood-red in *S. sanguineum*. Also, they lack the noticeably constricted 'waist' between abdominal segments 3–5 of *S. sanguineum* which gives that species a clubbed appearance. Females and immature males of *S. striolatum*/*S. nigrescens* are much browner than mature males. They can be separated from their *S. danae* counterparts by their lack of a large black triangular marking on the dorsal surface of the thorax. Non-melanic individuals can be readily distinguished from female and immature male *S. sanguineum* by the yellow longitudinal line on the outer surface of the legs, these being black in *S. sanguineum*. There are also differences in the shape of the accessary genitalia of males and the vulvar scale of females.

Habitat

S. striolatum/*S. nigrescens* occurs in a wide range of habitats including ditches, ponds, lakes, peaty bog pools, and, occasionally, slow-flowing streams and rivers.

Breeding biology

The territory of *S. striolatum* is not strongly localised, but consists of the area where it happens to be perched, usually determined by temperature requirements (Moore 1991d). The highest steady density is about 13 males per 100 m of water's edge. Copulation takes 10–15 minutes. Oviposition often occurs in tandem, with the downward movements of the male's abdomen making the female's abdomen touch the water and hence release the eggs (Moore 1952). Eggs that are laid in summer hatch within about six weeks, but those laid in autumn pass the winter in diapause and hatch the following spring. Larval development is generally completed in one year.

Flight periods

The flying period of *S. striolatum*/*S. nigrescens* is from the end of June to October, and occasionally November. Very occasionally, mass migrations of *S. striolatum* occur. Cynthia Longfield (1948) witnessed a vast migration during September 1947 along the south coast of Ireland involving probably over a million insects and lasting several weeks. They flew in from the sea in narrow columns and spread inland. Small-scale immigration to Britain and/or Ireland probably occurs most years.

Status and distribution

S. striolatum/nigrescens is the most common anisopteran in southern and central England, and most of Wales and Ireland. It is scarce in parts of northern England, and absent from most of southern and eastern Scotland. It would appear not to favour the higher upland areas. Melanic forms have been reported mostly from Scotland and Ireland, but also from north Wales, south-west England and Lincolnshire.

European and world distribution

It was from Scotland that Gardner obtained most of the few specimens that led him to redescribe *S. nigrescens* (Gardner 1955). He also reported it from Ireland and southern Norway. A record from southern Finland in 1980, based on a single larva,

Sympetrum striolatum (Charpentier)
Sympetrum nigrescens Lucas

Common darter
Highland darter

- ● 1975-90
- ○ 1950-74
- ○ Pre-1950

was later reidentified as *S. vulgatum* (Hämäläinen 1985). *S. striolatum* is widespread throughout most of Europe except northern Scandinavia and northern Russia, and is found east to Japan. It occurs in North Africa.

Sympetrum sanguineum (Müller)   **Ruddy darter**

Description   *S. sanguineum* is one of the small libellulids in which the abdomen of males is predominantly red. This coloration is blood-red, and is more uniform and brighter than male *S. striolatum*. There are two prominent black marks mid-dorsally on abdominal segments 8 and 9 and they may cause confusion with *S. striolatum* which possesses similar though less prominent markings. However, unlike *S. striolatum*, the abdomen is noticeably constricted at segments 3–5, giving it a clubbed appearance (similar to the black-bodied *S. danae*), and the pterostigmata of mature individuals are red, not brown. In immature males, and in females, the abdomen is predominantly yellow-brown with black markings. The dorsal surface of the thorax lacks the large black triangular mark that is characteristic of *S. danae*. The sides of the thorax are extensively marked with yellow and black, much brighter than in mature males. The hind wings of both sexes have a small but distinct saffron suffusion at their base. The legs are black.

Habitat   *S. sanguineum* breeds in the marshy margins of ponds, lakes (including old clay pits and gravel pits), canals and ditches, where there is an abundance of tall emergent plants such as horsetails, reed sweet-grass and bulrush. In coastal ditches, sea club-rush is often prevalent. It can breed in quite brackish conditions.

Breeding biology   It is uncertain whether *S. sanguineum* is territorial. Its highest steady density is about 16 males per 100 m of water's edge. Males maintain a small exclusion zone around themselves and chase off intruding males (Convey 1989). They have a rather 'skippy' flight, quite unlike *S. striolatum*. Oviposition takes place in tandem or alone. When in tandem, the pair adopt an undulating movement in flight during which the female's abdomen is swung downwards and the eggs released, sometimes singly, low down amongst shaded vegetation, less commonly over open water. *S. sanguineum* will oviposit in habitats which have temporarily dried up. The species can have both diapause and non-diapause eggs. The weed-dwelling larvae usually complete development in one year.

Flight periods   *S. sanguineum* is on the wing from late June to mid-September. It may be seen with other species that favour marshy fens and ditches, notably *Coenagrion pulchellum*, *Lestes sponsa* and *Libellula quadrimaculata*. It can occur with *S. striolatum*, a species seen more commonly over open water than *S. sanguineum*, which prefers the vegetated margins. Populations are probably augmented in most years by immigrants from the continent.

Status and distribution   In Britain, *S. sanguineum* has a south-easterly distribution. It is rare in the south-west and Wales, and is scarce in the north midlands, though there has been an increase in records recently. It breeds as far north as Barnsley, Yorkshire. Reports of a population crash in the 1970s were erroneous, and may have resulted from a misreading of an earlier BRC distribution map, which showed many more pre-1960 than post-1960 records. Many of these earlier records were the result of periodic large influxes of immigrants in the 1930s and 1940s, and did not necessarily represent breeding populations. Longfield (1949b) stated that *S. sanguineum* was probably increasing as a breeding species in Britain. This increase appears to have accelerated in the past decade or so, and has been noted in Essex (Benton 1988), Bedfordshire (Dawson 1988) and Gloucestershire (Holland 1983). However, *S. sanguineum* has disappeared from a number of localities, being very susceptible to permanent changes in water level due to improved drainage, and to natural seral changes in habitat. In Ireland, *S. sanguineum* has increased during this century. King and Halbert (1910) did not record it as Irish. Longfield (Corbet *et al.* 1960) referred to having given to Lucas one of the first pairs of *S. sanguineum* to be found in Ireland, taken in 1928. It is now fairly widely distributed; it is most commonly found in the fens and marl lakes of the midlands, and occurs frequently on turloughs.

European and world distribution   *S. sanguineum* occurs throughout most of Europe, except northern Scandinavia and some Mediterranean islands, and east to western Siberia. It is also found in North Africa.

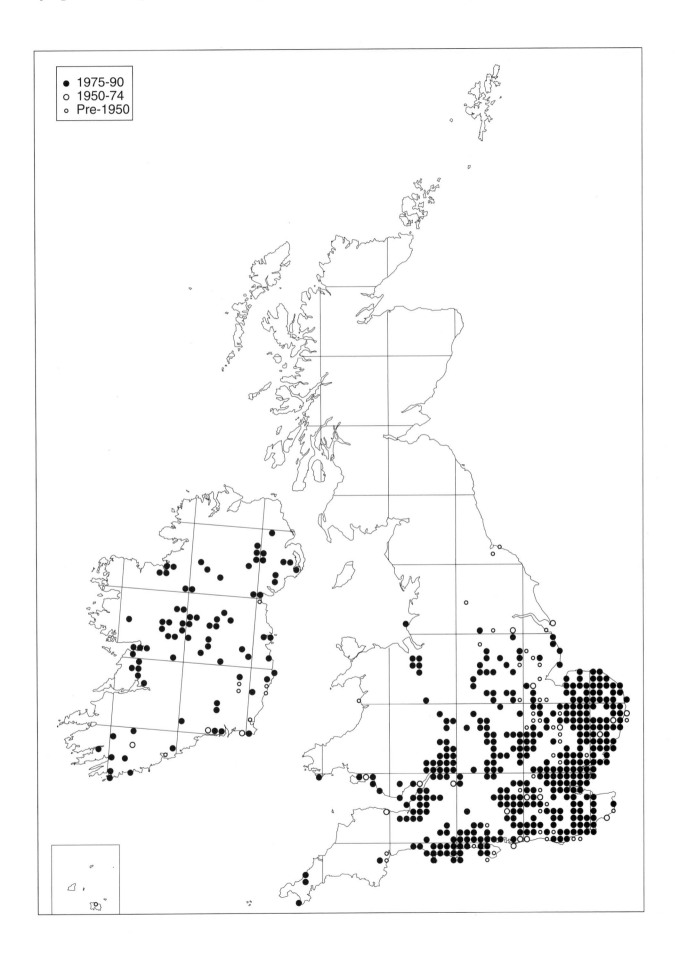

Description
S. danae is the smallest anisopteran found in Britain and Ireland, and the only species in which the abdomen of mature males is entirely black. The thorax is also black, with yellow markings laterally which become reduced in older specimens. The abdomen of males is constricted between segments 3–5 giving it a clubbed appearance similar to *S. sanguineum*, which has a blood-red abdomen. In immature males and females, the abdomen is amber-coloured dorsally, and has heavy black markings laterally which partially extend over the dorsal surface of segments 1, 8 and 9. The thorax is amber-coloured dorsally also, and has a large black triangular mark which readily separates *S. danae* from females of *S. sanguineum* and *S. striolatum/S. nigrescens*. The thorax has extensive black and yellow markings laterally. The wings of female *S. danae* have a small saffron suffusion at their base. As females mature, the amber coloration of the abdomen and thorax becomes khaki-brown. As males mature, the amber coloration becomes reduced as black extends over the whole body. The pterostigmata are black in both sexes.

Habitat
S. danae breeds in boggy pools, old peat cuttings, and the margins of peaty ponds and lakes where there is an abundance of emergent rushes and sedges. As a result, it is found mainly on heaths and moors, and occasionally also in acid fenland. In some years, *S. danae* may be encountered at atypical sites, far from known breeding areas; an indication of good powers of dispersal.

Breeding biology
S. danae is not strongly territorial. The population density rarely exceeds 17 males per 100 m of water's edge. The males hover and dart about over the emergent vegetation looking for females, and frequently settle on plant stems, rocks or on the ground. They have a dainty, skippy flight reminiscent of *S. sanguineum* and quite different from *S. striolatum/S. nigrescens*. During copulation, which takes several minutes, the male removes sperm from previous matings before inserting his own (Michiels & Dhondt 1988). Eggs are laid by females in tandem or on their own, and are flicked on to the surface of the water, peaty mud or exposed mats of vegetation such as *Sphagnum* moss, whilst in flight. The eggs overwinter in a state of diapause, and the larvae complete their development in one year (Harvey 1985). The larvae can survive the temporary drying out of their habitat (Valtonen 1986).

Flight periods
S. danae is on the wing from mid-July to October. Occasionally individuals may be seen in November. They occur with *Lestes sponsa*, *Aeshna juncea* and other species which favour similar habitat.

Status and distribution
S. danae is most commonly found in moorland and heathland areas, and is therefore widespread in western and northern districts of Britain, and in the lowland heaths of the south. It can sometimes be seen in very large numbers. It is absent from much of eastern England, Kent and east Sussex, where it has been lost from a number of former sites owing to agricultural improvements, drainage, and to the reclamation of heathland (Moore 1986). In Ireland it appears to be relatively scarce in southern and south-western districts, despite suitable habitat being present. The absence of *S. danae* from several former sites in the midlands is probably the result of habitat loss through drainage operations associated with large-scale peat extraction.

European and world distribution
S. danae is a circumboreal holarctic species. It occurs throughout much of northern Europe and, as different subspecies, across Asia to Japan. It is not found north of the Eurasian Arctic Circle. It occurs in North America. In the southern part of its European range, it is restricted to mountain areas such as the Pyrenees and the Alps.

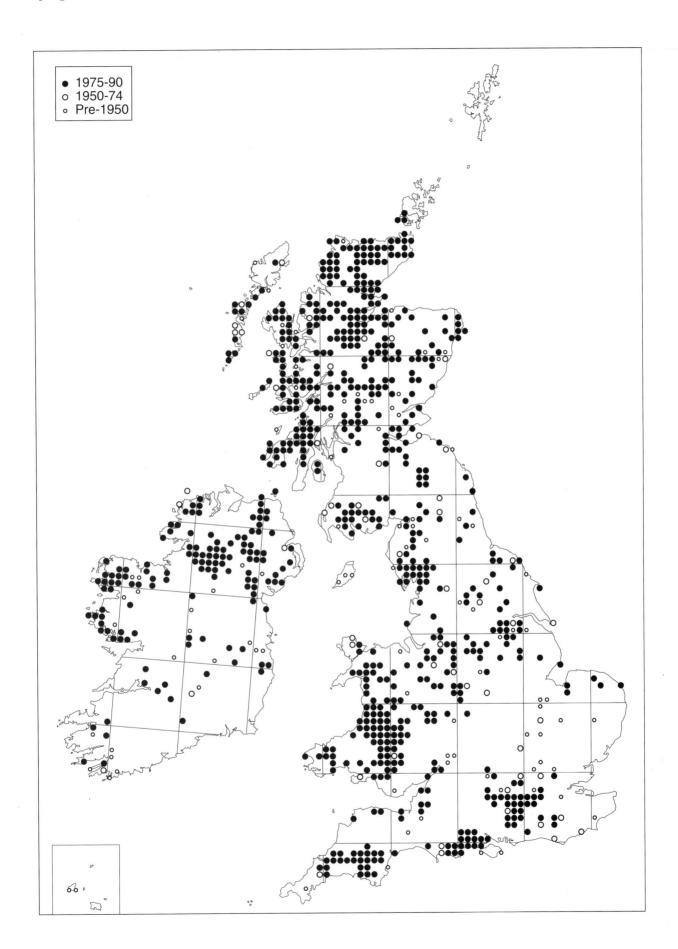

Leucorrhinia dubia (Vander Linden)   **White-faced dragonfly**

Description   *L. dubia* is a small dark libellulid which derives its name from its pale creamy white frons, clearly visible from the front in flight at close quarters. *Sympetrum danae* is also small and dark, but it lacks the white frons and the dark basal wing patches of *L. dubia*. In mature male *L. dubia*, the narrow abdomen is black with red markings on the dorsal and lateral surfaces of segments 2 and 3, reddish spots mid-dorsally on segments 4 and 5, and larger orange spots mid-dorsally on segments 6 and 7. These may become redder with age. The wings have dark black-brown patches basally, which are less extensive on the forewings, and red coloration mid-dorsally on and between the wing attachments. The thorax is black with faint red antehumeral stripes and lateral markings. In immature males and in females, the red and orange markings of mature males are pale creamy yellow.

Habitat   *L. dubia* breeds in acidic and usually oligotrophic bog pools which contain an abundance of submerged *Sphagnum* moss. Occasionally, on cut-over bogs, larvae will emerge from peat-stained pools with negligible amounts of submerged vegetation, but invariably these are at sites where *Sphagnum*-dominated pools are in close proximity. At some lowland sites, the submerged moss *Drepanocladus fluitans* is also plentiful. At several basin mire sites in the English midlands, the pools, up to 14 m deep, may have been formed as a result of the collapse of a *schwingmoor*. *L. dubia* is confined to waters with no fish (Henrickson 1988).

Breeding biology   *L. dubia* is territorial but its territories are not large. Interaction between *L. dubia* and *Libellula quadrimaculata* is discussed by Warren (1964), and is referred to more fully in the account of the latter species in this *Atlas*. Copulation takes place amongst low bushes or heather and is of short duration. The female oviposits by flying low over the bog pool, usually unaccompanied by the male, and dropping her eggs into the water or on to water-logged *Sphagnum* moss. The larvae, which live amongst submerged *Sphagnum*, usually take two years to develop.

Flight periods   *L. dubia* is on the wing from late May to the end of July. It may be seen with other species such as *Sympetrum danae*, *Aeshna juncea*, *Pyrrhosoma nymphula* and *Lestes sponsa*.

Status and distribution   The first authenticated record of *L. dubia* in Britain was at Thorne Moors, Yorkshire, on 28 July 1837 by William Beckitt, who passed a specimen to J C Dale (Limbert 1990). The species has a very disjunct distribution in Britain from Surrey to north Scotland. It has not been recorded from Ireland. Its strongholds are in Inverness-shire and Ross-shire. It appears to have declined in Perthshire and Argyllshire, not having been reported since 1972. *L. dubia* has declined notably in England over the past 35 years, having been lost from six sites between 1956 and 1976. Only seven breeding sites remain. Its sole Welsh locality, Fenn's and Whixall Moss, is at a site which straddles the border with England. The decline of *L. dubia* in Britain is due principally to the loss of habitat, caused by drainage associated with afforestation, commercial peat cutting and agricultural reclamation. Seral changes, which result in the drying out of the habitat and its encroachment by scrub and trees, are a danger at bogs which have already been damaged by human activity, and are most marked at the sites of former small-scale peat diggings (Key 1989; Eversham 1991). One site, in Surrey, was probably lost as a result of drying out in the drought of 1976. *L. dubia* occurs within several NNRs and an RSPB reserve. The appearance of *L. dubia* at an atypical, locally well-known site at Stone Edge, Derbyshire, in 1987–89 is now thought to have been an abortive attempt at introduction. *L. dubia* was reported from an atypical site at Walberswick NNR, Suffolk, in 1992 (Mendel 1992); none was seen there in 1993 or 1994.

European and world distribution   *L. dubia* is found throughout northern Europe, and east to Siberia. At the southerly limits of its range it is restricted to mountain areas such as the Pyrenees and Alps.

Leucorrhinia dubia (Vander Linden)   **White-faced dragonfly**

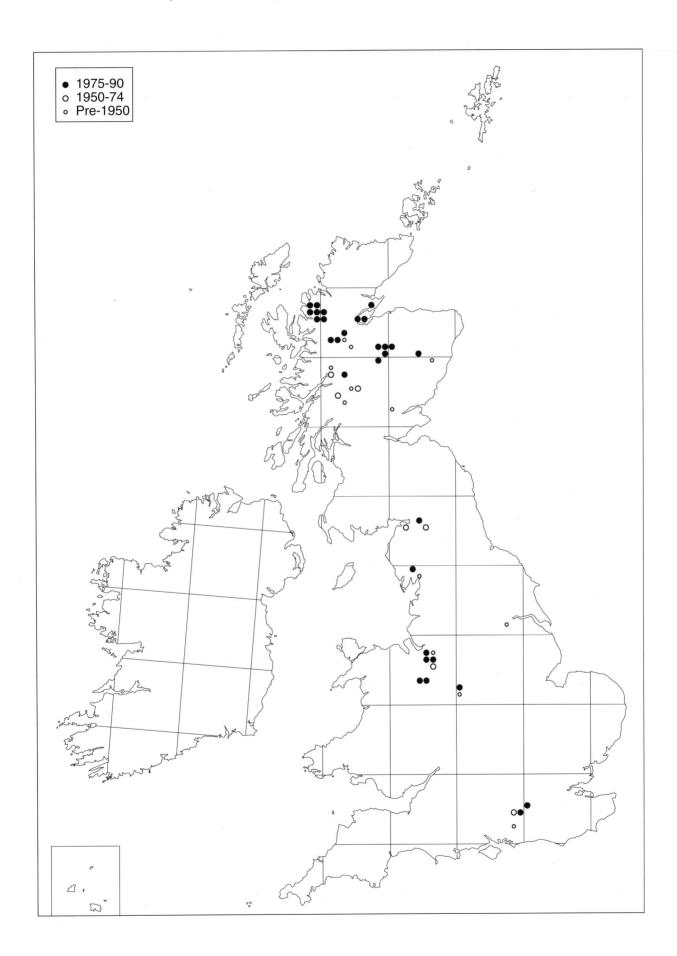

SPECIES RECORDED IN THE CHANNEL ISLANDS BUT NOT IN BRITAIN OR IRELAND

Lestes barbarus (Fabricius)

L. barbarus is similar in appearance to *L. sponsa* and *L. dryas*, but is larger and can be readily distinguished by the bi-coloured pterostigmata of mature individuals. These are dark brown except for the apical one-third which is white. *L. barbarus* breeds in ponds and ditches, including those that are slightly brackish. Eggs are laid in the tissues of emergent vegetation such as rushes and sedges, or into the overhanging branches of shrubs such as sallow. It is on the wing from the beginning of July to early October. It has been recorded from Jersey and Alderney. Whether it ever bred on Jersey is uncertain, but it almost certainly bred on Alderney in view of the considerable numbers seen at a pond there in 1900 (Walker 1900). It could not be found on Alderney during a survey in 1978 (Belle 1980), neither has it been seen on Jersey for many years (Silsby & Silsby 1988). Its European distribution is centred on the Mediterranean region, becoming scarcer in northern France, The Netherlands, Belgium and northern Germany. It is found east to Asia Minor, India and Mongolia.

Sympecma fusca (Vander Linden)

This brownish damselfly is closely related to the *Lestes* genus, but lacks the metallic green coloration and does not hold its wings half-open when at rest. It is predominantly fawn-coloured with a dark brown or black longitudinal marking on the dorsal surface of each abdominal segment reminiscent of female *Enallagma cyathigerum*. The dorsal surface of the thorax is dark black-brown, and faintly metallic, except for pale antehumeral stripes. The anal appendages of males immediately identify them as belonging to the Lestidae. It breeds in oligotrophic ponds and small lakes, and has an unusual life history. Eggs are laid in early spring into dead floating vegetation such as common reed, and hatch after three to six weeks. Larval development is completed in two months. Adults emerge in late July and August, and by late September they have all left the breeding site and dispersed to sheltered areas such as the edges of woods, often some distance away. Here they hibernate amongst tall grasses, their body coloration being good camouflage. *S. fusca* is one of only two European dragonflies to overwinter as an adult, the other being *Sympecma annulata* (Sélys-Longchamps). In spring they return to the water to recommence the breeding cycle. It has been recorded from Jersey (Le Quesne 1946), and is believed to have bred, but is probably now extinct (Silsby & Silsby 1988). *S. fusca* is widespread throughout southern and central Europe, thinning out northwards. Its range extends east to the Middle East and central Asia. It occurs in North Africa.

Crocothemis erythraea (Brullé)

Males of this libellulid are unmistakable with their broad, flattened and brilliantly red abdomen. The thorax is reddish brown, and the eyes are red above and purple below. In females the abdomen is yellowish brown with yellow lateral markings on segments 4–8. In both sexes there is a small amber-yellow suffusion at the base of the wings; more extensive on the hind wings. It breeds in shallow eutrophic ponds, paddy fields and drainage ditches. In the Mediterranean region it has two generations between April and November, but further north it has one and is on the wing from June to early September. It has been recorded from Jersey (Le Quesne 1946), and is believed to have bred, but has not been seen for many years (Silsby & Silsby 1988). *C. erythraea* is common in the Mediterranean region, but very local further north in central Europe. It is found east to the Middle East and Pakistan, and is widespread in tropical and North Africa. [See also footnote on p5.]

Sympetrum meridionale (Sélys-Longchamps)

In male *S. meridionale* the abdomen is predominantly reddish. In females it is yellowish brown. It differs from the *Sympetrum* species that have been recorded in Britain by the almost total lack of black markings on the sides of the thorax. An examination of the genitalia is necessary to confirm its identity. It breeds in shallow well-vegetated ponds and lakes. In its more usual southern haunts, its flight period is from late May to October. Its position on the British list rested on four records: two from the 19th century, and two from the early 20th century. These records were reappraised by F C Fraser (1957, 1958) who concluded that, for three of the four records, the identifications were suspect or that there were doubts about whether the specimens had been taken originally in Britain. He accepted the fourth record, 'from the environs of London' (Sélys 1846), because the original determination had been made by Sélys himself. In the case of the 1901 record from Dawlish, Devon, this specimen was recently re-identified as *S. striolatum* by S J Brooks (pers. comm.) at the Natural History Museum, London, where it is in the A E Gardner collection. A single female *S. meridionale* was recorded from Jersey on 5 August 1948 (Moore 1949) and sent to Cynthia Longfield at the Natural History Museum, London, who confirmed the identity. Its European distribution is centred on the Mediterranean region. It is found east to Kashmir and Mongolia, and occurs in North Africa.

Footnote: This species account has been modified since publication in 1996. It is now proper to the next section: *Immigrants and accidental species.*

IMMIGRANTS AND ACCIDENTAL SPECIES [See also footnote on p5.]

The populations of several species resident in Britain and Ireland are reinforced in some years by immigrants from the continent, notably *Aeshna mixta*, *Libellula quadrimaculata*, *Sympetrum striolatum* and *S. sanguineum*. There are also several other species which have occurred as immigrants and accidental visitors; none of them has so far succeeded in maintaining a permanent breeding population in Britain and Ireland, though several have bred in the Channel Islands. They include some of the most likely candidates to be discovered in, or to colonise, Britain or Ireland in the future.

Lestes viridis (Vander Linden)

This species is similar to *L. sponsa* and *L. dryas* in having a predominantly metallic green body, but is larger than either of them, and mature males do not develop any blue pruinescence (or only negligibly so). *L. viridis* breeds in ponds, canals and slow-flowing streams and rivers. Males defend vertical territories in trees overhanging the water margin. The female lays her eggs in the smaller branches of marginal bushes such as sallow. It is on the wing from early July to late September. The only British record is of a male captured at Shenley, Hertfordshire, on 11 August 1899 by E R Speyer. It was recorded at a number of localities on Jersey in the 1940s (Le Quesne 1946), and was rediscovered there in 1989; breeding was confirmed in 1990. On the continent, *L. viridis* is found throughout southern and central Europe as far north as Belgium and Germany. It occurs in the Middle East and North Africa.

Aeshna affinis (Vander Linden)

A. affinis is a small aeshnid, similar in size and general appearance to *A. mixta*, but the coloration of the abdominal spots of males is much brighter blue, highlighted by the black surrounds. Also, the pattern of these markings is different, most noticeably on the anterior segments. Additionally, the sides of the thorax are different in colour and pattern from *A. mixta*. It breeds in shallow ponds and ditches which possess an abundance of emergent vegetation, such as horsetails. It is a migratory species and is on the wing from late June to the end of August. There is only one confirmed British record, of a male, being taken at Romney Marsh, Kent, on 5 August 1952 by W E Dyson. The specimen is in the Natural History Museum, London. A field observation in 1992 (Holmes 1993) high-lights the need to net a specimen and examine it carefully in the hand for records of critical species to be acceptable. On the continent, the distribution of *A. affinis* is centred on the Mediterranean region. It is found east to China, and also in North Africa.

Hemianax ephippiger (Burmeister)

H. ephippiger bears a superficial resemblance to *Anax imperator* on account of the longitudinal black line, of irregular width, on the mid-dorsal surface of the abdomen. This line extends laterally on posterior segments, enclosing a pair of large pale spots on segments 8–10. It is a smaller dragonfly than *A. imperator* and, in males, the body is a sandy brown colour except for abdominal segment 2 which is bright blue in mature individuals. In females, the abdominal coloration is darker and duller, and segment 2 has only a weak blue-violet tinge. It breeds in small ponds. In Europe, *H. ephippiger* is observed mainly between March and October. It is strongly migratory and, until recent years, had been recorded on only six occasions in Britain, including once in the Shetland Islands, and on one occasion in Ireland (Merritt 1985). Since then a further six records have occurred, three of which were in 1988. The remaining three records were from Hampshire, Cambridgeshire and Devon, the latter record being of a male taken at Plymouth, Devon on 8 January 1992, and subsequently sent to the Natural History Museum, London. These recent records are reviewed by Silsby (1993). In Europe, *H. ephippiger* breeds sporadically in the Mediterranean region. Elsewhere it is a vagrant, and the only species of dragonfly to have been recorded from Iceland. It breeds in the drier regions of Africa, the Middle East and east to Pakistan.

Gomphus flavipes (Charpentier)

G. flavipes is very similar to *G. vulgatissimus*, but the abdomen is yellower and less club-shaped. Also, the black thoracic markings are slightly but significantly different, and the legs are yellow, striped longitudinally with black, unlike *G. vulgatissimus* in which they are almost entirely black. It breeds in rivers, and is on the wing from mid-June to early September. There is only one British record, that of a male taken near Hastings, Sussex, on 5 August 1818 by J F Stephens. In Europe it occurs mainly in the east, with only a few scattered records in the west, where it appears to be declining. It is an eastern Palaearctic species, ranging from eastern Europe and the Middle East to Manchuria.

Sympetrum vulgatum (Linnaeus)

This species is similar to, though slightly smaller than, *S. striolatum*. However, in mature males, the abdomen is more reddish and more constricted in the middle segments, though not to the extent of male *S. sanguineum*. Also, the tiny paired black spots on the dorsal surface of the abdomen are not enclosed in yellow rings as in *S. striolatum*. The black transverse line at the top of the frons extends down the inner sides of the eyes, unlike *S. striolatum* in which there is no lateral extension or, at most, a smudge. The accessary genitalia of males and the prominent vulvar scale of females are diagnostic. *S. vulgatum* breeds in ditches, ponds, lakes and slow-flowing rivers, and is on the wing from early July to October. It has been recorded in Britain on fewer than ten occasions, mostly from the London area, but also once from Torquay, Devon, and once from Kingston upon Hull, Yorkshire. None of the records is from recent years. It has been recorded several times from Jersey (Le Quesne 1946), but not from Ireland. On the continent, *S. vulgatum* occurs from eastern France to southern Scandinavia, and east to China. It appears to have increased in The Netherlands in recent years (Geijskes & van Tol 1983), and so may reach Britain more frequently in the future.

Sympetrum fonscolombii (Sélys-Longchamps)

In mature male *S. fonscolombii*, the abdomen is brighter red than *S. striolatum* and more parallel-sided. The veins in the proximal halves of the wings are red, thus distinguishing *S. fonscolombii* from all other *Sympetrum* species. In females these veins are yellowish and the abdomen is yellow-brown. In both sexes the pterostigmata are pale with a conspicuous black border along two sides, and there is a saffron patch at the base of the wings which may be quite extensive, though never as much as in *S. flaveolum*. It breeds in shallow static water bodies, and is on the wing from mid-June to October, earlier in southern Europe, where it may produce two generations in one year. *S. fonscolombii* is migratory and occurs sporadically in Britain, usually in mid- to late summer, although a male was recorded on 9 May 1987 at Broomhill Burrows, Pembrokeshire. The majority of records are from southern England, but it has occurred as far north as the Isle of May on the east Scotland coast, on 17 August 1911. There are two records from Co Cavan, Ireland, on 20 July 1941 and 27 July 1942. It has almost certainly bred occasionally in southern England (Longfield 1949c), but has been unable to sustain a population. It has bred on Jersey, where Le Quesne (1946) noted oviposition taking place in a canal on 11 May 1945. He continued to see adults there until July, then in August he found an immature female, the first specimen in this condition that he had seen that year. On 30 August, many exuviae and teneral adults were located at the site. He suggested that the evidence could indicate that the species may overwinter in the adult state. It is more probable that *S. fonscolombii* had undergone two generations in one year, which this species is known to accomplish in more southern latitudes, and that Le Quesne had missed a synchronous spring emergence toward the end of April. On the continent, *S. fonscolombii* is widespread in the Mediterranean region, and is found east to India, Mongolia and the Pacific. It occurs throughout Africa.

Sympetrum flaveolum (Linnaeus)

In *S. flaveolum* the parallel-sided abdomen is red in mature males, yellowish brown in females. The species is distinctive for having a broad saffron-yellow patch on the basal area of each wing. This is much more extensive than on any other *Sympetrum* except, occasionally, *S. fonscolombii* from which it can be distinguished by its black wing venation and dark pterostigma. It breeds in marshy ponds, ditches, and lakes, and the backwaters of slow-flowing rivers. It is on the wing from late June to October. *S. flaveolum* is migratory and occurs sporadically in Britain, mainly in the south although it occurred as far north as Keiss, Caithness, on 18 July 1945. It appears to be recorded less frequently now than it was before 1950. There is strong circumstantial evidence to suggest that *S. flaveolum* has bred in southern England on a few occasions (Longfield 1949c), but has been unable to sustain a population. It has been recorded from Jersey, and Belle (1980) suggests that it bred formerly on Guernsey and Alderney. There are no records from Ireland. It is found throughout Europe except the extreme south and north, and occurs east to Siberia and Japan. It is absent from Africa.

Sympetrum meridionale – see footnote on p110.

Pantala flavescens (Fabricius)

This brown libellulid is larger than any of the resident libellulids in Britain or Ireland, having an average overall length of 49–52 mm. The abdomen of both sexes is yellow-brown with a black longitudinal line, of uneven width, along the mid-dorsal surface which thickens posteriorly into black triangular marks on segments 8–10. The thorax is brown dorsally with yellow-brown sides. The wings of males may develop a small pale brown patch apically. There are two records from Britain. One is of a specimen captured in 1823 at Horning, Norfolk, by J Sparshall. This record is discussed by Fraser (1956) who had experience of it in India, and who, despite the doubts expressed by some leading entomologists of the 19th century as to how *P. flavescens* could have reached Britain, preferred to keep an open mind. The second record is of an individual taken at Bolton, Lancashire, in July 1951 by A Hazelwood, and which is now in the National Museums on Merseyside, Liverpool. It is believed to have arrived in Britain as a ship-borne immigrant with a consignment of bananas. Longfield (in Corbet *et al.* 1960) cites a case of a male *P. flavescens* sent to her by O G Watkins of Plymouth which was found flying around the wardroom of a British warship a few days before reaching Devonport Harbour from Singapore in 1955. It is a pantropical species, capable of migrating vast distances. It is found in Asia, Australasia, the Americas, Africa and many of the islands in the Indian Ocean and the Pacific Ocean. It only occurs sporadically in Europe.

POSSIBLE ADDITIONS TO THE BRITISH AND IRISH DRAGONFLY FAUNA

There are a number of other dragonfly species which have found their way on to the British list in the past. These are dealt with adequately by McLachlan (1884) and Lucas (1900). One of these species, however, requires a brief note here as it has been referred to in some recent publications. This is *Leucorrhinia pectoralis* (Charpentier), a larger and more robust dragonfly than *L. dubia*, which, at its nearest point to Britain, occurs at a few localities in northern France, The Netherlands, and Belgium, as well as Germany and southern Scandinavia, and east to Siberia, with a few southern European outposts in mountain areas. A specimen was taken near Sheerness, Kent, in June 1859, and exhibited in January 1860 at a meeting of the Entomological Society of London. McLachlan believed that the dragonfly was taken on board a fishing boat at the mouth of the Thames.

More recently, another species was added to the British list, by Fraser (1949): *Somatochlora alpestris* (Sélys-Longchamps). A single male, labelled 'Inverness, 7.vii.26, coll. K. Morton', had been given to Fraser some years earlier by Morton, intended as a specimen of *S. arctica* (Fraser 1947). Blackwood (1950), a friend of the late Morton, investigated the matter and was disappointed to conclude that the specimen could not have been taken by Morton on the date and place as labelled because he was in the Pyrenees at that time. In view of the European distribution of *S. alpestris* – Scandinavia and the mountain areas of central Europe – and its habitat requirement of tarns and *Sphagnum* bogs, and its close resemblance to our resident corduliids, it has been suggested that the species could be overlooked in Scotland. This is a possibility, but, as it is necessary to examine our native corduliids closely in order to separate one from another, the likelihood of a species from this distinctive family being overlooked is very slight.

This is not the case with two species of dragonfly which closely resemble only one resident species, and whose European distribution and habitat requirements make them possible candidates for discovery in Britain, in particular Scotland. They are *Aeshna subarctica* Walker, and *Leucorrhinia rubicunda* (Linnaeus). These are very similar in appearance to *A. juncea* and *L. dubia* respectively, and it is conceivable that an unsuspecting person could handle one and not realise its difference straight away. When three *L. dubia* were reported from Walberswick NNR, Suffolk, in May and June 1992, there was speculation that the presence of these individuals, or a breeding population if one existed, may have been the result of a recent immigration, and, additionally, that it could not be entirely ruled out that the individuals were *L. rubicunda* (Mendel 1992). There is little evidence to support the suggestion of immigration in Britain: the report of large numbers of *L. dubia* at Scarborough, Yorkshire, in 1900, at least some of which were observed flying in from over the sea (Imms 1900) being unsupported by specimens in any local or national collection. The question of the specific identity of the *Leucorrhinia* could be resolved in 1995, or sooner, if oviposition had occurred at the site, by the emergence of adults. However, the partial inundation of the area with sea water early in 1993 makes this less likely.

It could be argued that, with the greater number of people interested in dragonflies in recent years, the chance of additional species still awaiting discovery is so remote as to be discounted. This is not so - the discovery of *Coenagrion lunulatum* in 1981 in Co Sligo, Ireland, bears witness to that. This species must be a possible candidate for discovery in Britain, perhaps in Galloway, Cumbria or Anglesey where suitable habitat occurs. Reading through published documents from the 19th century, it is often apparent that leading entomologists just would not accept that they might have missed something. Fraser (1956) makes this point quite well. People have probably not changed that much, and we may all be guilty occasionally of seeing what we expect to see.

Many parts of Ireland still remain relatively under-recorded, especially in the south, and the likelihood of further discoveries being made is quite high. *Gomphus vulgatissimus*, an elusive species of slow-flowing rivers, perhaps awaits (re)discovery in Co Waterford or eastern Co Cork. *Libellula fulva* is another early summer riverine species that is a potential candidate. Care now needs to be taken that the expectation of finding *C. lunulatum* in Ireland does not lead to failure to detect *C. hastulatum* there, as these species are superficially similar, and they are known to coexist in Denmark (Robert 1958).

It is clear that at least three species have extended their range northward and westward in Britain during this century, namely *Aeshna mixta*, *Orthetrum cancellatum* and *Sympetrum sanguineum*. There is strong evidence that *S. sanguineum* has spread in Ireland too, and possibly *O. cancellatum* also. With global warming being predicted, it is quite possible that additional species will colonise Britain, appearing first in south-eastern counties closest to France and The Netherlands. Candidates for possible future colonists are not hard to find, and include all those species which breed up to the Channel coast.

Three species that would be high on the list are *Lestes barbarus*, *L. viridis* and *Sympecma fusca*. These have bred, or are thought likely to have bred, in the Channel Islands in the past and are described in the sections on the Channel Islands fauna or on immigrants. All three are relatively inconspicuous damselflies, similar to species which occur in Britain already, and they could easily be overlooked at sites in Sussex, Kent or Essex before being discovered. Certainly, odonatists in southern counties should make a point of checking closely a proportion of all damselflies that they encounter. With a general warming of the climate, perhaps one or more of our regular immigrants, namely *Sympetrum fonscolombii* and *S. flaveolum*, could succeed in establishing and maintaining a breeding population. Also, *S. vulgatum*, which is fairly widespread in The Netherlands and which has shown an increase in records there in recent years, could be a future colonist. In Ireland, a close watch should be kept for *A. mixta*.

It is evident that over the past 150 years, the dragonfly fauna of Britain and Ireland has gradually changed. Some species have declined and become extinct, whilst others have increased and spread to new areas. This process will, without doubt, continue.

SEASONAL OCCURRENCE

PREVIOUS REPRESENTATIONS OF FLIGHT PERIODS

Most records of dragonflies refer to adults, and the larval stages have received far less attention. Thus, in planning fieldwork, most recorders restrict themselves to the period of approximately May-October during which adult Odonata are on the wing. Individuals of a few species may be seen a little earlier or later, and there are occasional reports of adults seen in winter, usually associated with heated, or at least frost-free, pools in glasshouses or gardens (eg a teneral female *Sympetrum striolatum* in Cadogan Place Gardens, London, on 21 February 1943 (C Longfield, unpublished)).

The first published summaries of flight periods of British and Irish dragonflies were simple tabulations, based on the typical month of first emergence. Thus, 'Spring', 'Summer' and 'Autumn' species could be recognised (Longfield 1949a). Hammond (1977) provided a tabulation of flight periods by weeks, and distinguished the 'best time to observe the species' from 'earlier or later times when the species may be teneral or very adult' and 'exceptional dates due to a forward spring or prolonged summer'. This distinction is in contrast to much of the earlier published observations on flight periods, which tend to concentrate unduly on the very early or very late dates, and give less information on the time of peak numbers.

The trend to concentrate on extreme dates continues, for example as a regular feature of the **Brief notes and observations** section in the *Journal* or *Newsletter* of the British Dragonfly Society. Although 'first' and 'last' is an attractively simple concept, and appeals to the competitive spirit among recorders, it tells us little about how a species has responded to meteorological effects: maverick individuals often do not reflect the pattern of the majority. Ideally, one would like to be able to quantify the distribution of emergence and flight period in time, perhaps using the mean flight date and a measure of spread around this mean (such as the standard deviation), as has been successfully applied to butterfly phenologies (Brakefield 1987; Pollard 1992).

CURRENT DATA AND FUTURE STUDIES

The large numbers of records from the Recording Scheme permit a more detailed examination of dragonfly flight periods than has been possible previously. Of the 108 364 records received by the Scheme up to the end of 1990, 66 911 have a full date (day-month-year); when those records representing larvae or exuviae have been removed, there are still over 66 000 dated records which can be used in flight period studies. (Many more than 900 records of larvae or exuviae have been received, but, in most cases, adults were seen at the same time.)

MAIN AND OUTLYING FLIGHT PERIODS

Table 5 is based on the total dated records of each species. Solid symbols (●) are used for those weeks which contain 10% or more of the records of the species; the open symbol (○) is used for weeks when there are fewer than 10% of records. Isolated outlying dates are shown as (•).

The broad patterns are very similar to those presented by Hammond (1977), but with a tendency for the flight periods of most species to be longer. This is not surprising, because Hammond's tables appear to have been based largely on his own experience, which was concentrated in south-east England.

An alternative means of depicting flight periods is by use of histograms (Figure 8). This has been done in some continental atlases, such as Geijskes and van Tol (1983) and Maibach and Meier (1987). For the very common species, a histogram shows the peak(s) in numbers of records, which to some degree reflects the seasonal abundance of the species, but the histograms are also related to the pattern of recorder activity. For the scarcer species, the effects of repeated reporting of the same record may be significant: a sighting may be reported several times in the literature (and be extracted for the Recording Scheme by several different people), and specimens collected by the same person on the same day may find their way into many different museum and private collections. Thus, a single day's fieldwork may be responsible for a dozen or more entries in the database. This is useful to future workers who are reviewing the literature or seeking museum specimens for study, but multiple counts in a flight period histogram would be misleading. For these reasons, a simple tabulation is given, which it is hoped may be less prone to 'over-interpretation'.

A further confusion in examining flight period data gathered over a long period from a wide range of sources is the problem of year-to-year variation. The overall pattern represents the earliest and latest seasons, as well as 'typical' years; so, in any one year, a species will not have been observed on the full range of dates which the table suggests. As an illustration of this, all the records for *Ischnura elegans* for four consecutive years, 1984–88, are plotted in Figure 9; the year-to-year variation in this one species is as great as the apparent differences between it and some other species. This variation may be related to aspects of weather, but no simple correlation has yet been established.

Table 5. Flight periods of dragonflies in seven-day periods. The Table is generally based on data for Britain only, including records before the end of 1990; Channel Islands species and rare migrant species are omitted. Flight periods of dragonflies in Ireland will differ slightly from those in Britain, but there are insufficient records to present reliable tabulations for all species in Ireland separately. The flight period of Coenagrion lunulatum, which is not recorded from Britain, is based on its Irish records

Months (columns): Jan | Feb | Mar | Apr | May | Jun | Jul | Aug | Sep | Oct | Nov | Dec

SPECIES:

Aeshna caerulea
Aeshna cyanea
Aeshna grandis
Aeshna isosceles
Aeshna juncea
Aeshna mixta
Anax imperator
Brachytron pratense
Calopteryx splendens
Calopteryx virgo
Ceriagrion tenellum
Coenagrion armatum
Coenagrion hastulatum
Coenagrion lunulatum
Coenagrion mercuriale
Coenagrion puella
Coenagrion pulchellum
Coenagrion scitulum
Cordulegaster boltonii
Cordulia aenea
Enallagma cyathigerum
Erythromma najas
Gomphus vulgatissimus
Ischnura elegans
Ischnura pumilio
Lestes dryas
Lestes sponsa
Leucorrhinia dubia
Libellula depressa
Libellula fulva
Libellula quadrimaculata
Orthetrum cancellatum
Orthetrum coerulescens
Oxygastra curtisii
Platycnemis pennipes
Pyrrhosoma nymphula
Somatochlora arctica
Somatochlora metallica
Sympetrum danae
Sympetrum flaveolum
Sympetrum fonscolombii
Sympetrum sanguineum
Sympetrum striolatum/nigrescens

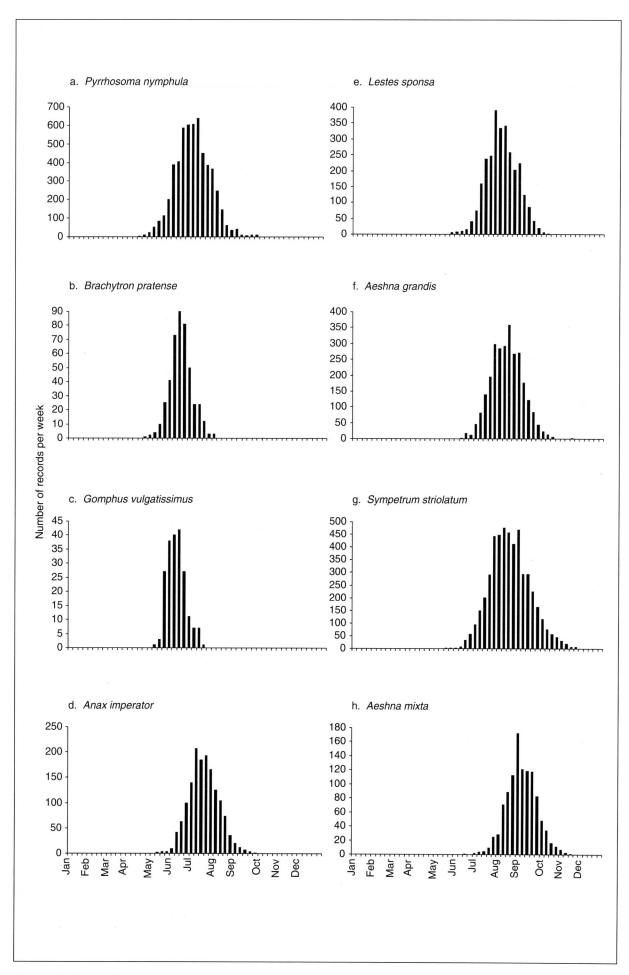

Figure 8. Flight period histograms for selected species

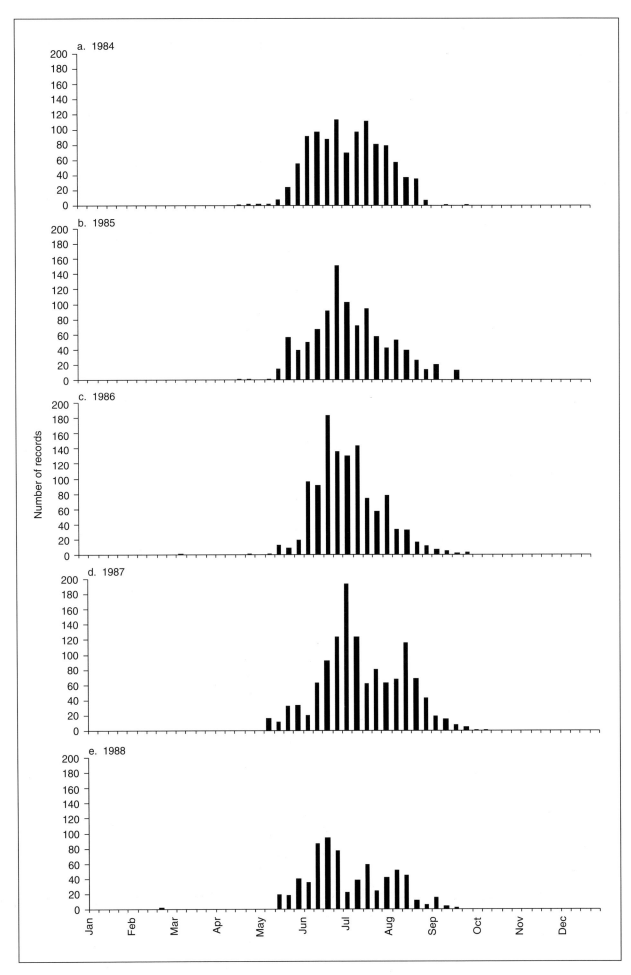

Figure 9. Flight period of *Ischnura elegans* each year from 1984 to 1988, showing annual variation

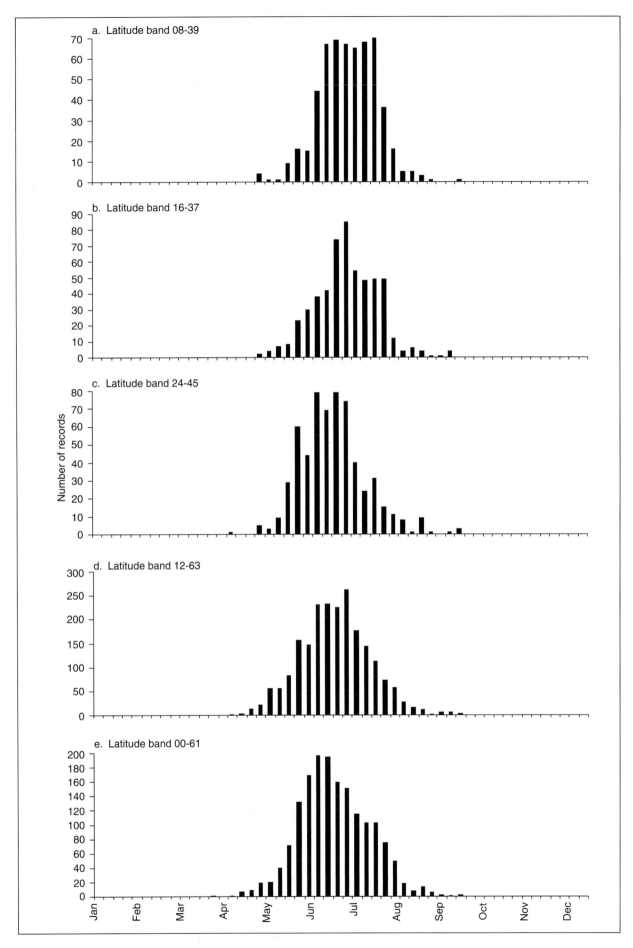

Figure 10. Latitudinal variation in flight period of *Pyrrhosoma nymphula*. Britain has been divided into five bands, each 200 km wide. The naming refers to the Ordnance Survey 100 km square numbers. Band a is the northern part of Scotland. Band e covers southern England and south Wales

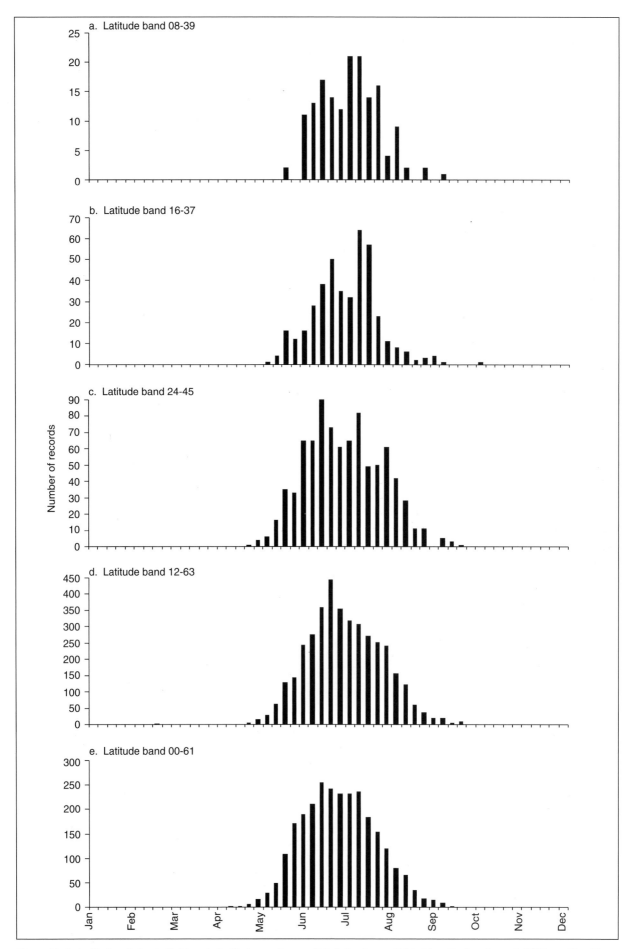

Figure 11. Latitudinal variation in flight period of *Ischnura elegans*. Britain has been divided into five bands, each 200 km wide. The naming refers to the Ordnance Survey 100 km square numbers. Band a is the northern part of Scotland. Band e covers southern England and south Wales

Finally, differences in recorder behaviour may confound a detailed analysis of flight period data, nationally or regionally. One cannot be completely certain that recorders start searching for adult Odonata at the absolute beginning of the season, particularly in northern and western areas where the early-season weather tends not to be conducive to recording adult Odonata. The simplest way to evaluate the effects of biases in the timing of recorder activity would be to establish the flight periods of species at a series of individual sites through regular monitoring. If a recorder is able to visit a transect at the same site each week, at about mid-day and in suitable weather, and logs the number of adult males of each species present (transects are described in the section on **Methods of recording**), the resulting pattern of flight periods is immune to most of the distortions caused by recorder bias.

REGIONAL VARIATION IN FLIGHT PERIODS

Another difficulty in interpreting flight period data is that a species may behave differently in different parts of Britain and Ireland. A tendency for species to fly later in the north than the south has often been remarked upon, but with few data to support it. Figures 10 and 11 show the latitudinal pattern of flight period for *Pyrrhosoma nymphula* and *I. elegans*. Whereas *P. nymphula* shows a clear trend to fly later in the north, and there appears to be a lag of as much as five weeks between south-west England and northern Scotland, *I. elegans* flies at almost exactly the same time throughout Britain. The causes of this surprising difference are still unknown: it could perhaps be due to life history differences between the species (in particular, the thermal cues which trigger emergence), or be related to habitat or microsite use and larval behaviour.

FUTURE RECORDING

The species maps presented in this *Atlas* portray the broad patterns of Odonata distribution in Britain and, to a lesser extent, in Ireland. In the latter country, there is still much recording to be done before comprehensive maps can be produced, although the position has improved remarkably in the past decade. There is little doubt that basic recording will continue to fill in the distribution patterns of the commoner species in parts of Britain, and to identify some new sites for scarcer species (see also the section on **Future distribution maps** in the **Fieldwork and data management** chapter).

The distribution of species is seldom static, and continued recording throughout the landscape will be needed to detect and monitor the changes which are taking place (Eversham 1994). Some species, such as *Aeshna mixta*, have attracted considerable attention in the context of possible climatic change (Watt, Ward & Eversham 1990). The example of *A. mixta* also stresses a requirement of future recording which is already being addressed for other reasons: the need to establish proof of breeding. Highly mobile species such as *A. mixta* can occur as adults tens or hundreds of miles away from breeding sites. However, there is clear evidence that the present range expansion of *A. mixta* is an extension of *breeding* range, and not merely an increase in northward mobility (or even a higher level of detection of such mobility by recorders). It has been observed emerging from ponds in Derbyshire, Nottinghamshire and Yorkshire.

Proof of breeding became a focus for recording in 1988, with the launch of the Odonata Key Sites Project (KSP) (Merritt 1988). This is primarily an initiative in support of conservation. Although the broad patterns of distribution of each species were well known, as were the locations of many of the more important breeding sites for scarcer species, it was not possible to evaluate fully these sites relative to others owing to the lack of comprehensive breeding data. The new recording card, the RA70 (Figure 12), provides space for information on each stage of the life cycle. The approach has already been used successfully at a county level, in the Cheshire dragonfly survey (Gabb & Kitching 1992). The authors have distinguished between proven, probable and possible breeding records. This distinction is of great importance, especially in relation to nature conservation, and it is hoped that county surveys in the future will follow their example.

The RA70 also encourages recorders to estimate the abundance of each species. Even an approximate indication of numbers present is an improvement on previous recording methods, and, taken over several years, KSP data are beginning to show which sites support significant populations of scarce species. No less valuable, it is becoming apparent which sites have unusually rich breeding assemblages (rather than merely having a long species list due to diligent observers noting species in transit). Given the continued support of recorders, the role of dragonflies in site assessment for nature conservation (Nature Conservancy Council 1989) can only increase.

Two other areas of enhancement in recording also seem likely to play an important part in future: the recording of immigrant species and movement by resident Odonata, and the thorough monitoring of individual sites.

Migrant butterflies such as the painted lady (*Cynthia cardui*) or the clouded yellow (*Colias croceus*) occur annually, and their occasional abundance attracts considerable attention. Similar movements among Odonata seem to be rarely detected. This may be because, unlike butterflies, the species of dragonfly most often involved are British/Irish resident species. The phenomenon is most obvious in the occasional arrival of species not normally present, such as *Hemianax ephippiger* or *Sympetrum fonscolombii*, records of which often find their way into the literature.

Movement of resident species is much more difficult to evaluate, but any species which is able to colonise new habitats must pass through the unsuitable countryside in between: if resident species are observed in apparently unsuitable sites, or occur only for a few days and are not breeding, they are almost certainly wanderers. The appearance of *S. danae* away from heathland pools and acid peatlands may represent such long-distance movement. A scatter of recent records of *Ischnura pumilio* away from established breeding sites, and an observation of numerous post-emergent individuals flying almost vertically up-wards on warm days suggests the possibility that *I. pumilio* may be a 'wandering opportunist' (Fox 1989).

Occasionally, dragonflies are seen flying in from the sea, sometimes in large numbers (Longfield 1948). Observers who spend all day in one place may see a steady stream of dragonflies pass them, flying along a river or over open countryside, perhaps all moving in the same direction. These may be rather rare events, but, if all observers are on the look-out, they may add up to a clearer picture of mobility within resident species. To this end, a recording form was drafted in 1991, and a revised version, the RA74 (Figure 13), was introduced in 1992.

ODONATA 6411

ODONATA 6411	LOCALITY		GRID REFERENCE		V-c. No.

VICE-COUNTY NAME

SOURCE

FIELD	
MUSEUM	
LITERATURE	
LOCAL BRC	

RECORDER(S)

CARD COMPILER

·DATE

ALTITUDE (metres)

NO.

NO.

ZYGOPTERA		Ad	Co	Ov	La	Ex	Em	ANISOPTERA		Ad	Co	Ov	La	Ex	Em
Calopteryx virgo	0102							Gomphus vulgatissimus	1502						
splendens	0103							Brachytron pratense	2101						
Lestes sponsa	0404							Aeshna caerulea	2201						
dryas	0405							juncea	2204						
Platycnemis pennipes	0504							grandis	2207						
Pyrrhosoma nymphula	0601							cyanea	2209						
Ischnura elegans	0801							mixta	2210						
pumilio	0805							isosceles	2212						
Enallagma cyathigerum	0901							Anax imperator	2401						
Coenagrion mercuriale	1002							Cordulegaster boltonii	2601						
pulchellum	1006							Cordulia aenea	2701						
puella	1007							Somatochlora metallica	2802						
lunulatum	1009							arctica	2804						
hastulatum	1010							Libellula depressa	3201						
Erythromma najas	1101							fulva	3202						
Ceriagrion tenellum	1301							quadrimaculata	3204						

CONSERVATION STATUS (For official use)

NNR	LNR	Trust N.R.	RSPB
SSSI	N.T.	Other N.R. (Please give details)	

		Ad	Co	Ov	La	Ex	Em
Orthetrum coerulescens	3302						
cancellatum	3309						
Sympetrum striolatum	3803						
sanguineum	3810						
danae	3812						
Leucorrhinia dubia	3903						

KEY TO COLUMN HEADINGS :

Ad = ADULT
Co = COPULATING PAIR
Ov = OVIPOSITING FEMALE
La = LARVA
Ex = EXUVIA
Em = PRE-FLIGHT EMERGENT

ESTIMATED NUMBERS :

A = 1

B = 2-5

C = 6-20

D = 21-100

E = 100-500

F = 500+

[ENTER LETTER IN APPROPRIATE BOX(ES). IF ESTIMATE IS NOT AVAILABLE, ENTER 'X'.]

HABITAT

COMMENTS AND OTHER SPECIES

SKETCH MAP OF SITE

INDICATE SCALE, DIRECTION OF NORTH, AND BREEDING LOCATIONS OF NATIONALLY OR LOCALLY UNCOMMON SPECIES. SHOW ADJOINING HABITATS IF POSSIBLE.

Biological Records Centre   **April 1988**   **RA70**

Figure 12. RA70 recording card, 1988

MIGRANT ODONATA 6411

LOCALITY

GRID REFERENCE

V–c No.

VICE–COUNTY NAME

SOURCE

FIELD
MUSEUM
LITERATURE
LOCAL BRC

RECORDER(S)

CARD COMPILER

DATE

ALTITUDE (metres)

NO.

NO.

NON–RESIDENT SPP.	Ad	Co	Ov	La	Ex	Em		Ad	Co	Ov	La	Ex	Em	KEY TO COLUMN HEADINGS :
Lestes barbarus 0401							Crocothemis erythraea 3601							
Lestes viridis 0407							Sympetrum vulgatum 3801							Ad = ADULT
Gomphus flavipes 1501							Sympetrum fonscolombei 3807							Co = COPULATING PAIR
Aeshna affinis 2211							Sympetrum meridionale 3808							Ov = OVIPOSITING FEMALE
Hemianax ephippiger 2501							Sympetrum flaveolum 3809							La = LARVA
Gomphus pulchellus 1506							Pantala flavescens 4201							Ex = EXUVIA

Em = PRE-FLIGHT EMERGENT

Other non–resident Odonata species

MOVEMENT OF RESIDENT SPECIES

SPECIES	ESTIMATED NUMBERS	COMMENTS

ESTIMATED NUMBERS :

A = 1

B = 2-5

C = 6-20

D = 21-100

E = 100-500

F = 500+

[ENTER LETTER IN APPROPRIATE BOX(ES). IF ESTIMATE IS NOT AVAILABLE, ENTER 'X'.]

WEATHER CONDITIONS

WIND SPEED AND DIRECTION

TIME OF DAY

HABITAT

SKETCH MAP OF SITE
INDICATE SCALE, DIRECTION OF NORTH, AND DIRECTION OF MOVEMENT

COMMENTS AND OTHER GROUPS eg BUTTERFLIES, BIRDS

CONTINUE OVERLEAF IF NECESSARY

Biological Records Centre November 1991

RA74

Figure 13. RA74 migrant recording form, 1992

Particularly in the case of resident species, but also for vagrants, there is much scope for examining the condition of individual dragonflies, particularly with respect to evidence of breeding behaviour. For species of Anisoptera, the inferior appendage of the male leaves 'copulation marks' (a pair of small circular impressions on either side of the junction of the compound eyes) on the female during mating. In some males which have mated, distinctive scratch marks are left on the dorsal surface of the abdomen where it has been clasped by the female. In those libellulids which possess a blue abdominal pruinescence, this may be rubbed off to reveal two dark patches dorsally. A layer of fine sediment coating the terminal portion of the abdomen of a female dragonfly may be indicative of earlier oviposition (Cham 1990).

The benefits of careful monitoring of single sites for Odonata have been discussed under **Methods of recording**. If sufficient sites are studied, monitoring will provide the fine detail for understanding regional and year-to-year variations in phenology, which may help elucidate changes in geographic distribution. It will also provide a yardstick against which to measure such changes. There are several species for which there is evidence of an extension of their range in Britain and/or Ireland, notably *Orthetrum cancellatum*, *S. sanguineum* and *A. mixta*. A further species, *Anax imperator*, may be undergoing a similar extension, although this is questionable at the moment, whilst another species, *I. pumilio*, is clearly re-establishing itself in regions from which no records have been received for many years. To provide detailed information about these, and possibly other, species (including contractions in range) will require geographically wide-ranging observations with increasing precision and regularity.

DRAGONFLIES AND NATURE CONSERVATION

Dragonflies have existed on the earth for over 300 million years. They belong to a much older group than most of their prey today: their larval and adult diet must have changed a great deal over the years. Their ability to eat almost anything that moves and is not too large has stood them in good stead.

During the last glaciation, some tundra dragonflies may have been able to survive in those parts of southern England and Ireland which were not glaciated, but the dragonfly fauna must have been exterminated over the rest of the country. The early separation of Ireland from Britain (perhaps before the end of the glacial), and the later separation of Britain from the continent made recolonisation more difficult when the climate improved. It is not surprising that Britain and Ireland have an impoverished dragonfly fauna when compared with the adjacent continent (see Table 1 in the **Introduction**). Today it is difficult to decide which continental species are absent from Britain and Ireland because the habitat or climate is not suitable and which because they have failed to cross the sea.

Since the last glaciation, there have been three main ecological situations to which dragonflies have had to adapt. First, there was the natural scene when man was a rare hunter/gatherer and had little effect on his environment. At that time, most of Britain and Ireland was covered by forest, but there were many tree-fringed lakes in the north, and large areas of swampy woodland and marsh in the valleys of lowland river systems. Apart from tarns, lochans and meres, small bodies of water were provided by ox-bow lakes and temporary pools made by fallen trees blocking streams, and by beaver (*Castor fiber*) dams. It is tempting to speculate on the dragonfly fauna of that time, but we have no direct evidence of it: dragonfly fossils are extremely rare in the Quaternary (Buckland & Coope 1991).

The second period was that of traditional agriculture based on manpower and horsepower. The forests were felled with flint and then metal axes, with a peak of activity in the Iron Age/Roman period; by the end of the first millennium AD, a large part of lowland Britain and Ireland consisted of agricultural land, though extensive wetlands survived in such areas as the Fens, the Somerset and the Humberhead Levels, and the Bog of Allen in the central Irish plain. During the period of traditional agriculture, and particularly from the 17th century onwards, swamps and meres were systematically drained, but, at the same time, thousands of ditches and farm ponds were dug.

Locks on rivers produced stretches of still water, as did dams supporting water mills and early iron works. The network of canals built in the 18th and early 19th centuries provided very large areas of dragonfly habitat. Nearly every large country house had a lake constructed in its park. Large areas of lowland heathland containing raised and valley bogs remained. For many species, outside of upland areas, there were probably more dragonfly habitats in the period of traditional agriculture than in the preceding period when forest predominated.

The third period started in the lifetime of some contributors to the Odonata Recording Scheme. It is the period of industrial agriculture, when machines have replaced horses, and herbicides the hoe, when deep drainage has been possible, and the vast majority of crops are treated with insecticides and fungicides. This period had its origin before the Second World War, but did not really become established until the 1950s. The shift from traditional to industrial agriculture has been largely detrimental to dragonfly habitats and hence to dragonflies. Yet, at the same time, developments in other industries have produced new habitats which are beneficial to dragonflies. The changing distribution and status of dragonflies recorded in this *Atlas* reflect the extent to which species, which had become adapted to the habitats produced by traditional agriculture over several thousand years, have responded to the new landscape which has arisen in less than half a century. In the following appraisal the probable effects of the changes on different species are described so that we can identify the conservation action which is now necessary in each type of landscape.

Farming is the most common land use in England, Wales and lowland Scotland, and much of Ireland. In lowland areas, the change from mixed farming to cereal and other arable production has had a considerable effect on dragonfly populations. Farm ponds, formerly used as drinking places for livestock, have been seriously neglected: often shaded by trees, overgrown with vegetation, or filled with rubbish. As a result, even common species such as *Coenagrion puella* and *Sympetrum striolatum* are now absent from large areas of farmland. However, such losses can be made good. Many ponds still exist, and if excessive tree growth and vegetation is cut back, and if they can be kept free of water polluted by slurry or fertilizer, they can be restored effectively. However, overgrown ponds may harbour rare invertebrates and plants that are adapted to such conditions and which may be of greater conservation value than the potential dragonfly fauna. In such circumstances, it would be better to construct a new pond altogether if a suitable site is available. Such a site should be chosen with care – a damp, boggy corner of a field may be important in its present state, and better left as it is. A biological survey is advisable at an early planning stage.

Changes on low-lying alluvial land have been more damaging to the dragonfly fauna, and are harder to rectify. When alluvial land is used for arable farming, it is advantageous to lower the water table. As a result, the networks of ditches, dug originally to drain the land of excess water, now sometimes dry out completely, or are kept free of aquatic plants by frequent herbicidal treatments. These activities destroy the habitat of those species which depend upon relatively undisturbed, unpolluted water with plentiful aquatic vegetation. It is not surprising that *C. pulchellum, Brachytron pratense* and *Lestes dryas* have declined in areas such as the Fens of Cambridgeshire and Lincolnshire, and Romney/Walland Marshes in Kent, and elsewhere. (*Aeshna isosceles* probably became extinct in the Fens in the 19th century as a result of improved drainage.) In the Broadland area of East Anglia, many grazing marshes are now unsuitable for *A. isosceles*. The special measures needed to maintain its habitat may often be impracticable outside nature reserves and designated land. *B. pratense* has benefited from conservation measures in parts of the Somerset Levels, as have *A. isosceles* and *Libellula fulva* at Strumpshaw Fen reserve in Norfolk, a reserve managed by the Royal Society for the Protection of Birds (RSPB) (Tickner, Evans & Blackburn 1991), and at the Suffolk Wildlife Trust's reserve at Castle Marsh (Leyshon & Moore 1993).

Another problem in low-lying alluvial areas, and in much of eastern England generally, is over-extraction of water from rivers and underground aquifers for crop irrigation and industrial and domestic use, thus further lowering the water table. Amongst river species, *Platycnemis pennipes* and *Calopteryx splendens* are especially affected. Dragonflies that favour marshes and shallow fens, and which are thus highly susceptible to seral changes, are particularly threatened, eg *Lestes dryas and S. sanguineum*. Clearly, dragonflies from low-lying alluvial land and neighbouring areas are having a hard time, and not just the scarcer species. Populations of relatively common species, eg *Pyrrhosoma nymphula*, also have declined. On intensively cultivated land, significant improvements to dragonfly habitats can be achieved by government action – by producing incentives for less intensive agriculture, by imposing stringent controls on water extraction and use, and by improving pollution control.

Outside of areas where cereal and vegetable growing is the main land use, animal husbandry prevails. The provision of piped water has greatly reduced the number of farm ponds. Increased use of nitrogenous fertilizers and increased stocking rates of dairy and beef cattle all lead to pollution of ponds, streams and rivers, both in lowland and upland areas. Accidental overflow and spillage of slurry have been particularly damaging to dragonfly populations. Habitats of *Calopteryx virgo, C. splendens, Cordulegaster boltonii* and *Platycnemis pennipes* have been damaged in this way. Pig slurry from intensive units is a major threat to a number of wetlands in Britain and Ireland. In sheep country, pollution of streams with sheep dip has caused local damage, notably in the 1960s when Dieldrin was used. However, in upland sheep country and in deer forests (see **Glossary**) in the Caithness and Sutherland Flow Country and other parts of Scotland, the main threat to dragonflies comes from afforestation with conifers.

Large-scale afforestation of moorland has taken place in Scotland, and elsewhere, this century. The main damage is caused by drainage operations prior to planting, and subsequently by acidification from runoff. Dragonflies which breed in blanket, valley or lowland cut-over bogs have suffered as a result. These include *Aeshna caerulea, Somatochlora arctica, Leucorrhinia dubia* and *Coenagrion hastulatum* – species which, in Britain, all have their headquarters in Scotland. Of these, only *S. arctica* is found in Ireland, in Co Kerry. It is essential that, at sites of new or replanted conifer forests, areas of bog are left undrained; that trees are not planted up to the margins of lochans; that a mix of tree species is used; and that open glades and rides are planned at an early stage. These measures are essential for providing shelter and feeding areas for dragonflies, as well as being important aids to dispersal in some species.

Raised bog formerly covered over 300 000 ha in Ireland (O'Connell 1987). Large-scale commercial peat extraction by giant milling machines for horticulture, electricity generation and domestic fuel has destroyed over 95% of the original bog habitat. Even so, in Ireland as well as at such sites in Britain, there may be scope for producing wetland habitats once the peat areas have been worked out, although these may be very different in character from the acidic bog habitats which they replace. Abandoned small-scale peat workings have provided, and still provide, many potential breeding sites for dragonflies. Species such as *C. lunulatum* in northern Ireland, and *Ceriagrion tenellum* and *L. dubia* in England may have benefited from such activities, along with many others, eg *Coenagrion pulchellum, Lestes sponsa, Aeshna juncea* and *Sympetrum danae*. At many of its sites in England, *L. dubia* has occupied pools formed by peat digging on lowland raised bogs. A major threat to English populations has been the drying out and consequent invasion by scrub and shading out of the site when a drained and cut-over bog is abandoned without adequate blocking of ditches. Nowadays, these cut-over bogs can only be protected adequately on managed nature reserves. Fortunately, for many of them, this is already the case.

Large areas of Britain were once covered by lowland heath. These were areas of shallow soils and low fertility, but their natural bogs and runnels produced habitats that were exceptionally good for dragonflies, eg *C. mercuriale, Ischnura pumilio* and *Orthetrum coerulescens*. The agricultural value of lowland heath was so low that from the 19th century onwards an increasing proportion has been afforested with conifers and, more recently, used for gravel and sand extraction or has been built on (Moore 1962; Webb 1986; Eversham 1991). Although destruction of heathland in East Anglia, Kent and Sussex has left the few remaining heathland sites extremely isolated, the small populations of *Ceriagrion tenellum, O. coerulescens* and *S. danae* seem able to survive so long as their localities are actively managed (Moore 1986); yet all are vulnerable to other pressures. In the last 50 years, much heathland has been reclaimed for agriculture. The result has been that this once-abundant habitat has largely disappeared, except where it is common land or used for military training, or has been deliberately conserved on nature reserves or through the Sites of Special Scientific Interest (SSSI) procedure. The threat to heathland was perceived relatively early, and a number of heaths are now National Nature Reserves (NNR), or are reserves managed by the county Wildlife Trusts, the Royal Society for the Protection of Birds (RSPB), or are designated SSSI. On many protected heaths, new pools could be dug, or produced with the judicious use of high explosives. These activities should also be encouraged in remaining areas of heath on the fringes of military training areas, and within conifer plantations – water points are needed for fire control and these can be constructed so that they are excellent habitats for dragonflies. However, it must be stressed that ponds should not be constructed on heathland runnels and streams unless a thorough biological survey has been undertaken first, because these habitats are important for a number of rare plants and invertebrates, including *Coenagrion mercuriale*, the only resident British dragonfly of importance in a European context. In former years, these sites were prevented from becoming overgrown with rank vegetation by the grazing of stock animals. Not surprisingly, this activity persists in the two most important areas for *C. mercuriale*, namely the New Forest in Hampshire, and Mynydd Preseli in

Pembrokeshire, and should be a feature of management plans for wet heathland in all areas.

In the period of industrial agriculture, extensive house building and road building schemes in Britain have produced a great demand for clay, chalk, gravel, sand and limestone. The large holes which the extractive industries leave behind are initially very inhospitable places for dragonflies, and may remain that way. But many have become full – or, better, partly full – of water, and have produced new habitats for over half the British and Irish species. *Orthetrum cancellatum* and *Enallagma cyathigerum* are early and very successful colonists, and are probably more abundant today than at any time in history. *I. pumilio* has recently been discovered breeding in flushes resulting from disturbed spring-lines in chalk and gravel pits in southern England and a number of quarries in northern Ireland, and is clearly an early colonist at several of these sites. *Brachytron pratense, Cordulia aenea, Somatochlora metallica* and *Libellula fulva* have all been reported from mature gravel pits in southern England where there are shallow, well-vegetated and gently sloping margins and, in the case of the two corduliid species, also shaded bays overhung with trees. There is great scope for dragonfly conservation in gravel pits, and other extractive pits, both at the stage of restoration and in the years that follow. Experience shows that they benefit from positive management.

We must conclude that the change from traditional to industrial agriculture has caused habitat loss and deterioration on a grand scale. Yet the total amount of dragonfly habitat, in Britain at least, may not have altered very much because of the great increase in new habitats in the form of flooded gravel, sand and clay pits, and garden ponds, in southern Britain. The total biomass of dragonflies – largely made up of very common species – may not have altered much either because, in addition to new habitats, there has been a great increase in the populations of several species during this century. *Aeshna mixta, O. cancellatum* and *Sympetrum sanguineum* are extending their ranges in Britain, as is the latter species in Ireland. *O. cancellatum* may possibly be increasing in Ireland, too.

However, whilst three species, at least, have extended their range, a further three, which were on the edge of their European range in Britain, have become extinct during the last 40 years. *Coenagrion scitulum* was lost when its two neighbouring sites in Essex were inundated with sea water in 1953. *C. armatum* became extinct a few years later when its sole remaining locality in Norfolk became choked with vegetation and dried out. *Oxygastra curtisii* was lost in the early

1960s from its single locality along the Moors River in Dorset (formerly Hampshire), probably as a result of pollution combined with other factors. These three cases demonstrate the need to conserve more than one site for rare species, whenever possible.

The loss of habitats in the last 50 years has stimulated conservation measures by both governmental and voluntary conservation organisations. Since the formation of the Nature Conservancy in 1949, it and its successor the Nature Conservancy Council and now the Country Councils (English Nature, the Countryside Council for Wales, and Scottish Natural Heritage) have built up and administer a system of NNRs. The objective of the system is to establish NNRs as representatives of all the main biotopes found in Britain. The NNRs have been selected primarily on their vegetational characteristics, not on the presence of particular plant or animal species. It has been assumed that this selection will conserve representative populations of most of the country's flora and fauna. Insofar as dragonflies are concerned, this assumption has been vindicated: all British dragonflies are found in one or more of the 234 National Nature Reserves, except for *Gomphus vulgatissimus* (Moore 1991e). However, this species occurs in at least three nature reserves managed by a voluntary Wildlife Trust, and in one National Trust property.

The NNR series is supported by the system of SSSIs. In recent years the criteria for selecting SSSIs have been refined (Nature Conservancy Council 1989). As a result, a larger number of types of water body have been notified and special criteria have been devised so that an SSSI can be selected for its dragonfly species alone. Localities containing strong populations of the rarest species are considered for notification, as are the best localities for scarce species in each 'area of search' (often an administrative county). Also, dragonfly communities with outstanding assemblages of species can be notified. The number of species which qualifies in a particular district varies because the number of species occurring in each region varies: an assemblage of 12 species is common in Hampshire but exceptional in Scotland. Scheduling land as an SSSI does not ensure total protection, but, since the passing of the Wildlife and Countryside Act in 1981, agricultural and forestry operations, as well as planning applications, are the subject of consultation with the statutory conservation bodies. Also, government money is available to compensate landowners and to give grants if an agreement is entered into with a Country Council to manage a site for nature conservation. The Countryside Stewardship Scheme also actively promotes the re-creation of biotopes of value for

nature conservation. An increasing number of SSSIs are acquired or managed as nature reserves by voluntary Wildlife Trusts, the RSPB and the National Trust, who may receive financial help from the Country Councils towards the costs of management. Comparable systems of site notification are in operation in both Northern Ireland and in the Republic of Ireland.

In early 1995, the UK government proposed the designation of over 200 Special Areas of Conservation (SACs) under the European Union Habitats Directive. Important dragonfly habitats are well represented in the SACs, including the New Forest, the Dorset heaths, Preseli in south Wales, and Loch Maree in Ross and Cromarty.

There has been a welcome increase in positive conservation measures to support dragonflies on both statutory and non-governmental nature reserves. These measures have not only maintained populations which were present when the reserve was established, but have provided new habitats which have been colonised by many species, including a number of rarities (Pickess 1989). The RSPB has produced guidelines for gravel pit management (Andrews & Kinsman 1990) which pay particular attention to the needs of dragonflies. The Joint Nature Conservation Committee and the RSPB, in association with National Power, have published a guide to habitat management for invertebrates (Kirby 1992), which takes account of dragonfly conservation.

Ponds, both natural and man-made, are largely transient habitats. Different species of plants and animals have become adapted to exploiting the different stages of pond succession from open water to wet woodland. Therefore, when the objective is to conserve aquatic plants and animals in general, such as on nature reserves, it is preferable to maintain a full range of successional types, by not over-managing existing ponds and by periodically creating new ones, rather than maintaining all ponds in a mid-successional stage (Biggs *et al.* 1994). This policy caters well for dragonflies, but is not feasible on most farms or gardens. There, careful management to maintain the mid-successional stages (well-vegetated and with areas of open water), when the pond's hydrology and vegetation is most varied, may be the only way to ensure the continued presence of a wide diversity of wildlife, including dragonflies. When the removal of invasive vegetation becomes necessary to maintain areas of open water, this is better done by periodically clearing a wedge of vegetation from shallow to deep water, than by clearing the whole pond at once.

Much of the initiative for making ponds on farms has come from the Farming and Wildlife Advisory Group (FWAG) which has a group in each county.

Over 40 counties have a full-time Farming and Conservation Adviser who, at the request of a farmer, supplies information on what there is of interest on the farm, how habitats should be managed, and how to obtain financial support for conservation activities. FWAG is an umbrella body consisting of farmers and all the main agricultural and conservation organisations. It is partly funded by government and partly by conservation bodies, industry and the farming community. Since 1983, when the FWAG was founded, 17 000 farms have been visited. As a result, hundreds of farmers have made new ponds or have rehabilitated old ones. In Wiltshire, some farmers formed a special group especially to construct and manage ponds on their land.

The success of these initiatives and comparable efforts by gardeners depends on using what we know about the biology and habitat requirements of dragonflies. Bearing in mind the need for care in choosing a suitable site, as mentioned earlier in this chapter, the basic requirements for making a good dragonfly pond are relatively simple.

- The pond must hold water throughout the year.

- Trees and bushes at the edge of the pond must not be allowed to get too large. It is important to prevent shading on the south side of the pond.

- The pond should include shallow areas and have gently shelving edges.

- The water must contain submerged, floating and emergent water plants for oviposition and for larvae to live amongst and emerge from.

- Reeds and bulrush must be controlled if they threaten to take over the pond.

- The pond must be kept free from pollution. It is particularly important to ensure that the pond is sited so that it does not receive drainage water from fields which are heavily treated with nitrogenous fertilizers or from ditches which can get contaminated with slurry or other runoff.

- If possible, ponds should be sited away from buildings and other places which support large populations of house sparrows (*Passer domesticus*), as these birds prey extensively on emerging dragonflies.

- In exposed locations, trees and bushes should be planted in close proximity to the pond (10–50 m), in order to provide sheltered feeding and resting areas for adults. Tall, rank grasses in such areas serve a similar function and should be encouraged.

- Ponds intended for dragonflies should not be stocked with fish, as they may compete with larvae for available food, or eat the larvae themselves, or with wildfowl, as these may seriously pollute the water with their excrement.

Colonisation of ponds by dragonflies is usually very rapid, especially in areas where other dragonfly habitats already exist. The process can be accelerated by planting emergent plants and submerged macrophytes after constructing the

Table 6. Conservation status and legislative designation of British and Irish Odonata species (the threat categories to which species have been assigned refer only to Great Britain, and cannot be regarded as a guide to the status of these species in Ireland)

Species	EII	EIV	B	WCA	1+	1	2	3
Oxygastra curtisii	+	+	+		+			
Coenagrion mercuriale	+		+					+
Aeshna isosceles				+		+		
Coenagrion armatum					+			
Coenagrion scitulum					+			
Coenagrion hastulatum							+	
Lestes dryas							+	
Somatochlora arctica								+
Libellula fulva								+

Key:

EII   EC 'Habitats and species' Directive, Annex II (Special Areas of Conservation to be designated)
EIV   EC 'Habitats and species' Directive, Annex IV (special protection for species)
B   Bern Convention, Appendix II (special protection for species)
WCA   Wildlife and Conservation Act 1981, Schedule 5 (special protection for species)
1+   Red Data Book (RDB) Category 1+, believed extinct
1   RDB Category 1, Endangered
2   RDB Category 2, Vulnerable
3   RDB Category 3, Rare

At the pan-European level, van Tol and Verdonk (1988) recognise both *Coenagrion mercuriale* and *Oxygastra curtisii* as endangered, and list *Coenagrion lunulatum, C. scitulum* and *Gomphus vulgatissimus* as vulnerable

pond. One of the authors did this on his own pond in a Cambridgeshire village, which was made according to the specifications outlined above. Seventeen species were recorded on it during the first five years, 14 in the first season. Fourteen have bred successfully (Moore 1991c).

In Britain and Ireland, numerous organisations and individuals are concerned to conserve dragonflies whenever possible. The British Dragonfly Society (BDS) is at the forefront of such activities. It has set up a Dragonfly Conservation Group, which advises on all aspects of dragonfly conservation. It provides a formal link with the statutory conservation agencies for England (English Nature), Scotland (Scottish Natural Heritage) and Wales (Countryside Council for Wales), and with the Department of the Environment for Northern Ireland and the Joint Nature Conservation Committee. The BDS also has representation on a number of fora, such as the Peatland Conservation Consortium, the Pond Conservation Group and the Joint Committee for the Conservation of British Invertebrates. It has produced illustrated leaflets on pond construction (British Dragonfly Society 1992) and on the management of wetlands for dragonflies (British Dragonfly Society 1993), and a code of practice on collecting. The BDS has also been closely involved with the national WATCH programme, bringing an awareness of dragonflies to children.

International liaison on conservation is achieved through the Societas Internationalis Odonatologica and through the Odonata Specialist Group of the Species Survival Commission of the International Union for the Conservation of Nature and Natural Resources. Several countries, including Britain, cover dragonfly species in their conservation legislation (see Table 6). However, the conservation of habitats is immeasurably more important as a means of conserving dragonflies.

Table 6 shows the dragonfly species which are included in European or British legislation and conventions. Additionally, the Red Data Book species are listed, as sites for these species qualify for consideration as SSSIs (Nature Conservancy Council 1989). Note that the Red Data Book status is taken from Shirt (1987), but a revision is due soon.

Definitions of RDB categories are given by Shirt (1987). Although most Red Data species occur in 15 or fewer 10 km squares, the criteria for inclusion in the RDB are based on threat (eg rate of habitat loss and species decline), and not simply rarity; so that threatened species which occur in rather more than 15 squares may still be included in the RDB.

Additionally, the following species are listed as Nationally Scarce in the SSSI Guidelines (NCC 1989). The usual definition of 'Nationally Scarce' is that a species occurs in 16–100 10 km squares in Britain; the species marked * have been recorded in more than 100 squares since 1980.

> *Aeshna caerulea*
> *Brachytron pratense* *
> *Ceriagrion tenellum*
> *Coenagrion pulchellum* *
> *Cordulia aenea*
> *Gomphus vulgatissimus*
> *Ischnura pumilio* *
> *Leucorrhinia dubia*
> *Somatochlora metallica*

LITERATURE AND REFERENCES

SOURCES OF INFORMATION

Dragonflies by Corbet, Longfield and Moore (1960), and *A biology of dragonflies* by Corbet (1962) provide a thorough introduction to the subject, and review the older literature in detail. *Dragonflies* by Miller (1987) brings the subject up-to-date, as well as providing illustrated keys for identification. *The dragonflies of Great Britain and Ireland* by Hammond (2nd edition, revised R Merritt 1983) also has keys and large illustrations. The colour photographs in *A complete guide to British dragonflies* by McGeeney (1986) are useful adjuncts to his keys and descriptions.

The dragonflies of Europe by Askew (1988) is an essential reference work for those studying dragonflies on the continent of Europe. However, it is a large book, and some may find *A field guide to the dragonflies of Europe and North Africa* by Aguilar, Dommanget and Prechac (English edition 1986) or *Dragonflies and damselflies of Britain and northern Europe* by Gibbons (1986) more portable.

Each of the available guides has its merits and its drawbacks, and each will appeal to some readers. A tabular review of identification guides is provided by Jones (1987).

The British Dragonfly Society produces its own *Journal*, with two issues each year. Its articles are full of interest to those concerned primarily with British and Irish species. It includes book reviews. On the world scale, the Societas Internationalis Odonatologica (SIO) produces *Odonatologica* four times a year, as well as *Notulae Odonatologicae* for shorter articles. *Odonatologica* provides a comprehensive abstracting service, as well as containing a large proportion of the papers on dragonflies which are published.

LARVAL IDENTIFICATION

The identification of larvae and exuviae to species is becoming increasingly important in the context of Odonata monitoring. The papers by Gardner (1954, 1955) were reprinted in Corbet *et al.* (1960), and again in Hammond (1977, 1983). Hammond's work was intended to be accompanied by a second volume, to be written by Gardner, dealing in detail with larvae, but unfortunately Gardner's untimely death prevented this.

These same keys provided the basis for others, such as those in Miller (1987), and the keys in Askew (1988) also rely heavily on Gardner for British and Irish species. The keys by Carchini (1983) to the

larvae of Italian Odonata (written in English and well illustrated) introduce a few new identification features, and are differently structured, so provide some alternative. However, there remain several difficulties in determining larvae and exuviae to species. In particular, it should be noted that all keys so far published are intended for use with final instar larvae, and that they will be correspondingly less reliable if applied to earlier stages. Almost all key features are readily seen on exuviae. Many of the characters used in the key are far easier to interpret if reference material is available, so it is worthwhile collecting a range of exuviae before attempting to use the keys.

Identifications based on the number of labial setae are not always reliable: in particular, the separation of *Lestes dryas* from *L. sponsa*, and of *Ischnura pumilio* from *I. elegans* by means of counting the setae on the prementum and the labial palps is not infallible. Female *Lestes* larvae are more reliably separable in late instars by the size and proportions of the genitalia. In *I. elegans*, the spines on the lateral ridges of abdominal segments 7 and 8 are stouter than those on the ventral surface; there is no such size difference in *I. pumilio*. There appears at present to be no reliable means of separating *Coenagrion puella* and *C. pulchellum* as larvae. The separation of *Sympetrum sanguineum* and *S. striolatum/nigrescens*, based on the relative length of the lateral spine on abdominal segment 9, can cause difficulties for inexperienced observers. A solution to such problems is to take a few larvae home and breed them out. Some useful information on this subject is given by Butler (1985).

REFERENCES USED IN THIS *ATLAS*

The information contained in the individual species accounts is based on the work of numerous authors, as well as on unpublished information. It would be impractical to include references for every statement. Therefore, if a statement is derived from the following works, or from papers referred to in their bibliographies, it is not usually given a separate reference.

World distribution	Askew (1988)
General biology	Corbet, Longfield & Moore (1960)
	Corbet (1962)
Conservation status in Europe	Maibach & Meier (1987) van Tol & Verdonk (1988)
Adult population densities	Moore (1964, 1991c)

The references which are given below are to be found in the text of this *Atlas* and draw attention to some (but only some) recent studies.

REFERENCES

Aguilar, J. d', Dommanget, J.L. & Prechac, R. 1986. *A field guide to the dragonflies of Europe and North Africa.* English ed. London: Collins.

Allport, A.M. 1985. A further note on the occurrence of the migrant hawker *Aeshna mixta* in Yorkshire. *Yorkshire Naturalists' Union Bulletin,* **4**, 6.

Andrews, J. & Kinsman, D. 1990. *Gravel pit restoration for wildlife: a practical manual.* Sandy: Royal Society for the Protection of Birds.

Askew, R.R. 1982. Roosting and resting site selection by coenagrionid damselflies. *Advances in Odonatology,* **1**, 1-8.

Askew, R.R. 1988. *The dragonflies of Europe.* Colchester: Harley.

Averill, M.T. 1989. Emergence attitudes in *Gomphus vulgatissimus* (L.). *Journal of the British Dragonfly Society,* **5**, 37-39.

Balfour-Browne, F. 1904. A bionomical investigation of the Norfolk Broads. *Transactions of the Norfolk and Norwich Naturalists' Society,* **7**, 661-673.

Banks, M.J. & Thompson, D.J. 1985. Lifetime mating success in the damselfly *Coenagrion puella. Animal Behaviour,* **33**, 1175-1183.

Banks, M.J. & Thompson, D.J. 1987. Regulation of damselfly populations: the effects of larval density on larval survival, development rates and size in the field. *Freshwater Biology,* **17**, 357-365.

Belle, J. 1980. Survey of the dragonfly fauna of the Sarnian Islands. *Report and Transactions of La Société Guernesiaise,* **20**, 465-481.

Benton, E. 1988. The dragonflies of Essex. *Essex Naturalist,* **9**. London: Essex Field Club.

Benton, E. & Payne, R.G. 1983. On the rediscovery of *Lestes dryas* Kirby in Britain. *Journal of the British Dragonfly Society,* **1**, 28-30.

Berry, R.J. 1988. *Biological survey: needs and network.* London: Linnean Society of London.

Biggs, J., Corfield, A., Walker, D., Whitfield, M. & Williams, P. 1994. New approaches to the management of ponds. *British Wildlife,* **5**, 273-287.

Blackwood, G.G. 1950. The possible occurrence of *Somatochlora alpestris* in Scotland. *Scottish Naturalist,* **62**, 31-32.

Bond, K.G.M. 1989. *Aeshna cyanea* (Müller), Odonata Aeshnidae, a dragonfly new to Ireland. *Irish Naturalists' Journal,* **23**, 73-74.

Brakefield, P.M. 1987. Geographical variation in, and temperature effects on, the phenology of *Maniola jurtina* and *Pyronia tithonus* (Lepidoptera, Satyrinae) in England and Wales. *Ecological Entomology,* **12**, 139-148.

British Dragonfly Society. 1988. *Code of practice on collecting dragonflies in the United Kingdom.* Purley: British Dragonfly Society.

British Dragonfly Society. 1991. Instructions to authors (includes list of recommended scientific and vernacular names). *Journal of the British Dragonfly Society,* **7** (1).

British Dragonfly Society. 1992. *Dig a pond for dragonflies.* Purley: British Dragonfly Society.

British Dragonfly Society. 1993. *Managing habitats for dragonflies.* Purley: British Dragonfly Society.

Brooks, S.J. 1988. Book review: *The dragonflies of Europe,* by R.R. Askew. *Journal of the British Dragonfly Society,* **4**, 46-48.

Brooks, S.J. 1989. The dragonflies (Odonata) of London: the current status. *London Naturalist,* **68**, 109-131.

Brooks, S.J. 1993. Review of a method to monitor adult dragonfly populations. *Journal of the British Dragonfly Society,* **9**, 1-4.

Brownett, A. 1994. Resource partitioning in the genus *Calopteryx:* an unsolved problem of odonatology. *Journal of the British Dragonfly Society,* **10**, 6-11.

Buckland, P.C. & Coope, G.R. 1991. *A bibliography and literature review of Quaternary entomology.* Sheffield: Collis.

Butler, S. 1983. Notes on finding larvae of *Somatochlora arctica* (Zetterstedt) in N.W. Scotland. *Journal of the British Dragonfly Society,* **1**, 4-5.

Butler, S. 1985. Rearing dragonfly larvae. *Journal of the British Dragonfly Society,* **1**, 74-77.

Carchini, G. 1983. A key to the Italian odonate larvae. *Societas Internationalis Odonatologica rapid communication* (Supplement), **1**.

Cham, S.A. 1990. A study of *Ischnura pumilio* (Charpentier) with particular reference to the state of maturity of the female form *aurantiaca. Journal of the British Dragonfly Society,* **6**, 42-44.

Cham, S.A. 1991. The scarce blue-tailed damselfly *Ischnura pumilio* (Charpentier): its habitat preferences in south-east England. *Journal of the British Dragonfly Society,* **7**, 18-25.

Cham, S.A. 1992. Ovipositing behaviour and observations on the eggs and prolarvae of *Ischnura pumilio* (Charpentier). *Journal of the British Dragonfly Society,* **8** (2), 6-10.

Chelmick, D.G., ed. 1979. *Provisional atlas of the insects of the British Isles, part 7, Odonata.* 2nd ed. Huntingdon: Institute of Terrestrial Ecology.

Chelmick, D.G. 1983. Observations on the ecology and distribution of *Oxygastra curtisii* (Dale). *Journal of the British Dragonfly Society,* **1**, 11-14.

Clarke, D.J. 1994. Notes on the larva and generation time of *Aeshna caerulea* (Ström) in Scotland, with particular reference to the south-west. *Journal of the British Dragonfly Society*, **10**, 29-36.

Clarke, D.J., Hewitt, S.M., Smith, E.M. & Smith, R.W.J. 1990. Observations on the breeding habits and habitat of *Aeshna caerulea* (Ström) in Scotland. *Journal of the British Dragonfly Society*, **6**, 24-29.

Colley, L.T. 1983. *Coenagrion mercuriale* (Charpentier) in Anglesey, north Wales. *Journal of the British Dragonfly Society*, **1**, 27.

Convey, P. 1989. Post-copulatory guarding strategies in the non-territorial dragonfly *Sympetrum sanguineum* (Müller) (Odonata: Libellulidae). *Animal Behaviour*, **37**, 56-63.

Corbet, P.S. 1957. The life-histories of two summer species of dragonfly (Odonata, Coenagriidae). *Proceedings of the Zoological Society of London*, **128**, 403-418.

Corbet, P.S. 1962. *A biology of dragonflies.* London: Witherby. (Reprinted 1983, Faringdon: Classey.)

Corbet, P.S. & Harvey, I.F. 1989. Seasonal regulation in *Pyrrhosoma nymphula* (Sulzer) (Zygoptera: Coenagrionidae). 1. Seasonal development in nature. *Odonatologica*, **18**, 133-145.

Corbet, P.S., Longfield, C. & Moore, N.W. 1960. *Dragonflies.* London: Collins. (Reprinted 1985.)

Cotton, D.C.F. 1981. Some new records and an appraisal of the published records for *Ischnura pumilio* (Charpentier)(Odonata: Coenagriidae) in Ireland. *Entomologist's Gazette*, **32**, 59-64.

Cotton, D.C.F. 1982. *Coenagrion lunulatum* (Charpentier) (Odonata: Coenagrionidae) new to the British Isles. *Entomologist's Gazette*, **33**, 213-214.

Dale, C.W. 1901. Notes on British dragonflies. *Entomologist*, **34**, 53.

Dandy, J.E. 1969. *Watsonian vice-counties of Great Britain.* London: Ray Society.

Dawson, N. 1988. Forty years on: a comparison of the dragonfly fauna of Bedfordshire in the 1940s with the situation today. *Journal of the British Dragonfly Society*, **4**, 25-28.

Dommanget, J-L. 1987. *Étude faunistique et bibliographique des odonates de France.* (Inventaires de faune et de flore, **36**.) Paris: Secrétariat de la Faune et de la Flore.

Doubleday, H. 1871. A list of the Odonata (Dragon-flies) occurring in the neighbourhood of Epping. *Entomologist's Monthly Magazine*, **8**, 86-87.

Drake, C.M. 1990. Records of larval *Lestes dryas* Kirby in Essex during 1987. *Journal of the British Dragonfly Society*, **6**, 34-41.

Drake, C.M. 1991. The condition of *Lestes dryas* Kirby larval populations in some Essex grazing marshes in May 1990. *Journal of the British Dragonfly Society*, **7**, 10-17.

Evans, F. 1989. *A review of the management of lowland wet heath in Dyfed, west Wales.* (Nature Conservancy Council contract surveys, no. 42.) Peterborough: Nature Conservancy Council.

Evans, M.W.F. 1845. *British Libelluldae or dragon flies.* London: Bridgewater.

Evans, W. 1911. Scottish dragonflies. *Annals of Scottish Natural History*, **20**, 14-25.

Eversham, B.C. 1991. Thorne and Hatfield Moors: implications of land use change for nature conservation. *Thorne and Hatfield Moors Papers*, **2**, 3-18.

Eversham, B.C. 1994. Using invertebrates to monitor land use change and site management. In: *Invertebrates in the landscape: invertebrate recording in site evaluation and countryside monitoring*, edited by P.T. Harding, 36-45. *British Journal of Entomology and Natural History*, **7** (supplement), 36-45. (Proceedings of the National Federation for Biological Recording Annual Conference.)

Eversham, B.C. & Arnold, H.R. 1991. Introductions and their place in British wildlife. In: *Biological recording of changes in British wildlife*, edited by P.T. Harding, 44-59. (ITE symposium no. 26.) London: HMSO.

Foster, G.N. 1994. Evidence for pH insensitivity in Odonata of peat pools. *Journal of the British Dragonfly Society*, **10**, 40-44.

Fox, A.D. 1987. *Ischnura pumilio* (Charpentier) in Wales: a preliminary review. *Journal of the British Dragonfly Society*, **3**, 32-36.

Fox, A.D. 1989. *Ischnura pumilio* (Charpentier) (Odonata: Coenagrionidae) - a wandering opportunist? *Entomologist's Record*, **101**, 25-26.

Fox, A.D. 1991. How common is terrestrial oviposition in *Somatochlora metallica* Vander Linden? *Journal of the British Dragonfly Society*, **7**, 38-39.

Fraser, F.C. 1940. Historical, biological and ecological notes on *Oxygastra curtisii* (Dale) (order Odonata). *Journal of the Society for British Entomology*, **2**, 45-53.

Fraser, F.C. 1947. Is *Somatochlora alpestris* Sélys (Odon., Corduliidae) a British species? *Entomologist's Monthly Magazine*, **83**, 86-87.

Fraser, F.C. 1949. *Odonata.* (Handbooks for the identification of British insects, **1** (10).) London: Royal Entomological Society.

Fraser, F.C. 1956. A restatement of the case of *Pantala flavescens* (F.) (Odon., Libellulidae) as a casual visitor to Britain. *Entomologist's Monthly Magazine*, **92**, 347-350.

Fraser, F.C. 1957. Historical notes on the occurrence of *Sympetrum meridionale* Sélys (Odon., Libellulidae) in Britain. *Entomologist's Monthly Magazine*, **93**, 42-47.

Fraser, F.C. 1958. Some further notes extracted from the Sélys-Dale correspondence bearing on the occurrence of *Sympetrum meridionale* (Sélys) in Britain (Odon., Libellulidae). *Entomologist's Monthly Magazine*, **94**, 151-153.

Gabb, R. & Kitching, D. 1992. *The dragonflies and damselflies of Cheshire.* Liverpool: National Museums and Galleries on Merseyside.

Gardner, A.E. 1954. A key to the larvae of the British Odonata. Part I. Zygoptera. Part II. Anisoptera. *Entomologist's Gazette*, **5**, 157-171, 193-213.

Gardner, A.E. 1955. A study of the genitalia of the two species *Sympetrum nigrescens* Lucas and *S. nigrifemur* (Sélys) with notes on their distribution (Odonata: Libellulidae). *Entomologist's Gazette*, **6**, 86-108.

Gaunt, R.G. 1984. A remarkable emergence of *Aeshna cyanea* at a small pond in the Forest of Dean. *Journal of the British Dragonfly Society*, **1**, 45-46.

Geijskes, D.C. & van Tol, J. 1983. *De libellen van Nederland (Odonata).* Hoogwoud (N.H.): Koninklijke Nederlandse Natuurhistorische Vereniging.

Gibbons, R.B. 1986. *Dragonflies and damselflies of Britain and northern Europe.* Twickenham: Country Life/Hamlyn.

Goyvaerts, P. 1979. *Cordulia aenea* (Odonata: Corduliidae), a new county record. *Irish Naturalists' Journal*, **19**, 329.

Graves, P.P. 1947. Odonata at Killarney. *Irish Naturalists' Journal*, **9**, 61-63.

Hämäläinen, M. 1985. Note on 'nigrescens-like' specimens of *Sympetrum striolatum* (Odonata, Libellulidae) in the Aland Islands. *Notulae Entomologicae*, **65**, 68.

Hammond, C.O. 1977. *The dragonflies of Great Britain and Ireland.* London: Curwen.

Hammond, C.O. 1983. *The dragonflies of Great Britain and Ireland.* 2nd ed., revised R. Merritt. Colchester: Harley.

Harding, P.T. & Sheail, J. 1992. The Biological Records Centre -a pioneer in data gathering and retrieval. In: *Biological recording of changes in British wildlife*, edited by P.T. Harding, 5-19. (ITE symposium no. 26.) London: HMSO.

Harley, J.L. 1975. *Ordnance Survey maps: a descriptive manual.* Southampton: Ordnance Survey.

Harvey, I.F. 1985. *Larval spacing behaviour of two species of damselfly (Odonata: Zygoptera).* PhD thesis, University of Dundee.

Harvey, I.F. & Corbet, P.S. 1985. Territorial behaviour of larvae enhances mating success of male dragonflies. *Animal Behaviour*, **33**, 561-565.

Heath, J. 1971. Insect distribution maps scheme progress report 1971. *Entomologist*, **104**, 305-310.

Heath, J. ed. 1978. *Provisional atlas of the insects of the British Isles, Part 7, Odonata.* Huntingdon: Institute of Terrestrial Ecology.

Henrickson, B-I. 1988. The absence of anti-predator behaviour in the larva of *Leucorrhinia dubia* (Odonata) and the consequences of their distribution. *Oikos*, **51**, 179-183.

Hinnekint, B.O.N. 1987. Population dynamics of *Ischnura e. elegans* (Vander Linden) (Insecta: Odonata) with special reference to morphological colour changes, female polymorphism, multiannual cycles and their influence on behaviour. *Hydrobiologia*, **146**, 3-31.

Holland, S.J. 1983. Dragonfly Survey Reports - 1. Gloucestershire. *Journal of the British Dragonfly Society*, **1**, 1-3.

Holmes, J.D. 1984. Rapid larval development in *Brachytron pratense* (Müller). *Journal of the British Dragonfly Society*, **1**, 38.

Holmes, J.D. 1993. A probable sighting of *Aeshna affinis* in Avon. *Journal of the British Dragonfly Society*, **9**, 17-18.

Holmes, J.D. & Randolph, S. 1994. An early emergence (one year life cycle) of *Libellula depressa* Linnaeus and *Anax imperator* Leach. *Journal of the British Dragonfly Society*, **10**, 25-28.

Imms, A.D., ed. 1938. In: *The Victoria history of the county of Cambridgeshire and the Isle of Ely*, **1**, 92-93. London: Oxford University Press.

Imms, A.D. 1900. A probable case of immigration in *Leucorrhinia dubia* V.d.L. *Entomologist's Monthly Magazine*, **11**, 189.

Jenkins, D.K. 1991. A population study of *Coenagrion mercuriale* (Charpentier) at a New Forest site. Part 4. A review of the years 1985 to 1989. *Journal of the British Dragonfly Society*, **7**, 1-3.

Jones, R.A. 1987. Odonata book review. *Proceedings & Transactions of the British Entomological and Natural History Society*, **20**, 120-121.

Khan, R. 1983. Observations of wood-mice (*Apodemus sylvaticus*) and hobby (*Falco subbuteo*) feeding on dragonflies. *Journal of the British Dragonfly Society*, **1**, 15.

Kaiser, H. 1974. Verhaltensgefüge und Temporialverhalten der Libelle *Aeshna cyanea*. *Zeitschrift für Tierpsychologie*, **34**, 398-429.

Kemp, R.G. & Vick, G.S. 1983. Notes and observations on *Gomphus vulgatissimus* (Linnaeus) on the River Severn and River Thames. *Journal of the British Dragonfly Society*, **1**, 22-25.

Kemp, R.G.K. 1988. Is *Gomphus vulgatissimus* (L.) exclusively a riverine species in the British Isles? *Journal of the British Dragonfly Society*, **4**, 8-9.

Key, R.S. 1989. Peat cutting and invertebrate fauna of lowland peatland with particular reference to the Humberhead Levels mires of Thorne and Hatfield Moors.

In: *The ecology and conservation of cut-over raised mires*, edited by R. Meade & W. Fojt, 32-37. Peterborough: Nature Conservancy Council.

King, J.J.F.X. & Halbert, J.N. 1910. A list of the Neuroptera of Ireland. *Proceedings of the Royal Irish Academy*, **28B (2)**, 29-112.

Kirby, P. 1992. *Habitat management for invertebrates: a practical handbook.* Sandy: Royal Society for the Protection of Birds, for the Joint Nature Conservation Committee.

Kloet, G.S. & Hincks, W.D. 1945. *A check list of British insects.* Stockport: privately published.

Kloet, G.S. & Hincks, W.D. 1964. *Small orders and Hemiptera.* (Handbooks for the identification of British insects, **12** (1).) London: Royal Entomological Society.

Lawton, J.H., Prendergast, J.R. & Eversham, B.C. 1994. The numbers and spatial distributions of species. In: *Systematics and conservation evaluation*, edited by P. Forey, C.J. Humphries & R.I. Vane-Wright, 177-195. Oxford: Oxford University Press.

Le Quesne, W.J. 1946. The dragonflies of Jersey. *Bulletin Annuel de la Société Jersiaise*, **14**, 213-216.

Le Quesne, W.J. 1951. Entomological report for 1950. *Bulletin Annuel de la Société Jersiaise*, **15**, 297.

Leyshon, O.J. & Moore, N.W. 1993. A note on the British Dragonfly Society's survey of *Anaciaeschna isosceles* at Castle Marshes, Barnby, Suffolk, 1991-1992. *Journal of the British Dragonfly Society*, **9**, 5-9.

Limbert, M. 1985. Three rare Yorkshire dragonflies. *Yorkshire Naturalists' Union Bulletin*, **4**, 4.

Limbert, M. 1990. Notes on the Dorchester nymph, *Leucorrhinia dubia* (Vander Linden). *Journal of the British Dragonfly Society*, **6**, 18-19.

Longfield, C. 1937. *The dragonflies of the British Isles.* London: Warne.

Longfield, C. 1948. A vast immigration of dragonflies into the south coast of Co. Cork. *Irish Naturalists' Journal*, **9**, 133-141.

Longfield, C. 1949a. *The dragonflies of the British Isles.* 2nd ed. London: Warne.

Longfield, C. 1949b. The dragonflies of the London area. *London Naturalist*, **28**, 80-98.

Longfield, C. 1949c. The breeding status of *Aeshna mixta* Latreille (Odonata) and notes on the evidence of breeding in *Sympetrum flaveolum* (L.) and *S. fonscolombii* (Sélys). *Journal of the Society for British Entomology*, **3**, 84-88.

Longfield, C. 1954. The British dragonflies (Odonata) in 1952 and 1953. *Entomologist*, **87**, 87-91.

Lucas, W.J. 1900. *British dragonflies (Odonata).* London: Upcott Gill.

Lucas, W.J. 1904. *Agrion hastulatum, Aeshna juncea* and *A. isosceles. Entomologist*, **37**, 85.

Lucas, W.J. 1908. Notes on the British dragonflies of the 'Dale Collection.' *Entomologist's Monthly Magazine*, **44**, 198-203.

Lucas, W.J. 1909. Notes on the British dragonflies of the "Dale Collection". *Entomologist's Monthly Magazine*, **45**, 79-83.

Lucas, W.J. 1912. British Odonata in 1911. *Entomologist*, **45**, 171-173.

Lucas, W.J. 1930. *The aquatic (naiad) stages of the British dragonflies (Paraneuroptera).* London: Ray Society.

Macan, T.T. 1974. Twenty generations of *Pyrrhosoma nymphula* (Sulzer) and *Enallagma cyathigerum* (Charpentier) (Zygoptera: Coenagrionidae). *Odonatologica*, **3**, 107-119.

McGeeney, A. 1986. *A complete guide to British dragonflies.* London: Cape.

Mackenzie Dodds, R. 1992. Inverted emergence of *Ischnura elegans* (Vander Linden) at Ashton Water Dragonfly Sanctuary. *Journal of the British Dragonfly Society*, **8** (2), 13-15.

Marren, P.R. and Merritt, R. 1983. Scarce species status report 2. A review of *Coenagrion hastulatum* (Charpentier) in Britain. *Journal of the British Dragonfly Society*, **1**, 16-19.

McLachlan, R. 1865. Notes on the occurrence of *Aeshna borealis* and other dragonflies at Rannoch. *Entomologist's Monthly Magazine*, **2**, 117-118.

McLachlan, R. 1870. Occurrence of *Cordulia metallica*, Van der Lind.: a dragonfly new to Britain. *Entomologist's Monthly Magazine*, **7**, 38.

McLachlan, R. 1884. The British dragon-flies annotated. *Entomologist's Monthly Magazine*, **20**, 251-256.

McLachlan, R. 1900a. *Agrion hastulatum* Charp., a new British dragonfly. *Entomologist's Monthly Magazine*, **11**, 226.

McLachlan, R. 1900b. Dragonflies in Inverness-shire and Sutherland. *Entomologist's Monthly Magazine*, **11**, 241.

McLachlan, R. 1900c. The exact locality for the Aviemore example of *Agrion hastulatum. Entomologist's Monthly Magazine*, **11**, 263.

Maibach, A. & Meier, C. 1987. *Atlas de distribution des libellules de Suisse (Odonata) (avec liste rouge).* Neuchâtel: Centre Suisse de Cartographie de la Faune.

Mayo, M.C.A. & Welstead, A.R. 1983. *Coenagrion mercuriale* (Charpentier) on the flood plains of the River Itchen and River Test in Hampshire. *Journal of the British Dragonfly Society*, **1**, 20-21.

Mendel, H. 1992. *The dragonflies of Suffolk.* Ipswich: Suffolk Naturalists' Society.

Merritt, R. 1983a. Scarce Species Status Report 1. *Coenagrion mercuriale* (Charpentier) with notes on habitat. *Journal of the British Dragonfly Society*, **1**, 9-12.

Merritt, R. 1983b. An introduction to the study of dragonflies in Devon. *Nature in Devon*, **4**, 7-28.

Merritt, R. 1985. The incidence of *Hemianax ephippiger* (Burmeister) in Britain and Ireland. *Journal of the British Dragonfly Society*, **1**, 105-106.

Merritt, R. 1987. The origins and early history of the British Dragonfly Society: a personal account. *Journal of the British Dragonfly Society*, **3**, 21-27.

Merritt, R. 1988. Key Sites Project. *Odonata Recording Scheme Newsletter*, **10**, 1-12.

Merritt, R. & Vick, G.S. 1983. Is *Sympetrum nigrescens* Lucas a good species? *Journal of the British Dragonfly Society*, **1**, 7-8.

Michiels, N.K. & Dhondt, A.A. 1988. Direct and indirect estimates of sperm precedence and displacement in the dragonfly *Sympetrum danae* (Odonata: Libellulidae). *Behavioural Ecology and Sociobiology*, **23**, 257-263.

Miller, P.L. 1987. *Dragonflies*. Cambridge: Cambridge University Press.

Miller, P.L. & Miller, A.K. 1989. Post-copulatory 'resting' in *Orthetrum coerulescens* (Fabricius) and some other Libellulidae: time for 'sperm handling'? (Anisoptera.) *Odonatologica*, **18**, 33-41.

Milne, B.S. 1984. The dragonfly fauna of the Ouse Valley gravel pits. *Journal of the British Dragonfly Society*, **1**, 55-57.

Moore, B.P. 1949. *Sympetrum meridionale* Sélys (Odon., Libellulidae), new to the Channel Islands. *Entomologist's Monthly Magazine*, **85**, 23.

Moore, N.W. 1952. Notes on the oviposition behaviour of the dragonfly *Sympetrum striolatum* Charpentier. *Behaviour*, **4**, 101-103.

Moore, N.W. 1953. Population density in adult dragonflies (Odonata - Anisoptera). *Journal of Animal Ecology*, **22**, 344-359.

Moore, N.W. 1962. The heaths of Dorset and their conservation. *Journal of Ecology*, **50**, 369-391.

Moore, N.W. 1964. Intra- and interspecific competition among dragonflies (Odonata). An account of observations and field experiments on population density control in Dorset 1954-1960. *Journal of Animal Ecology*, **33**, 49-71.

Moore, N.W. 1975. Butterfly transects in a linear habitat 1964-1973. *Entomologist's Gazette*, **26**, 71-78.

Moore, N.W. 1980. *Lestes dryas* Kirby - a declining species of dragonfly (Odonata) in need of conservation: note on its status and habitat in England and Ireland. *Biological Conservation*, **17**, 143-148.

Moore, N.W. 1986. Acid water dragonflies in eastern England – their decline, isolation and conservation. *Odonatologica*, **15**, 377-385.

Moore, N.W. 1991a. The last of *Oxygastra curtisii* (Dale) in England? *Journal of the British Dragonfly Society*, **7**, 6-10.

Moore, N.W. 1991b. Where do adult *Gomphus vulgatissimus* (L.) go during the middle of the day? *Journal of the British Dragonfly Society*, **7**, 40-43.

Moore, N.W. 1991c. The development of dragonfly communities and the consequences of territorial behaviour: a 27 year study on small ponds at Woodwalton Fen, Cambridgeshire, UK. *Odonatologica*, **20**, 203-231.

Moore, N.W. 1991d. Male *Sympetrum striolatum* (Charpentier) 'defends' a basking spot rather than a particular locality. *Notulae odonatologicae*, **3**, 112.

Moore, N.W. 1991e. Recent developments in the conservation of Odonata in Great Britain. *Advances in Odonatology*, **5**, 103-108.

Moore, N.W. 1995. Experiments on population density of male *Coenagrion puella* (L.) by water (Zygoptera: Coenagrionidae). *Odonatologica*, **24**, 123-128.

Moore, N.W. & Corbet, P.S. 1990. Guidelines for monitoring dragonfly populations. *Journal of the British Dragonfly Society*, **6**, 21-23.

Nature Conservancy Council. 1989. *Guidelines for selection of biological SSSIs*. Peterborough: Nature Conservancy Council.

Nelson, B. 1986. The Odonata of the North of Ireland. *Journal of the British Dragonfly Society*, **2**, 21-23.

O'Connell, C., ed. 1987. *The IPCC guide to Irish peatlands*. Dublin: Irish Peat Conservation Council.

O'Farrell, A.F. 1950. The J.J.F.X. King collection of British Odonata. *Entomologist*, **83**, 14-18.

Parr, M.J. 1969. Comparative notes on the distribution, ecology and behaviour of some dragonflies (Odonata). *Entomologist*, **102**, 151-161.

Parr, M.J. 1970. The life histories of *Ischnura elegans* (Van der Linden) and *Coenagrion puella* (L.) in south Lancashire. *Proceedings of the Royal Entomological Society of London A*, **45**, 172-181.

Parr, M.J. 1973. Ecological studies of *Ischnura elegans* (Van der Linden) (Zygoptera: Coenagrionidae) II. Survivorship, local movements and dispersal. *Odonatologica*, **2**, 159-174.

Parr, M.J. 1976. Some aspects of the population ecology of the damselfly *Enallagma cyathigerum* (Charpentier) (Zygoptera: Coenagrionidae). *Odonatologica*, **5**, 45-57.

Parr, M.J. & Parr, M. 1979. Some observations on *Ceriagrion tenellum* (de Villers) in southern England (Zygoptera: Coenagrionidae). *Odonatologica*, **8**, 171-194.

Perring, F.H. 1992. BSBI distribution maps scheme - the first 40 years. In: *Biological recording of changes in British wildlife*, edited by P.T. Harding, 1-4. (ITE symposium no. 26.) London: HMSO.

Perring, F.H. & Walters, S.M. 1962. *Atlas of the British flora.* London: Nelson.

Pickess, B.P. 1987. How far will larvae of *Orthetrum cancellatum* (L.) travel for their emergence? *Journal of the British Dragonfly Society*, **3**, 15-16.

Pickess, B.P. 1989. The importance of RSPB reserves for dragonflies. *RSPB Conservation Review,* **5**, 30-34.

Pinniger, E.B. 1947. *Coenagrion scitulum,* Rambur, a dragonfly new to Britain. *London Naturalist*, **26**, 80.

Poethke, H-J. 1988. Density-dependent behaviour in *Aeshna cyanea* (Müller) males at the mating place (Anisoptera: Aeshnidae). *Odonatologica*, **17**, 205-212.

Pollard, E. 1979. A national scheme for monitoring the abundance of butterflies: the first three years. *Proceedings and Transactions of the British Entomological and Natural History Society*, **12**, 77-90.

Pollard, E. 1992. Monitoring populations of a butterfly during a period of range expansion. In: *Biological recording of changes in British wildlife*, edited by P.T.Harding, 60-64. (ITE symposium no. 26.) London: HMSO.

Porritt, G.T. 1910. *Agrion armatum,* Charp., at Stalham Broad, Norfolk. *Entomologist's Monthly Magazine*, **21**, 161-162.

Porritt, G.T. 1912. *Agrion armatum,* Charp., in the Norfolk Broads. *Entomologist's Monthly Magazine*, **48**, 163.

Prendergast, J.R, Quinn, R.M., Lawton, J.H., Eversham, B.C. & Gibbons, D.W. 1993. Rare species, the coincidence of diversity hotspots, and conservation strategies. *Nature*, **365**, 335-337.

Prendergast, N.H.D. 1988. The distribution and abundance of *Calopteryx splendens* (Harris), *C. virgo* (L.) and *Platycnemis pennipes* (Pallas) on the Wey river system (Hampshire and Surrey). *Journal of the British Dragonfly Society*, **4**, 37-44.

Rippey, I. & Nelson, B. 1988. Odonata in the north of Ireland 1986/87. *Journal of the British Dragonfly Society*, **4**, 13-19.

Robert, P-A. 1958. *Les Libellules (Odonates).* Neuchâtel and Paris: Delachaux et Niestlé.

Ruppell, G. 1985. Kinematic and behavioural aspects of flight of the male banded agrion *Calopteryx splendens* L. In: *Insect locomotion*, edited by M. Gewecke & G. Wendler, 195-204. Berlin: Parey.

Schmidt, E. 1978. Die Verbreitung der Kleinlibelle *Coenagrion armatum* Charpentier 1840 in Nordwestdeutschland (Odonata: Coenagrionidae). *Drosera*, **2**, 39-42.

Sélys-Longchamps, E. de. 1846. Revision of the British Libellulidae. *Annals and Magazine of Natural History*, **18**, 217-227.

Sélys-Longchamps, E. de. & Hagen, H.A. 1850. Revue des Odonates ou Libellules d'Europe. *Mémoires de la Société Royale des Sciences de Liège,* **6**, xxii+408.

Shirt, D.B., ed. 1987. *British Red Data Books: 2. Insects.* Peterborough: Nature Conservancy Council.

Silsby, J. 1993. A review of *Hemianax ephippiger*, the vagrant emperor. *Journal of the British Dragonfly Society*, **9**, 47-50.

Silsby, J.D. & Silsby R.I. 1988. Dragonflies in Jersey. *Journal of the British Dragonfly Society*, **4**, 31-36.

Siva-Jothy, M.T. 1987. Variation in copulation duration and the resultant degree of sperm removal in *Orthetrum cancellatum* (L.) (Libellulidae: Odonata). *Behavioural Ecology and Sociobiology*, **20**, 147-151.

Skelton, M.J.L., ed. 1974. *Insect Distribution Maps Scheme: Orthoptera, Dictyoptera and Odonata preliminary distribution maps.* Huntingdon: Biological Records Centre.

Smith, E.M. 1984. Some observations at breeding sites of emeralds (Corduliidae) in Scotland. *Journal of the British Dragonfly Society*, **1**, 37-38.

Smith, E.M. & Smith, R.W.J. 1984. *Brachytron pratense* (Müller) and other Odonata of the Black Lochs, Argyll. *Journal of the British Dragonfly Society*, **1**, 51-54.

Speight, M.C.D. & Legrand, J. 1984. *Coenagrion lunulatum* (Odonata): morphology of the female and notes on a second Irish colony. *Irish Naturalists' Journal*, **21**, 237-242.

Speyer, E.R. 1909. On the occurrence of *Somatochlora metallica,* Van der Lind., in Sussex. *Entomologist's Monthly Magazine*, **45**, 227-233.

Stace, C.A. 1991. *New flora of the British Isles.* Cambridge: Cambridge University Press.

Stephens, J.F. 1835-37. *Illustrations of British entomology*, **4**. London: Baldwin and Cradock.

Taylor, J.W. 1894-1921. *Monograph of the land and freshwater Mollusca of the British Isles.* 3 volumes & 3 parts (unfinished). Leeds: Taylor Bros.

Thickett, L.A. 1991. Inverted emergence by *Ischnura elegans* (Vander Linden). *Journal of the British Dragonfly Society,* **7**, 33.

Tickner, M., Evans, C. & Blackburn, M. 1991. Restoration of a Norfolk Broad: a case study of Strumpshaw Fen. *RSPB Conservation Review*, **5**, 72-77.

Tol, J. van & Verdonk, M.J. 1988. *The protection of dragonflies and their biotopes.* Strasbourg: European Committee for the Conservation of Nature and Natural Resources.

Trail, J.W.H. 1878. List of Lepidoptera and other insects of 'Dee'. *Transactions of the Natural History Society, Aberdeen.*.

Ubukata, H. 1975. Territorial behaviour of *Cordulia aenea*. *Insectarium, Tokyo* ,**12** (9), 196-199 (Japanese). (Abstract in *Odonatologica* **5**, 301.)

Ubukata, H. 1986. A model of mate searching and territorial behaviour for 'flier' type dragonflies. *Journal of Ethology*, **4**, 105-112.

Valtonen, P. 1986. On the odonate fauna of a Finnish forest pond occasionally drying up. *Notulae odonatologicae*, **2**, 134-135.

Walker, F.A. 1900. Dragon-flies in the Island of Alderney: including *Lestes barbara*, F. *Entomologist's Monthly Magazine*, **11**, 189.

Warren, R.G. 1964. Territorial behaviour of *Libellula quadrimaculata* L. and *Leucorrhinia dubia* Van der L. (Odonata, Libellulidae). *Entomologist*, **97**, 147.

Watt, A.D., Ward, L.K. & Eversham, B.C. 1990. Invertebrates. In: *The greenhouse effect and terrestrial ecosystems of the UK*, edited by M.G.R. Cannell & M.D. Hooper, 32-37. (ITE research publication no. 4.) London: HMSO.

Webb, D.A. 1980. The biological vice-counties of Ireland. *Proceedings of the Royal Irish Academy*, **80B,** 179-196.

Webb, N.R. 1986. *Heathlands*. London: Collins.

Welstead, A.R. & Welstead, N.I. 1983a. Illustration of the variation in pigmentation of the dorsal surface of the 8-10th abdominal segments of male *Ischnura pumilio* (Charpentier) in the New Forest, Hampshire. *Journal of the British Dragonfly Society*, **1**, 26.

Welstead, A.R. & Welstead, N.I. 1983b. A key to identify females of three species of Coenagriidae. *Journal of the British Dragonfly Society*, **1**, 43-44.

Wildermuth, H. 1986. Zur Habitatwahl und zur Verbreitung von *Somatochlora arctica* (Zetterstedt) in der Schweiz (Anisoptera: Corduliidae). *Odonatologica* ,**15**, 185-202.

Winsland, D.C. 1983. Some observations of *Erythromma najas* (Hansemann). *Journal of the British Dragonfly Society*, **1**, 6.

Winsland, D.C. 1985. Preliminary site and pH evaluation for assessing the distribution of *Coenagrion mercuriale* (Charp.) in the New Forest. *Journal of the British Dragonfly Society*, **1**, 89-93.

Appendix 1. GLOSSARY

Acid, acidic Soil or water with a low pH (below 7), usually base-poor

Aeshnid Member of the family Aeshnidae (represented in this *Atlas* by the genera *Aeshna*, *Anax*, *Brachytron*, *Hemianax*)

Alkaline Soil or water with a high pH (above 7) and usually base-rich

Alluvium, alluvial Fine sediment deposited by a river or the sea. Alluvial soils are highly fertile

Anal appendages Projections on the terminal abdominal segment of adult dragonflies. In male Zygoptera, there are two pairs, the superior (upper) and inferior (lower) appendages. In male Anisoptera, there is a pair of superior appendages, but only a single inferior appendage (the epiproct). In females, there is a single pair of anal appendages which may be long (eg aeshnids), short (eg libellulids) or rudimentary, as in most damselflies. The male uses his anal appendages to hold the female by the prothorax (Zygoptera), head (most Anisoptera) or both (Aeshnidae) during mating and in the tandem position

Anisoptera Suborder of Odonata, the 'true dragonflies', containing the larger, more robust and actively hawking species

Antehumeral stripes A pair of pale stripes on the dorsal surface of the thorax

Basin mire Bog formed in a natural hollow or depression

BDS British Dragonfly Society

Biotope A major land use/vegetation type; 'habitat' (*qv*) is often used loosely as a synonym of biotope, but should be used only when referring to habitats of a named species

Blanket bog or mire Extensive area of bog in areas of high rainfall, found mainly in north and west Scotland and west Ireland

Bog Acidic wetland on peat

Boreal Northern; in Europe, pertaining to northern Russia and most of Scandinavia

Boreo-alpine Northern, and also occurring in the Alps (and often in other European mountains)

Boreo-montane Northern, also found in mountains further south

BRC Biological Records Centre, ITE Monks Wood

Breck Inland sandy heathland area of Norfolk and Suffolk (see Figure 14)

Britain England, Scotland, Wales and nearby associated off-shore islands; not including the Irish Republic or Northern Ireland, or the Channel Islands

Broads, Broadland Area of fens and shallow lakes in Norfolk and Suffolk (see Figure 14), the lakes originating in medieval peat digging

Burren, The A mainly upland region in north Co Clare, Ireland, characterised by extensive limestone pavement (see Figure 14)

Calcareous Rich in lime (calcium carbonate)

cf Compare with

Circumboreal	Occurring in a band encompassing the North Pole, ie in northern Europe, North America and northern Asia; not necessarily extending inside the Arctic Circle
Channel Islands	Jersey, Guernsey, Alderney, Sark and Herm (see Figure 14)
Co	County (used mainly in Ireland)
Coenagrionid	Damselfly of the family Coenagrionidae (represented in this *Atlas* by the genera *Ceriagrion*, *Coenagrion*, *Enallagma*, *Erythromma*, *Ischnura*, *Pyrrhosoma*)
Connemara	Area in west Co Galway, Ireland (see Figure 14)
Corduliid	Member of the family Corduliidae (represented in this *Atlas* by the genera *Cordulia*, *Somatochlora*, *Oxygastra*)
Costa	Vein running along the leading edge of the wing
Cut-over bog	Area of bog (currently, mainly lowland raised mires) from which the vegetation and surface layers of peat have been removed as a result of peat digging; long-abandoned cuttings may develop secondary vegetation which contains some of the species found in intact bogs
Damselfly	Member of the suborder Zygoptera, which as adults are usually the smaller, slender-bodied Odonata, and which hold their wings closed, or nearly closed, over the abdomen when at rest
Deer forest	In Scotland, land in the uplands which is not suitable for growing crops, usually open (without trees) and including the pool-dominated and boulder-strewn blanket bogs of the north-west and central Highlands
Diapause	An obligatory dormant or 'resting' stage in the life cycle. In Britain, usually a means of passing the winter
Distal	The part of a limb or wing toward the apex, furthest away from the centre of the body or the point of attachment (*cf* proximal)
Emergence	Change from aquatic larva to winged adult
Eurytopic	Able to occupy a wide range of biotopes; having very broad habitat requirements (*cf* stenotopic)
Eutrophication	Nutrient enrichment of water, often with nitrates and phosphates from agricultural fertilizer runoff
Fen	Basic to slightly acid wetland, usually on peat
The Fens, Fenland	Inland part of East Anglia, and southern Lincolnshire, much of which was formerly fen (*qv*) (see Figure 14)
Femur	'Thigh', the upper (basal) of the two long sections of each leg, usually the stouter (pl. **femora**)
Flush	Mineral enrichment caused by moving water; a wet area or seepage on sloping ground
Frons	The 'forehead' or upper part of the face of an insect
FWAG	Farming and Wildlife Advisory Group
Galloway	Area of south-west Scotland comprising the historic counties of Wigtownshire and Kirkcudbrightshire (= Stewartry District) (see Figure 14)

Genus	A group of closely related species; the first half of a species' specific name – eg *Lestes dryas* is in the genus *Lestes* (pl. **genera**)
Habitat	The biotope in which a species lives. Often used loosely as a synonym of biotope (*qv*), but should strictly be used only when referring to a named species or group of species
Heathland	Area of nutrient-poor, acid soil, usually sandy or gravelly, often dominated by low-growing ericaceous shrubs, especially heather. Often used in a wider sense to encompass low-lying moors on peat, including cut-over bogs (*qv*)
Highest steady density	For each species, the highest number of adult males to be expected along 100 m of water edge, only rarely exceeded. It is controlled by territorial or aggressive interactions between males
Highlands	Area of northern Scotland (see Figure 14)
Holarctic	Occurring in the Palaearctic (*qv*) and in North America and Greenland
Hyaline	Translucent, glass-like
Iberian peninsula	Spain and Portugal
Instar	Period between larval moults, a growth stage. The 'last larval instar' is that from which the adult emerges
Introduction	Moving individuals of a species to a site from which it is absent. If the species formerly occurred at the site, the term 'reintroduction' is used. Dragonfly larvae are often introduced accidentally when ponds are stocked with water plants
Ireland	The Irish Republic and Northern Ireland
JNCC	Joint Nature Conservation Committee
Kintyre	Peninsula in south-west Scotland (see Figure 14)
KSP	Key Sites Project, a project for recording dragonflies and establishing proof of breeding, launched by BRC in 1988
Lake District	Upland area in Cumbria, England, with many large lakes
Larva	Term used for the aquatic immature stages of a dragonfly or other insect (pl. **larvae**). See also **nymph**
Lestid	Member of the family Lestidae (represented in this *Atlas* by the genera *Lestes* and *Sympecma*)
Levels	Low-lying, often coastal, area of fen, bog and other wetlands; originally used for seasonal cattle grazing, many such areas have been drained for agriculture or cut for peat (eg Somerset Levels, see Figure 14)
Libellulid	Member of the family Libellulidae (represented in this *Atlas* by the genera *Crocothemis*, *Leucorrhinia*, *Libellula*, *Orthetrum*, *Pantala*, *Sympetrum*)
Machair	Flat area of grazed calcareous dune grassland on west coasts of Scotland, Ireland and the Hebrides
Macrophytes	Aquatic and emergent vascular plants (ferns, horsetails and flowering plants)

Marl	A whitish clay soil with a high lime content
Massif Central	Mountain range in south-eastern France
Maturation	Of adult dragonflies, the physiological changes and development of body colour preparing the insect for breeding. The maturation period is often spent away from water
Mesotrophic	Having moderate levels of dissolved nutrients
Mynydd Preseli	Extensive area of lowland heath and upland moorland (to 468 m) in Pembrokeshire (now Dyfed). Parts with base-rich spring-fed runnels which support important populations of *Coenagrion mercuriale*
New Forest	Large area of mainly unenclosed heathland, woodland, acid grassland and valley mires in Hampshire, England (see Figure 14)
Node	The position on the leading edge of the wing at which there is a break in the costa (*qv*), resulting in a slight notch
NNR	National Nature Reserve
Nymph	Aquatic immature stage of dragonfly or other insect which does not pass through a pupal stage. (Strictly, a **nymph** has a similar body form to the adult into which it develops; its developing wings are visible externally as buds, and it changes directly into an adult, whereas a **larva** differs greatly from the adult, and undergoes a pupal stage during which the wings are formed. The two terms are now usually treated as synonyms, and larva is preferred in most modern publications on Odonata)
Oligotrophic	Nutrient-poor water, with low levels of nitrate, phosphate, calcium, etc, and usually acidic
Oviposition	Egg laying and associated behaviour
Ovipositor	An apparatus for inserting eggs in tissues of plants, or into sediment. It is situated on the ventral surface of abdominal segments 8 and 9 of females of some dragonfly species (see also **vulvar scale**)
Ovipositor valves	The ovipositor is made up of three pairs of processes, of which the main pair (the valves) forms the greater part (see **vulvar scale**)
Palaearctic	Zoogeographic region comprising Europe, North Africa, western Asia, Siberia, northern China, and Japan
Phenology	The seasonality of natural phenomena, such as life histories; used in reference to flight periods of insects, particularly in relation to climatic conditions
Pingo	A more or less circular mound or depression in glacial deposits, caused by the action of ice. Pingos often occur in groups, and when water-filled form rich and diverse ponds
Pre-flight emergent	Newly emerged adult dragonfly which has not yet taken its maiden flight, and so provides absolute proof of successful breeding
Pronotum	Plate on the dorsal surface of the prothorax, covering the 'neck' of Odonata which joins the head to the rest of the thorax
Proximal	The part of a limb or wing nearest the base, closest to the centre of the body or the point of attachment (*cf* distal)
Pruinescence	A powdery bloom, giving a pale blue or grey colour to parts of the body of some dragonflies when fully mature

Pterostigma	A usually darkened, sclerotised cell of the wing venation, adjoining the costa toward the apex of the wing. It functions as an inertial regulator of wing twisting (pl. **pterostigmata**)
qv	See, refer to
Raised mire, raised bog	Shallowly domed bog, usually on the floodplain of a lowland river; the dome of peat supports a water table above that of the surrounding alluvium
Relict	Left behind, a surviving population in a small part of a formerly wider geographic range
RSPB	Royal Society for the Protection of Birds
Schwingmoor	Associated with some basin mires, a floating raft of vegetation (including *Sphagnum* mosses) or peat, overlying deep water or semi-fluid peat
Sere, seral	A natural succession of plant communities leading to climax vegetation (usually tree cover): in still freshwater habitats, succession tends to lead from open water, through marshy vegetation to terrestrial habitats
Sphagnum	Genus of bog mosses, responsible for peat formation in bogs; they can form an undulating surface of moss hummocks with wetter hollows or pools in between. They provide important oviposition sites and larval habitat for many dragonflies
Spring species	A dragonfly whose larvae pass the winter in diapause in their last larval instar, and which usually have a synchronous emergence in the spring or early summer (*cf* summer species)
SSSI	Site(s) of Special Scientific Interest, scheduled under the Wildlife and Countryside Act 1981
Stenotopic	Confined to a narrow range of biotopes, or to a single biotope; with very specific habitat requirements (*cf* eurytopic)
Summer species	A dragonfly whose larvae spend the winter in the penultimate or earlier larval instar. Diapause occurs in the egg stage of some species. Emergence is not usually synchronised, and takes place in mid- to late summer (*cf* spring species)
Tandem	A male and a female dragonfly coupled together before or after mating; some species remain coupled during egg laying
Teneral	Recently emerged adult dragonfly whose cuticle has not fully hardened and darkened. (Used in a much wider sense than 'pre-flight emergent, *qv*)
Territory	An area or space defended by an animal, usually in competition with members of its own species
Tibia	'Shin', the lower (distal) of the two long sections of each leg
Turlough	In Ireland, a temporary shallow lake in limestone country which fills and empties through fissures in response to changes in local water table
United Kingdom	Britain and Northern Ireland, excluding the Irish Republic; a political rather than a biogeographic unit
Valley mire or bog	Bog formed in small, shallow valleys or channels along which there is some water flow, often slight. Most common type of bog on English heathland

Var.	*Varietas* or variety: a form of a species which looks distinct, but which occurs mixed with typical examples of the species, and is not geographically or genetically separated
Vulvar scale	A backwardly projecting flap on the ventral surface of abdominal segment 8, extending below segment 9, in females of some dragonfly species which lay their eggs freely in water (rather than in plant tissue). The eggs are exuded from the vulvar opening, which lies above the vulvar scale. Also called **vulvar lamina**
WATCH	Educational programme initiated by the Royal Society for Nature Conservation (the Wildlife Trusts), to encourage children to understand wildlife and the countryside
Weald	Clayey and sandy area of Kent and Sussex, between the North and South Downs, characterised by fast-flowing streams and abundant woodland (see Figure 14)
Wheel position	Position adopted by a male and female dragonfly during mating: the male grasps the female's head (most Anisoptera) or prothorax (Zygoptera) or both (Aeshnidae) with his anal appendages, then the female curls her abdomen forward so that her primary genitalia situated near the tip of her abdomen contact the male's accessory genitalia, on the underside of his second abdominal segment
Zygoptera	Suborder of Odonata comprising the damselflies (*qv*)

Highlands

Kintyre

Galloway

Lake District

Connemara

The Burren

Broads

Fens

Breck

Mynydd Preseli

Somerset Levels

Weald

Channel Islands

New Forest

Figure 14. Map showing geographic areas referred to in the **Species accounts** and defined in the **Glossary**

Appendix 2. LIST OF PLANT NAMES

Plant species in the text of the *Atlas* are referred to by their English names. The following provides their scientific names, in accordance with Stace (1991). Where the names have recently been changed, the best-known synonyms are given in brackets.

Alder	*Alnus glutinosa*	Sallow	*Salix* sp.
Amphibious bistort	*Persicaria amphibia* (*Polygonum amphibium*)	Scots pine	*Pinus sylvestris*
		Sea club-rush	*Bolboschoenus maritimus* (*Scirpus maritimus*)
Bilberry	*Vaccinium myrtillus*		
Birch	*Betula* sp.		
Black bog-rush	*Schoenus nigricans*	Sedge	*Carex* sp.
Blunt-flowered rush	*Juncus subnodulosus*	Slender sedge	*Carex lasiocarpa*
Bog asphodel	*Narthecium ossifragum*	Soft rush	*Juncus effusus*
Bogbean	*Menyanthes trifoliata*	Spiked water-milfoil	*Myriophyllum spicatum*
Bog-myrtle	*Myrica gale*		
Bog pondweed	*Potamogeton polygonifolius*	Stoneworts	Characeae
		Sundew	*Drosera* sp.
Bog-sedge	*Carex limosa*	Unbranched bur-reed	*Sparganium emersum*
Bottle sedge	*Carex rostrata*	Water horsetail	*Equisetum fluviatile*
Branched bur-reed	*Sparganium erectum*	Water-lily	*Nuphar lutea* or *Nymphaea alba*
Broad-leaved pondweed	*Potamogeton natans*		
Bulrush	*Typha latifolia*	Water-plantain	*Alisma plantago-aquatica*
Common club-rush	*Schoenoplectus lacustris* (*Scirpus lacustris*)	Water-soldier	*Stratiotes aloides*
Common cottongrass	*Eriophorum angustifolium*	Western gorse	*Ulex gallii*
		White beak-sedge	*Rhynchospora alba*
Common nettle	*Urtica dioica*	White water-lily	*Nymphaea alba*
Common reed	*Phragmites australis* (*P. communis*)	Willow	*Salix* sp.
		Yellow flag	*Iris pseudacorus*
Common spike-rush	*Eleocharis palustris*	Yellow water-lily	*Nuphar lutea*
Common water-crowfoot	*Ranunculus aquatilis*		
Compact rush	*Juncus conglomeratus*		
Deergrass	*Trichophorum cespitosum*		
Duckweed	*Lemna* sp.		
Floating sweet-grass	*Glyceria fluitans*		
Flowering-rush	*Butomus umbellatus*		
Fool's water-cress	*Apium nodiflorum*		
Frogbit	*Hydrocharis morsus-ranae*		
Grasses	Poaceae (Gramineae)		
Greater bladderwort	*Utricularia vulgaris*		
Great fen-sedge	*Cladium mariscus*		
Hard rush	*Juncus inflexus*		
Hazel	*Corylus avellana*		
Heather	*Calluna vulgaris*		
Horsetail	*Equisetum* sp.		
Jointed rush	*Juncus articulatus*		
Lesser bladderwort	*Utricularia minor*		
Lesser spearwort	*Ranunculus flammula*		
Marsh cinquefoil	*Potentilla palustris*		
Marsh St John's-wort	*Hypericum elodes*		
Pondweed	*Potamogeton* sp.		
Purple moor-grass	*Molinia caerulea*		
Reed canary-grass	*Phalaris arundinacea*		
Reed sweet-grass	*Glyceria maxima*		
Round-leaved sundew	*Drosera rotundifolia*		
Rush	*Juncus* sp.		

Appendix 3. VICE-COUNTY BOUNDARIES

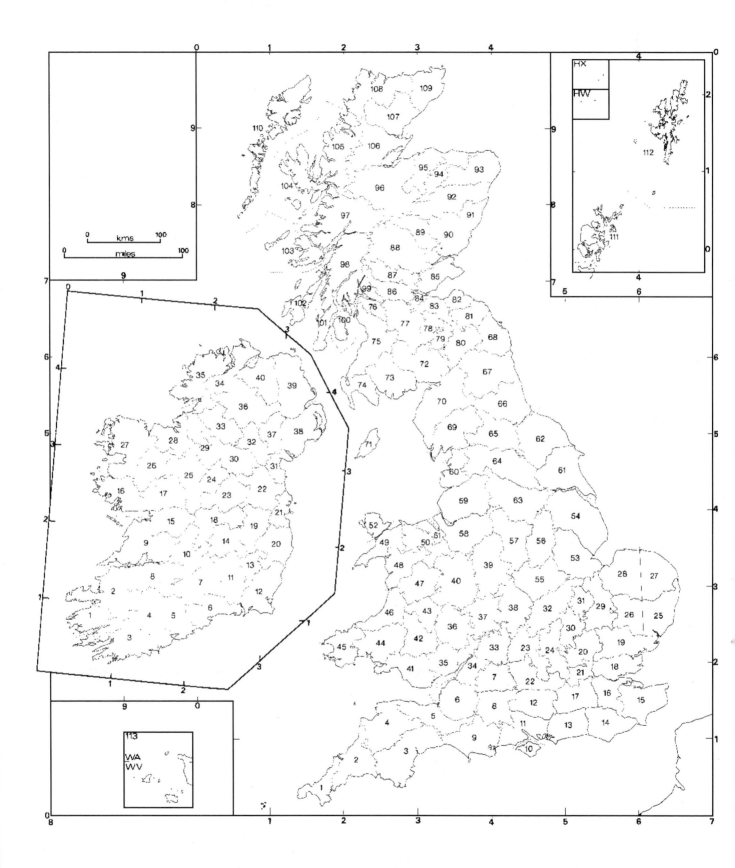

THE VICE-COUNTY NUMBERS AND CORRESPONDING VICE-COUNTIES

ENGLAND AND WALES

1. West Cornwall (with Scilly)
2. East Cornwall
3. South Devon
4. North Devon
5. South Somerset
6. North Somerset
7. North Wiltshire
8. South Wiltshire
9. Dorset
10. Isle of Wight
11. South Hampshire
12. North Hampshire
13. West Sussex
14. East Sussex
15. East Kent
16. West Kent
17. Surrey
18. South Essex
19. North Essex
20. Hertfordshire
21. Middlesex
22. Berkshire
23. Oxfordshire
24. Buckinghamshire
25. East Suffolk

26. West Suffolk
27. East Norfolk
28. West Norfolk
29. Cambridgeshire
30. Bedfordshire
31. Huntingdonshire
32. Northamptonshire
33. East Gloucestershire
34. West Gloucestershire
35. Monmouthshire
36. Herefordshire
37. Worcestershire
38. Warwickshire
39. Staffordshire
40. Shropshire (Salop)
41. Glamorgan
42. Breconshire
43. Radnorshire
44. Carmarthenshire
45. Pembrokeshire
46. Cardiganshire
47. Montgomeryshire
48. Merionethshire
49. Caernarvonshire
50. Denbighshire

51. Flintshire
52. Anglesey
53. South Lincolnshire
54. North Lincolnshire
55. Leicestershire (with Rutland)
56. Nottinghamshire
57. Derbyshire
58. Cheshire
59. South Lancashire
60. West Lancashire
61. South-east Yorkshire
62. North-east Yorkshire
63. South-west Yorkshire
64. Mid-west Yorkshire
65. North-west Yorkshire
66. Durham
67. South Northumberland
68. North Northumberland (Cheviot)
69. Westmorland with North Lancashire
70. Cumberland
71. Isle of Man
113. Channel Isles

SCOTLAND

72. Dumfriesshire
73. Kirkcudbrightshire
74. Wigtownshire
75. Ayrshire
76. Renfrewshire
77. Lanarkshire
78. Peeblesshire
79. Selkirkshire
80. Roxburghshire
81. Berwickshire
82. East Lothian (Haddington)
83. Midlothian (Edinburgh)
84. West Lothian (Linlithgow)
85. Fifeshire (with Kinross)
86. Stirlingshire

87. West Perthshire (with Clackmannan)
88. Mid Perthshire
89. East Perthshire
90. Angus (Forfar)
91. Kincardineshire
92. South Aberdeenshire
93. North Aberdeenshire
94. Banffshire
95. Moray (Elgin)
96. East Inverness-shire (with Nairn)
97. West Inverness-shire
98. Argyll Main

99. Dunbartonshire
100. Clyde Isles
101. Kintyre
102. South Ebudes
103. Mid Ebudes
104. North Ebudes
105. West Ross
106. East Ross
107. East Sutherland
108. West Sutherland
109. Caithness
110. Outer Hebrides
111. Orkney Islands
112. Shetland Islands (Zetland)

IRELAND

H.1. South Kerry
H.2. North Kerry
H.3. West Cork
H.4. Mid Cork
H.5. East Cork
H.6. Waterford
H.7. South Tipperary
H.8. Limerick
H.9. Clare
H.10. North Tipperary
H.11. Kilkenny
H.12. Wexford
H.13. Carlow
H.14. Laois

H.15 South-east Galway
H.16. West Galway
H.17. North-east Galway
H.18. Offaly
H.19. Kildare
H.20. Wicklow
H.21. Dublin
H.22. Meath
H.23. Westmeath
H.24. Longford
H.25. Roscommon
H.26. East Mayo
H.27. West Mayo

H.28. Sligo
H.29. Leitrim
H.30. Cavan
H.31. Louth
H.32. Monaghan
H.33. Fermanagh
H.34. East Donegal
H.35. West Donegal
H.36. Tyrone
H.37. Armagh
H.38. Down
H.39. Antrim
H.40. Londonderry

INDEX TO SPECIES